HUNTER: THE VIGIL
NIGHT STALKERS

Alex Greene|Martin Henley|Howard Wood Ingham|
John Newman|Malcolm Sheppard

CREDITS

Concept and Design:
Justin Achilli, Richard Thomas, Chuck Wendig

Authors:
Alex Greene, Martin Henley, Howard Wood Ingham, John Newman, Malcolm Sheppard

Developer:
Chuck Wendig

Editor:
Scribendi.com

Art Direction and Design:
Mike Chaney

Layout and Design:
Jessica Mullins

Creative Director:
Richard Thomas

Production Manager:
matt milberger

Artists: Vince Locke, Avery Butterworth, Jim DiBartolo, Efrem Palacios, Ken Meyer Jr, Matias Tapia, Sam Arraya, Sean Phillips, Andrea Sorrentino, Phil Hilliker & Jessica Mullins

Cover Artist:
Chad Michael Ward

COMING NEXT FOR HUNTER:

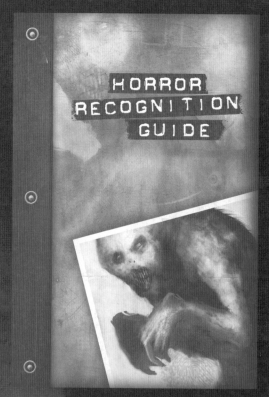

HORROR RECOGNITION GUIDE

WHITE WOLF PUBLISHING
2075 WEST PARK PLACE BOULEVARD
SUITE G
STONE MOUNTAIN, GA 30087

HUNTER: THE VIGIL
NIGHT STALKERS

TABLE OF CONTENTS

FRANK'S STORY

Where all this is going: Frank will find his daughter. It will not be as conclusive as Frank wants it to be. In fact, it will be, at the very best, bittersweet for Frank. Frank will go home without her, thinking: at least she's alive.

Frank makes certain choices; the choices we make are often what keep us from losing hope altogether, even when there is no reason to have any hope at all.

LONDON'S TRUE DETECTIVE STORIES

Frank's ringtone is Kenny Rogers' "Coward of the County." Out of habit, he lets it play through the chorus. He expertly, regretfully flicks the cigarette end across the pub car park, wishing for the God-knows-how-many-th time that the law hadn't forced him to smoke outside.

He sighs, looks at the phone. He doesn't know the number. *Click.*

"Yeah?"

"Is this Mister Crowe?" It is a young man's voice; London accent, the kind that the kids in the hoodies around here try to emulate with varying success.

"*Detective Inspector Crowe.*"

"Yeah."

"What do you want, son?"

"You got a daughter, yeah?"

Frank chokes, composes himself, and remains silent.

"Mister Crowe?" The boy sounds more confident.

"Is this some sort of a joke, son?" He uses the Authority Voice, the one that used to freeze shoplifters and bag-snatchers in their tracks, the one he started using when he was just a beat copper, fresh out of training; when they still had beats.

"No. No. I'm a friend of Bianca's. I thought you'd want to know where she was. I hear you been looking for her."

Frank says nothing.

"She's in trouble."

"What sort of trouble?"

The voice gives Frank three names, an address. It hangs up without a goodbye.

Frank Crowe, then: 48 years old, born in the East End of London. A Detective Inspector in the South Wales Constabulary. A bit seedy, perhaps, his once-expensive sheepskin coat smelling of spirits and stale tobacco, a shadow on his chin that no amount of shaving can eradicate. He'd object if told, but he conforms to the stereotype of the journeyman detective from fiction: Chief Inspector Heat, Inspector Lestrade, the bloke John Thaw played in The Sweeney, maybe Gene Hunt if you're so inclined. A good police officer, if a little reckless; but then, the recklessness that gets you suspended is the same recklessness that gets you promoted to Detective Inspector in the first instance.

Frank is a widower. He has a daughter, aged 19, with a string of offenses as long as Frank's arm. He lost her just as he lost his wife.

He owns a picture that Bianca made when she was seven, drawn in little kid fashion, of daddy in a police officer's uniform and her dressed as a princess, all in pink; with a little tiara. His Princess. He had it Blu-tacked incongruously behind his desk for years, between the whiteboard and the police notices, fading, turning brown, becoming as tatty and ruined as their relationship.

He can close his eyes and see her even now, as she was the last time they spoke; the scotch only makes it more vivid, adds colors he can't see when he's sober. He sees her through shards of glass in a door, slammed and smashed in a single motion, sixteen, walking out for the last time, turning on a stiletto heel, a tightly-pulled bleach-blond ponytail swishing in the air.

He remembers trying to reason with her, in his own way. "You'll come to a bad end, you will. Mark my words, girl," he says, even now, struggling with a wet dogend rescued from a saucer so he won't have to make eye contact. "What would your mother say?"

"Nothing," she replies, black-smudged eyes as hard as his own. "She wouldn't say anything. She's dead."

Frank sits in his sepia lounge, staring into space, trying to figure out how to go to sleep. He removes a sputtering cigar with yellowed fingers and stubs it out into a scummy mug. "Bloody women!"

He pauses, picks up another picture, a family photo — the one that shows a smiling, athletic man, his wife with the feather perm and the blue eye shadow and the chandelier earrings, their smiling toothy daughter with the long, mousy hair.

"Sorry, Pauline."

He turns the picture so it lies face downwards, then stretches himself across the sofa, the heady haze of the scotch beginning to kick in at last.

⌖

Frank shivers, rubs his hands together, blows on them, and paces the length of the pedestrian subway, listening to the occasional car above.

"Frank?"

He turns; a younger man, tow-headed, bespectacled, dressed in old but clean clothes. This is Simon May.

"Yeah."

"How's things, Frank?" Simon approaches, his hands in his pockets.

"Been better, son. But you can talk. I'm not the only one been looking for you."

Simon nods, licks his lips. "They haven't found me."

"I found you."

"I wanted you to." He looks around. "So did you get away with it?"

"Yeah. Sort of. The tape proved I didn't have much choice. Self defense, see. And the other tapes... they proved we were right about him." Frank tries not to let the other man see him shudder. "But the breaking and entering, see. Bit of a sticking point. And having the golf club handy in the first place. Got an indefinite suspension. Without pay."

"Sorry to hear that, Frank."

"You won't be turning yourself in." It's a statement, half an order.

"No. No, I won't. I don't think it'd end well."

Frank lights another cigarette.

"What happened, Frank?"

Frank tells Simon about the call, about how Bianca is in some sort of trouble; he asks the younger man for a favor. Asking nearly kills him. Simon appreciates this, makes no comment, asks no condition. It would kill Frank even more to know how the other man pities him.

⊱—✦—⊰

Frank is nodding off when the man taps at the car window; he nearly strangles himself with the car seatbelt, he jumps so hard. The man is waiting.

He stares at the steering wheel, considers just motoring off.

The tapping again: tap, tap.

Frank takes a deep breath, exhales swiftly. Then he winds down the window.

"Excuse me, but why are you watching the factory?"

The man looks like he's the wrong side of sixty, wearing a black coat, collar turned up. Slicked-back hair in an iron-gray widow's peak; heavy black brows, eyes lost in shade, aquiline nose, sardonic half-smile. He has a French accent. He reminds Frank a bit of Sacha Distel, but since every Frenchman Frank has ever met reminds him of Sacha Distel, this should not really be a surprise. Thinking of Sacha Distel reminds him of Pauline. "The Good Life" was one of her favorite songs.

"Don't know what you're talking about, mate."

"Sir, I have spent a very long time watching various places. This place, that place. I know when one is practicing the art of surveillance."

"I was on the way to Billericay. To my daughter's. I got lost. I was just checking the map—"

"You are six miles down a side road. Behind a bush."

"Said I was a bit lost."

"I see." The old man bites his lip, looks to one side for a second, leans forward, both hands on the roof of the Escort, face almost inside the window. "Sir, I have a problem."

"What's that to do with me?" For Frank, the usual mode of defense is assault. Verbal, physical, it makes no odds.

"I am rather thinking that it has everything to do with you."

"I don't like your tone."

"My apologies. I meant nothing of it. I simply meant that since I wanted to break into the factory too—"

"What?"

Frank is not sure how the old man ends up sitting next to him in the car, even less sure how he ends up explaining why he has driven half-way across the country to sit in a car outside a factory that makes feed for farm animals.

⌐═─⌐

The old man's name is Mr. Thélème. Frank doesn't catch the first name. Something does not sit right with Frank about the man. He looks too hard at Frank and pauses before speaking as if trying not to laugh. He offends Frank's sense of dignity.

They're at the fence, next to the one spot they're half-sure isn't covered by the CCTV. Frank puts down the golf club for a second and pulls out a Tesco carrier bag from his coat pocket.

"Steak," he explains. "With Mogadon in it. For the dogs."

"You got that from a detective film, didn't you?" says the other man.

"Worth a go, innit?"

"And if it does not work?"

Frank pulls a stun gun from a pocket. And then he puts it away, and pulls a revolver out from a holster inside his coat. Thélème makes one of those Gallic shrugs Frank has occasionally heard of.

In the end, the dogs completely ignore the steak, and Frank has to use Plan B; shortly after that, here comes the security guard. He walks up to the fence, sees Mr. Thélème and challenges him, but doesn't see Frank until it's too late. Frank shoots an arm through the gaps in the rods and grabs the man's collar. The guard loses his footing and falls into the fence; Frank zaps him in the neck before he can even yell. Frank's up the fence, using a pair of wire cutters to snap the razor wire, pushes it back with the club. And he's over, Mr. Thélème behind him.

"See? Easy," says Frank, straightening out his coat.

The Frenchman half-smiles.

"Please yourself, sunshine," says Frank.

The cameras move, five-second sweeps. Conceivably, a man could make it across the grounds into the shadows without being seen. But the guard will be missed soon. They must be swift.

The camera shifts; they run. And again, and again.

Before Frank really knows where they are, the two of them are crouched between the factory wall and a row of skips, their contents under tarpaulins.

It takes a minute for Frank to realize how bad the smell is. He rises slightly, raises a hand to lift the edge of the tarpaulin. Mr. Thélème puts a hand on his wrist. Frank stares at him.

"Mr. Crowe. I know what's in there."

Frank shrugs the man's hand off and then he looks.

When the pause of comprehension has elapsed, Frank puts the tarp right like it's red-hot, flings himself back against the wall, slumps to the ground, eyes wide, mouth slack.

Mr. Thélème looks away.

"There were children in there," says Frank. "A kid. She can't have been more than three."

The other man looks away, tight-lipped.

Frank puts his hand on Mr. Thélème's arm.

"You didn't know," Mr. Thélème says.

Frank composes himself. "What is this?"

Frank never supported naming and shaming, but he's like a lot of parents when faced with evidence of pedophiles and child-killers: he remembers how once he used to imagine it happening to his own child, and it causes him more distress than he is capable of admitting. He recalls the face of the little girl he saw, and it morphs in his head into the face of his own daughter, when she was a little girl, when she drew the picture that sits right now, folded up in the pocket of his blazer.

Thélème speaks after a long silence. "Animal feed. They make livestock feed. You know this."

"What?"

"You will see that building, there." A slender finger points at the farther of the two pre-fabricated factory units, with vast doors. "That is where they make the feed for the farm animals. This is the storage. For the ingredients."

"You mean, they're killing people, so they can turn them to pig feed."

"No. That they turn these people into the livestock feed is because, I think, that they have to do something to dispose of the bodies, and they think that they might as well make a profit."

"And?"

"We have to go there." Mr. Thélème points to the other pre-fab unit. He then turns and points to a spot 10 feet above and to the left of Frank, where a camera is trained directly on them. "And it seems our stealth has been for nothing."

Frank's fingers tighten on the handle of the golf club. "I'm staying. I'm seeing this through."

"Good for you, Inspector Crowe." Thélème stands up and strides into the open yard. "No point in hiding. Shall we?"

Frank goes cold, but he stands up and follows the old man across the concrete. No one stops them. No alarm rises.

The factory unit has the same vast doors as the other, and a second door for human access, locked with a number pad. Thélème leans close to the door and whispers something.

Frank is about to push him aside and bash the door in with his golf club, when the door clicks, and opens without Thélème pushing it. A whiff of... sulfur? ...reaches Frank's nostrils, and for a moment, it looks like there is someone standing in the shadows behind the door. He hears Thélème whisper merci, but as they walk in and the door, on a spring closer, snaps shut behind them, he can see that no one is there.

"Here. How did you—?"

"I had someone come in here ahead of me," says Thélème. "No, he is gone, now."

It is all the explanation Frank gets.

⌐═─⌐

The corridor ends in a locker room; half a dozen green work coats hang on pegs opposite lockers that could exist anywhere. Beside them, on a hook, a ring of keys. And a door which presumably leads to the shop floor. But the place stinks to high heaven, even here.

Thélème motions for Frank to go first.

Frank walks into the first aisle, and the smell is so bad, he feels like throwing up, and would do so if he had eaten today. In the dark, it looks like the warehouse section of his one trip to Ikea, all aisles full of goods, stacked in rows, twenty, thirty feet high. Frank can hear a sound like a vast toilet cistern refilling; and another noise, a mewling noise like a cat. It's the sound of a person. Sobbing.

Thélème behind him hits a green button on the wall next to the door and the lights come up. Bang, bang, bang, bang: vast fluorescent lights bang on, one after the other, gradually illuminating the further reaches of the unit.

"Christ Almighty," says Frank.

They're cages. Hundreds upon hundreds of them, shelf upon shelf, row upon row. Each is a four-foot cube and each contains a man, woman or child, naked, crouching in their own excrement. Each inmate is chained. And every cage has a feeding trough. Every ethnicity is here, but the majority of people here are black or Asian. Frank looks at a cage containing an unconscious young woman. The shackles at her wrists and neck cover angry welts on her skin. Her arms are covered with track marks. She looks so very pale.

In the next cage a man looks up and starts to say something, weakly in a language Frank doesn't know. In a third, a teenage boy turns his head away. And in all of them: manacles, disease, track marks.

Frank vomits anyway, ejecting stomach acid into the middle of the floor.

He wipes his mouth and his eyes. "This has got to end," says Frank.

"That was my idea," says Thélème. "Which is why we must go to the office."

"But we have to—"

"No. We cannot waste the time. We must find the offices and get what we need."

"I'll call the police."

"Inspector Crowe, do you think they will do anything? Ask yourself, why, if this business fronts itself with the sale of animal feed, why the Health and Safety Executive has never inspected the factory, or why the sections of your government that manage industry have never been here, or to any of the other factories?"

"Others."

"This is only one of nine. The first was in Devon, I believe. They have even opened a factory in the United States."

"We have to get these people out. We have to tell someone. The press. The Daily Mail. They'd print it."

"No, Mister Crowe. Any journalist who comes here receives a notice from your government that kills the story. If you try to put it on the Internet, they will dismiss it as a crazy conspiracy theory. If they do not run this country, Mr. Crowe, they run enough of it to ensure that no one knows or cares what is happening to these people. The ring of keys, hanging up in the locker room. Did you not think that was careless? Or the single security guard on patrol? These people are not bothered about being caught."

Frank raises an eyebrow. Then he turns, and runs back to the locker room. Now holding the ring of keys, he runs along an aisle, looking in the cages, and then stops. He fumbles with the keys, tries three or four until he manages to undo the padlock. Inside, a little girl cowers in the filth. She is maybe three or four. He undoes the same for the manacles, half-climbing inside and holding the girl as he frees her. She begins to cry, but does not struggle. He takes her out and wraps his old sheepskin coat around her.

"Inspector Crowe, why did you do that?" says Thélème, strolling back down the aisle of this place as if it were a library corridor and he a browser. "It will only slow us."

"Fuck off, Pierre. I'm getting someone out of here. Hold this." He hands Thélème the golf club and picks the girl up.

"But what good will it do, if we cannot save ourselves?"

⸙

Hundreds upon hundreds of them, shelf upon shelf, row upon row.

Each is a four-foot cube and each contains a man, woman or child, naked, crouching in their own excrement. Each inmate is chained. And every cage has a feeding trough. Every ethnicity is here, but the majority of people here are black or Asian.

Frank looks at a cage containing an unconscious young woman. The shackles at her wrists and neck cover angry welts on her skin. Her arms are covered with track-marks. She looks so very pale

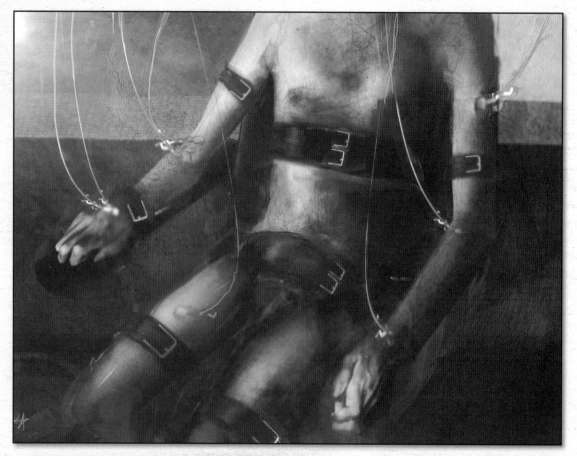

Out the other side of the prison, past an area containing forklift trucks and hoppers, they find a room as pale and sterile as the main shop floor is filthy. Three gurneys stand in the corner; white cabinets line three of the walls. What looks like a half a dozen dentists' chairs, equipped with sturdy-looking straps, sit in a row in the middle of the room. The little girl shrinks in Frank's arms, and begins to try to get away. Frank holds her.

"It's all right, sweetheart. I won't let anyone hurt you again."

Thélème sighs, strides over to the huge metal door that sits at the other side of the room. He cocks his head to one side, as if listening, whispers merci again and keys a number in the keypad. A click; Thélème turns the wheel and the door opens, letting a blast of cold air into the room.

Mr. Thélème walks into the refrigerated room; Frank, holding the girl tightly to his chest, follows.

It seems to go on forever: rows and rows of bags of blood, hanging on rack after rack.

"This is why we are here, Inspector Crowe."

"They're bleeding them to death."

"That is so."

"They're organ traffickers. Only with blood. They're organizing black-market transfusions."

"Would that it were something so sordid."

"What?"

"Do you think that this place would be so protected if it were simply a means of organizing blood for illicit transfusions when you live in a country where a transfusion is easy to come by and free of charge? Who would pay? Where is the profit? No, the blood is needed for another purpose. This should be self-evident."

"What, though?"

"Vampires. They are selling the blood to vampires."

"Oh, fuck off. I am sick to the back teeth of you constantly taking the piss, you smug French bastard."

"I am quite serious."

"I'll show you who's serious." Frank puts the child down on the floor, gently. Then he takes the golf club from the older man and smashes the temperature controls, which are set into the wall beside the door.

He walks back into the clinical suite. He opens the cupboards one by one and scatters and smashes the contents: cases of surgical instruments, sample bottles, test tubes, hypodermic needles in plastic bags, beakers, and indeterminate pieces of hand-held medical machinery. He overturns the chairs and gurneys, one by one. When he is done, he is red-faced and breathless. He stands in the middle of the devastation, leaning hands on thighs. Mr. Thélème walks in and raises an eyebrow.

"Right," says Frank, pausing for breath between each word. "Let's find that office."

<hr />

An alarm begins to ring.

"Took 'em long enough," says Frank.

The girl is curled up in the swivel chair in the manager's office; the lock on the door has been shot out. Frank is regretting this a little, but he tells himself that a siege would be pointless.

The two men stand at the desk, looking at the PC screen.

"You'd have thought he'd have a password or something," says Frank.

"The man probably doesn't even know how to set one up," says Mr. Thélème. "Do you?"

"No. It's not the point. They don't seem to give a fuck, the careless bastards."

"That is precisely it. They have no care for security. They have things under control at a much higher level than this."

The sound of an engine outside.

"They coming?" says Frank.

"I expect they are investigating your work at the factory unit."

Frank still has the keys in his pocket.

"You are aware that this is where they will take us, Mr. Crowe."

"Yeah."

"I have something."

Windows has opened up. The manager is using the default wallpaper. Right on the desktop sits a folder called Accounts, next to an icon called ERP.

"There isn't a printer here."

Thélème holds up a USB flashdrive.

It takes the private security firm's men another half an hour to get to the manager's office, by which time Frank, the girl, and Mr. Thélème have gone. The computer is in bits across the carpet, its case battered by a blunt object.

⌖

After dropping off Mr. Thélème with some relief, Frank's first port of call is the Casualty department in Basildon. He tells the nurse the girl is his grand-daughter, and that she's called Pauline, and that something terrible has happened to her. Then, when they wheel her into the rooms, he leaves.

When they see what's happened to her, they'll ask questions, and probably call the police. And no one will ever know who she is, because she can barely even talk. She'll probably end up in a children's home somewhere. She'll have a pretty miserable life, too, but it'll be longer and better than anything she'll have experienced there.

He feels a pang of regret about an hour later, as he sits in the Internet café, drinking milky tea (two sugars). But he knows he's old, and not cut out to bring up a child on his own.

Which was the problem, really.

He plugs the USB stick into the front of the computer. He flails around a bit, but doesn't have too much trouble opening the output files.

The document containing the raw materials manifest is presented in circumspect language, and if Frank had not seen what those raw materials were, he might not have made the connections he has. But he sees shipments of people, from China, from Iraq, from the Sudan, from Nigeria.

Frank has always been one of those people with no time for immigrants. They're spongers. Out to take our jobs. Steal our benefits. But he's not a monster. Frank understands with a jolt exactly what it is they are doing. Thélème told him there were nine of these places. That means thousands of people every year. He feels sick again.

He skims through the other files, looking for the one that matters to him, that was the reason he went... there. Sales. A list of amounts, dates, clients, and a column with one of two values, F and V.

F goes to farms, livestock companies, food suppliers. Companies. Factory farms. V is bought in smaller amounts, by private individuals.

He hopes the voice on the phone was wrong... but no, there: one, two... seven large sales in the space of a month, all V. Clear as day. Sold to Ms. Crowe.

INTRODUCTION

Vampires own the night. The city goes dark. Shadows fall across suburban streets and farm fields. The sun goes down and the barest sliver of a moon comes up — not much light, not much light at all.

Those hunters whose Vigil pits them against the fiends of the night know a true fear of the dark. When you hunt the spider, you must venture into the web. To hunt the vampire, you must first stalk the night. And that's a terrifying prospect. Beneath the piss-yellow glow of a flickering streetlight, who knows what hungry thing waits just out of sight? In a dark club whose heart pulses with a driving beat, who can say what callous monsters have stuffed themselves into expensive suits and brought a false blush of life to the cheeks — wolves wriggling into the skins of sheep. In a penthouse of glass and steel, a cabal of vampires buy and sell souls and cackle as they do so, and in the lowest bowels of the sewers, a nest of hardly-human leeches writhe in coagulating puddles of blood. Hunters know that vampires have their territories — oh, that block's got the blood witches entrenched, and that housing project is in the squeezing grip of some thug 'banger bloodsucker gang. But really smart hunters know this is just a ruse. The vampires claim the whole *night* as their territory. These creatures of death own the darkness.

And hunters want to take it back.

Embracing Darkness

Here's why vampires are scary: they're basically us. Hunters see it — vampires are really just the dark side of humanity. Like the moon to the sun, like sin to virtue, like death to life. For the most part, these accursed undead look like anybody else, and even the ones who have become so monstrous still retain some glimmer of humanness (the glint of mercy in a milky eye, a wedding ring on a gnarled and pale finger, a decades-old love letter folded perfectly and kept in the heel of the monster's expensive shoe). *That's* what's truly frightening: that they're us; that we could become *them*. If they were pure monster, just a seething throng of uncaring evil rising up out of Hell, well, that's scary because it's implacable, but it's not precisely sinister, is it? Vampirism is an infection of both body and spirit. It's a disease you can catch. Hunters know it. They've seen too many of their own taken and turned — either made to suckle at a succubus' breast to get at the sweet blood, or simply murdered outright and dragged unwittingly into the mock life of the vampire.

Hunters fight for the light, both inside and out. Some vampires fight for that light, too, but find that it always lies just out of reach — the darkness is too deep, too pervasive, and over time they give in. The hunger cannot be denied. Sin must be fed. The soul — if any part of it is even left within the vampire, and some hunters argue that nary a sliver remains — will shrivel on the vine like plants kept from the sun.

I saw their starved lips in the gloam,
With horrid warning gaped wide,
And I awoke and found me here,
On the cold hill's side.
—John Keats, "La Belle Dame sans Merci"

Beast and Abyss

Beast I am, lest a beast I become. Stare too long into the Abyss, and you become the Abyss. And all that jazz.

Hunters fear vampires for another reason — proximity. Hunting them takes a toll. It's not like hunting other monsters. You get close to their ways, their *nocturnal society*, and it's like wrestling with feral pigs: you'll get some mud on you. Think of it like going undercover. When a detective goes undercover — and we're talking *deep* cover, here — he gets close to the evils of man. He rubs elbows with the gnarliest, nastiest motherfuckers. To get near them, he has to do things. Things his soul won't ever forgive. He can't help it. Soon, he starts to think like them. Even if it's just a little bit, it's too much.

Hunters descend into nightmare when bringing the Vigil to bear against the bloodsuckers. They must walk the night. They must wander into the beast's lair. Some hunters play one set of vampires against the other. They make deals, Faustian bargains of blood and souls. They're close to evil. Some hunters see the vampires are pure monsters, and by failing to see even the tiniest glimmer of humanness within the fiends, they lose something. Perspective. Mercy. And their souls darken. Other hunters go the opposite way: they see too much within the vampires that they understand. That maybe they respect, or even *like*. The cruelty and callousness of the creatures of the night is very seductive. They have sway over men's minds. Hunters can lose bits of their soul there, too.

The Blood's the Thing

For vampires, it's all about the blood. Sticky. Wet. Sweet like nectar. Bitter like pennies. For a vampire, the blood is both brutal and sensuous — gross arterial spray arced across a white wall, or a bead of luscious red trickling down a bared thigh. It is both grotesque and sexual, a curse and a blessing. Hunters are going to encounter the blood when they encounter vampires, because it's what drives the creatures of the night. They're going to see it rent from a vampire's gut. They're going to feel it forced into their mouths from an opened wrist. Down the drain. On the ceiling. Staining teeth. The blood's the thing, see?

The Whys and Wherefores

Why hunt a vampire? The obvious thing is revenge. Vampires cannot help but set off chains of events — murder a teenage girl or turn her into a bloodthirsty fiend, and the father wants justice done.

For some hunters, it's not about revenge, but about justice (though some could argue that those are two sides of the same coin). Vampires are monsters. They hide amongst the herd. They're a cancer that needs cutting out.

But the conflict isn't always so easy as justice or revenge.

Vampires know things. They are keepers of mighty secrets, potent lore, and powerful resources. Hunters might want those things for themselves. Maybe that means beheading some foolish fang and taking what he has, but maybe it means making a deal — "Want to work together?" How to oust the pack of Lupines that've been stalking the roads just outside the city, roads that both the hunter and the vampire need open? Vampires have territory. They have power. They have access. All things a hunter might desire. The hunt can be selfish — and vampires appreciate a selfish motive.

How to Use This Book

Throughout the book, you'll find several tales that tie into one another — the stories of Frank, the Chevalier Thélème, and Frank's daughter Bianca. All people affected by the insidious vampiric menace.

Chapter One: Night Country gives you glimpses into the ceaseless struggle of hunter and vampire. Hunters are vulnerable and mortal, but the Vigil is eternal — and vampires know a thing or two about eternity. In-character artifacts help show how vampires have shaped the hunt.

Chapter Two: At Stake describes how the hunters deal with vampires. How does Network Zero or the Malleus Maleficarum bring the Vigil to bear against the society of the night? You'll find information on how all the compacts and conspiracies wage their tireless wars against the fangs, and you'll also find some new compacts and conspiracies (such as the Cainite Heresy) that bear unique grudges against the vampires.

> ## VIGIL AND REQUIEM
>
> This book is not meant to replace **Vampire: The Requiem**. If you don't have that book, you don't need it. You'll find what you need in this book, whether it's about the struggle between hunter and vampire, or a myriad of "vampire systems" to utilize in your story.
>
> If you *do* have **Requiem**, you have two choices: use this book for its angle on hunters, but then use **Requiem** for the basic systems; or use this book and **Requiem** in tandem. This book presents some new rules and takes on the vampire, and they can just as easily be mixed and matched with what's found in **Requiem**. That works well to keep players on their toes, as a sense of honest mystery goes a very long way.

Chapter Three: Drawing Blood is your one-stop shop for systems. New Endowments, Tactics and Merits meant to help a hunter carry the fight to the vampires' doorsteps? Done. The mysterious Rites of Denial, wielded by a willfully ignorant Cainite Heresy? Absolutely. Rules on how to create believable and unique vampire antagonists for use in your story? No doubt.

Chapter Four: The Nocturnal offers a look at what vampires *mean* in your story. What vampire archetypes will best suit your tale? What threats do they represent? What kinds of iconic scenes can play out in your tale? In addition, you'll get yet another look at Philadelphia, this time framed from the viewpoint of *hunter versus vampire*.

Death, sex, disease, grief. The vampire personifies all of those things that we fear, all of those things we have, over time, made taboo. The vampire has a human face, maybe even the face of someone we knew, someone we loved. The vampire is the corruption of everything we want: sexual potency, eternal youth, health.

The vampire preys on the innocent. The vampire is a murderer. The vampire is a rapist. This is what the hunter knows: don't let the glamour and the romance blind you to the fact. The undead are the greatest threat the invisible world has to offer. If even they don't know it, it makes no difference.

At least, that's what you have to believe if you want to survive as a vampire hunter. You mustn't lose your way. Start sympathizing with them, start imagining that they're still human, still worthy of pity or mercy, and they'll have you in their clutches.

Yeah, it's the only way.

Found in Ancient Tombs

The very beginning of human consciousness was perhaps marked by the awareness of mortality. What surprise, then, that the earliest myths of humankind concerned the walking, hungry dead?

These old stories come from long, long ago, but are no less pertinent for us today. Human beings only live for a finite time. But we stay dead forever. And if we walk, we walk forever.

In the most ancient times, the vampire was perhaps far more open about his depredations than he is now. People knew such things existed, and accepted that they were a danger. If few people rose up to fight them, it's perhaps a testament to the other ways in which vampires could hide. In Egypt, the vampires became central for a time to the cult of the gods, and brought about the downfall of a king and the destruction of his eternal reputation.

But only the most subtle monsters depended upon cults and conspiracies. Consider the story of the Sirens: according to Homer, Odysseus, on his travels, eludes a bevy of carnivorous bird-women, whose song seizes the heart of humans and lures them to their deaths. The Greek myths tell us they were the companions of Persephone, who, lest we forget, was the wife of Hades, with one foot in the land of the living and one in the land of the dead.

Secret texts owned by the Aegis Kai Doru and the Loyalists of Thule give other versions of the story. The friendship with Persephone is more of a poetic, figurative sort of relationship, a metaphor to describe a creature neither wholly dead nor wholly alive, suggesting that in fact the Sirens were as much ghost and corpse as bird and woman. They openly used their powers to inspire dread, fear and love; they fed openly by night. If "Odysseus" (really a composite of a dozen or more ancient monster-killers) faced them down, it is telling that the accounts show him neither killing the monsters nor they him; simply that he survived the encounter was victory enough.

Throughout the whole vast shadowy world of ghosts and demons there is no figure so terrible, no figure so dreaded and abhorred, yet dight [sic] with such fearful fascination, as the vampire, who is himself neither ghost nor demon, but who yet partakes the dark natures and possesses the mysterious and terrible nature of both.

— Montague Summers, The Vampire

Meanwhile, in ancient India, the Buddhist king Ashoka supposedly faced a blood-drinking monster that had styled itself as a *Deva*, a divinely-powered being on a par with a Hindu god. Enlightened as he was, the creature's power to make others worship it did not work on him. He defeated the *Deva*, so the story goes, in philosophical discussion: he convinced the creature that it really was divine, and it walked naked into the dawn, fooled by its own arrogance into a suicidal act. Modern-day vampire hunters would be better off not trying Ashoka's tactic, of course: however the event panned out, if it happened at all, it most certainly did not end quite like that. The story as recorded is a morality tale, and as such holds its lessons (pride as downfall being one of them), but the secret of killing a vampire that has managed to get the ordinary people around him to worship him as a god is not one of them.

As far as scholars in the older and better-informed conspiracies and compacts know, something seems to have happened about the time of the Western Roman Empire to cause vampires to follow the example of their Egyptian forebears rather than that of the Greek or Indian examples. No one really knows why that should be. The likelihood is the dead don't know that either. It's a mixed blessing. While the public are mercifully spared the knowledge of the greatest of the supernatural horrors, the vampire has become adept at hiding from view. The disbelief of the masses can be as much a hindrance to the dedicated hunter as it is an aid.

Akhenaten (1336BCE)

An anonymous Egyptian document, supposedly translated from a fragmentary 14th-Dynasty papyrus kept by the Ascending Ones of New York:

Amenhotep, Ruler of Thebes, the Strong Bull, Appearing in Truth, One Establishing Laws, Pacifying the Two Lands, Great of Valor, Smiter of the Asiatics, passed on to the Field of Green, and when the mourning of Egypt passed, all recognized his eldest son Amenhotep as Pharaoh.

But Amenhotep son of Amenhotep did not honor his father's name. He did not honor the Gods of the Twin Kingdoms, nor did he honor the palace of his father, nor even did he honor the holy city of Thebes.

As time went on, he only sought the worship of the sun-disc Aten, and built a city to his god, and he took the name Akhenaten, Strong Bull, Beloved of Aten, Great King of Akhetaten, Who Bears the Name of the Aten.

He presented to all the slaying of Amun-Re in the sight of all. He proscribed the writing and the very speaking of the names of the Gods.

And this is our secret: we knew that he was right to do so, and he did so with our blessing.

Akhenaten knew that to venerate the Aten-Sun was to defy the ones who rules the night, who had over-run Thebes and Luxor, who had ruled his father as surely as they prepared to rule him.

And what is more: the two Great Cults who guarded the God-King had been impotent, for the dead had violated the True Way that the Great Ennead had ordained. They had dared to rule over the living. They had placed themselves in the way of Anubis and Amemet and the Field of Green. They had made the people of the Twin Nation their provender.

The day came when even the Cult of Set, whom we had entrusted with the protection of the night as we had protected the day, fell, too. The vampires came among them, and killed their priests and captains, and made our brothers dead and hungry; they in turn made more of their kind from the faithful of the Cult of Set. And those they did not kill and make to rise they forced to drink of their blood, that they might love them and die for them.

And they thought that we did not know. But the light of the Sun reveals all things, and although the Phoenix dies at sunset, it rises with the dawn, and we learned all things anew each night.

We protected the king, and it was I who forsook the Great Gods of the Nile and who counseled him to make himself Akhenaten, and to build a City of the Aten where the dead, who could not bear the sun, were not.

And while we made the new city our own, we took to learning how best to ascend beyond the Phoenix, to protect both day and night without our erstwhile brothers' knowledge, for they still smiled, and shook our hands, and claimed friendship.

I saw the Hand of Horus, First Captain of the Phoenix, brew a potion that would never permit him to sleep, and I saw him fight the dark, and die.

I saw the Vigilant of Isis, the Second Captain of the Phoenix, brew a potion that might keep him from sleep, and add a single drop of a cobra's poison. And I saw him fight the dark, and die.

And I, the Child of Osiris, Seed of the Infertile, First Priest, saw that I must create my own drug, and I made myself pure. I ascended. And when I had made myself strong, then I brewed my potion, and then I steeped it in the venom of the cobra, and then I drank, and I became the first of the Ascended.

And on that night the war began.

While we had readied ourselves, the corruption that had replaced our brothers had made their own plans. They had plied the priests of the Great Ennead with their blood and had made them their slaves.

And having chained the hearts of the priests of the Twin Lands, they set them to raising the ire of the army and the mob; they said that Akhenaten was mad, or that he was possessed by a demon and that the soul of the beautiful queen was not her own, that she had been sacrificed to the darkness.

And then Akhenaten died. There was no mystery in that. He was old, and he was tired, and he grew ill.

The Queen, and Akhenaten's son, the boy Pharaoh Tut-Ankh-Aten took the throne together, but they were not as strong as the old king, and they could not maintain the peace. Came the night when a battle raged in the streets of the City of Aten. The Cult of the Phoenix and the followers of the Sun ranged against the mob and the priests, and the army and the Traitor Cult of Set.

We fought well. But we failed. The enemy took the city and they took the palace. They killed the queen, and they forced the boy to execrate his own father, to damn the memory of that great king to be forgotten, that his soul might dwindle to nothing and be exiled from the Field of Green. Then, when the child was old enough, they killed him and replaced him with their puppet, the high priest Ay.

We took our revenge, and took our cue from our erstwhile allies, grooming our own Pharaoh in waiting. We came by day. And the Cult of Set crumbled to dust in our hands.

The verdict of the priests could not be undone. We could only urge the new Pharaoh to add Ay to the execration of his predecessors. We abandoned politics. We retreated into the shadows, leaving behind the palaces of the powerful for the alleys of the city, for the company of the unwashed and the disenfranchised.

We left behind the ashes of the Cult of Set. But we will never forget.

Story Hooks: Conspiracies and Cults

• The Followers of Set and the Cult of the Phoenix

Don't tell the Ascending Ones, but the Cult of Set survived. Like their ancient friends-turned-enemies, they don't know their counterparts have survived, and even if they did stumble upon them, they probably wouldn't recognize them for what they are. Still, even if none of the vampires who now control that ancient cult were walking in the days of Akhenaten and Ay, they're still the followers of Typhon Set, and still dedicated to evil (of *course* they're dedicated to evil—they're vampires).

In a game context, the real question is what does the Cult of Set actually *do*? And this is something of a wider question. It's all very well ascribing eons-old motivations to monsters and hunters alike, but what does time mean in the cold light of the present day (or night, for that matter)? In story terms, ancient cults and conspiracies have to do things, and while the history is part of the reason and motivation behind what it is they do, the important thing is what they do.

What the Cult of Set does—what they still do—is foment chaos. They do it in small ways—consider how a vampire killing one security guard could cause all sorts of knock-on effects, as a CCTV camera screen doesn't get watched, as someone who should have been stopped walks into a shopping precinct and detonates the ten pounds of C4 strapped to his waist....

And they do it in larger ways. Vampires worm their way into the corridors of power. They corrupt politicians, scientists and church leaders alike. They use power to their own advantage.

And not for its own sake. For the sake of chaos. For the sake of the collapse of society, because it's what their god represents.

It begins with a mailman posting the wrong letter through a door; suddenly, someone important is blackmailed. Someone commits suicide. Or a relationship falls apart. A vacuum in a job or a breakdown in communication keeps vitally important money from some civic project—perhaps the roads aren't fixed in one part of town, or a rehab center has to close down, or the necessary annual check on the city bridge is reduced to one man looking at it for about two minutes and going, "looks fine to me."

The drug problems in town escalate; dealers move in. The police move in. Gun battles and drive-by shootings increase in frequency. The wrong man gets shot by the cops. A riot results. The whole area becomes a no-go.

The bridge falls down. People die. People grieve. A man loses his wife in the disaster. He loses sleep. He works in the subway system. He's tired, preoccupied. He makes an error. A train crashes. More people die.

Gradually, society disintegrates, and it's only through the small things, the little issues. The vampire conspiracy needs to do very little... and then sit back and wait for the fabric of human culture to be fragmented enough for them to stand up and take advantage of it.

Who can stop them? Who will be able to halt the plot before things get too bad? Or is it already too late?

Even if an investigator manages somehow to trace a chain of events back to the vampires—and why would he?—who in their right mind is going to believe that these events *can* be traced back to a drink getting spiked, or a letter being misdelivered, or a traffic signal being faulty? It's not that the vampires know themselves what the mischief they conceive leads to. In fact, they're responsible for hundreds, even thousands of small errors and acts of mischief a year, and it's only a few that lead to the chaos they desire.

And of course, ordinary people are wholly responsible for causing chaos themselves.

Even so, it is possible to uncover the machinations of the Cult of Set. But the Followers of Set have been gently unraveling the threads of human interaction for over three thousand years. Even if a covey of blood-drinkers become handfuls of dust at the end of a story, is there any hope of stopping the chain of chaos the Setites began so long ago?

• Vampire Cults

One interesting fact about the Cult of Set is that not all of its followers—in fact, very few of them—are vampires.

Many of the Followers of Set are ordinary people, and not all of those necessarily know that their masters are vampires. A group of hunters might think that they're investigating a cult or even another hunter conspiracy, and only when they reach the top do they have a chance of understanding what they're really facing.

The Cult of Set isn't the only vampire cult out there. Above all, vampires are manipulators. They lie. People follow vampires unknowingly because vampires are magnetic and scary and sexy and, in conversational terms, powerful. Often, they don't even know that they're doing it, because so many vampires have the power to manipulate emotions, memories and even thoughts. A businessman might find the woman in black who wants him to get some accounts for her as creepy as hell, but even if she isn't using mind-warping powers on her witless acquaintance, he's going to do what she says anyway, because she's also dangerous and really *hot*.

But plenty of the human agents of the undead know exactly what it is they're serving. Some do it because they're scared. Some do it because they think they're in love (or lust, anyway) with a vampire. And a lot of them do it because they want to be vampires themselves, and the vampires keep promising immortality and power... and maybe they even grant a few of their most loyal with that "gift" of thralldom through a taste of their blood (though it must be asked: how many of the immortal minions of vampires think that they actually *are* vampires?)

And then there are those who have been seduced in some way. A lover or spouse who is still devoted to her now-undead better half. A sex offender or serial killer who's been promised all the victims he might ever want. A gangster whose boss doesn't come out in the day any more.

A hooker whose pimp has developed... unusual tastes. Hunters facing well-placed vampires may have to deal with dozens of human cultists before getting to the big score.

The Circoncellions (418CE)

From an open letter, entitled De Ultimo Avium Minervae, attrbuted to the name Valens Valentinus, preserved in one copy in a library held by the Aegis Kai Doru in Marrakesh:

Our nation has abandoned Minerva; Minerva has in turn abandoned us.

I fought for Eugenius, my brothers. This you know. I was barely more than a boy, but I was already sworn to Minerva as one of her Birds, and I knew the stakes that had been set. Eugenius was our last hope. When the murderer Theodosius displayed his head before the people of Rome, the old gods finally turned their backs on Rome, and only disasters have followed in the wake of the Christians gaining their last victory. Barbarians have contaminated our once glorious armies. The Christians, so busy fighting among themselves, cannot see how they fail to keep destruction from Rome's gates. And our Empire stands as two empires now, each stunted and weak, where once an inviolable and mighty empire stood.

But we must endure.

I have recently returned from Africa, and I have a proposal. But my proposal depends on a story.

I had followed the Cainites to Africa.

The Cainites were another Christian faction among many. As far as I can glean, they were led into some kind of "error" about 50 years ago by a leader whom they realized was a vampire, and whom they destroyed. They made something of a nui-

sance of themselves, for they tried—in vain—to alert the other Christians to the monsters who inhabited the city below, and grew ever more strident as their entreaties fell upon deaf ears. The other Christians drove them out of Rome.

Some found their way to Constantinople, where they were no more welcome. Between the Christians, who accused them of heresy, and the vampires they enraged and frightened with their public sermons, the Cainites died.

Some found their way to the North, to Britain. But we lost track of them in the year of the civil war with Magnus Maximus. But the Cainites who made their way to Carthage fell in with the Circoncellions, for one simple reason. The Circoncellions knew about the vampires.

You may know of the Donatists. They had been the product of a century-old controversy among the Christians of Africa concerning some trifle I do not understand. In their typically Christian obstinacy, they allowed no accord to be reached. One of the factions, the party of one Donatus, had finally been outlawed. Forced into the desert, they became Circoncellions: they dwelled in desert crypts, and they supported their families through banditry.

As you may surmise, others claimed the crypts, and for decades, a small war has raged between the Circoncellions and the desert dead, who compete for territory and prey with the Donatists.

And this is why the Cainites joined them so easily. I had followed their trail for five years or more when I finally traced them. I left Carthgae with a single horse, and I ventured into the desert. On that first night, I took shelter in a tomb which bore on its walls some signs I recognised as being of the Donatists. But it hadn't been theirs for a long time, and had I not known the Red Rituals, I would have died, or worse.

It took three days to find them. They are adept at hiding, these Circoncellions, but the greatest difficulty for me came at night; the territory known as the Circoncellions' hunting ground is now mostly claimed by the monsters, who feed off each other as much as on the people of the region. Indeed, were it not for the intervention of the very outlaws I sought, the last of the four creatures I encountered would have killed me.

I lay there on the sand in the light of a desert moon, my hands grasping the wrist whose hand grasped my throat, and I prepared to meet my ancestors in the realm of Pluto. I closed my eyes—and then I heard a hoarse voice hiss the words: Cain, qui est?

I opened my eyes; a blade beheaded the creature with a single stroke. It grazed my forehead, drawing blood. The wrist crumbled beneath my fingers; the headless body followed. Removing the grave-ash from my robes, I looked up to see three men in Berber robes who were by no means friendly.

They would have killed me, had I not begun quickly to explain why I sought them out. I had a gift for them.

They blindfolded me and took me to their camp. Their families were in a terrible state. Their children were starving and diseased. Men and women alike, their faces uncovered, were burned to leather by the sun and sand. But all of them knew how to fight, man, woman, child.

These were my Circoncellions, and the Cainites who had brought them over to their cause.

Who lived apart from the world that they might face the dead.

But their numbers were dwindling. The monsters and the soldiers of the Empire alike had driven them to this; some of their former friends now tore at the throats and drank the blood of travelers they would once have simply robbed.

Brothers, I taught them the first of the Red Rituals: The Denials.

Forgive me. It came to me that our time as warriors against the night has gone, and that we must pass on our knowledge to others better suited to the world as it is.

We live in a world where the one god has replaced the many, where the hard word of the cenobite and the hermit carry more weight than the words of the philosopher and the sophist. The ages change, and the Age of Iron becomes replaced by a yet worse age, an age of Rust and Darkness.

An age of unwavering belief, of obstinacy, of violence without glory. The Birds of Minerva are finished. We must find new hands to do our work.

Story Hooks: Heretics

• Sources

Hunter compacts and conspiracies like to think themselves autonomous; truly, though, others pull their strings. Even those whose leaders are known to the membership have masters whose motives are often difficult to discern. From where does Task Force: VALKYRIE get its funding? Who *are* the Cheiron Group's Board of Directors? What does the Lucifuge really want? And why *does* Ambrogio Baudolino meet with her, for that matter?

The Cainite Heresy still exists. Its leaders receive communiqués from an unnamed (and perhaps unnamable) source, which offer everything from intelligence on the vampires they hunt, right down to the Rituals of Denial, the blood-magics they use to fight the dark.

But who are the Cainites' Sources? This document suggests that they were, at least at one point, the last remnants of the Birds of Minerva (see **Hunter: the Vigil,** p. 18). But that doesn't mean that it's true, or that even if it was true then, it's true now.

ROMAN CONNECTIONS

Storytellers interested in the ultimate origins of the Cainite Heresy can find more on where they came from and how they drove off their original master in the **Vampire: the Requiem** supplements **Requiem for Rome**, p.174 and **Fall of the Camarilla**, pp. 134-141.

• Outsiders

The Circoncellions were, in some respects, terrorists. They were certainly outlaws and outsiders. The thing is, that's very much the position of the monster hunter in society. You go around heavily armed, wanting to kill things that most people don't even believe in? Someone's going to think you're mad.

Nor consider the fact that vampires, of all the monsters, are the walking corpses with their claws sunk deep into the jugular of society itself.

The civic leaders you trust, the church ministers, the top-level respectable gangsters... they're all under the control of the undead. Some of them might even know it. Maybe the President is, too, although he's got Task Force: VALKYRIE to look out for him. But who's running TF:V...?

And so it goes. The point is that vampire conspirators have at their disposal a lot of the means to make hunters' lives miserable beyond simply floating outside their window at night, beckoning and hissing blasphemies. Although they can do that too, if they like.

But first comes the bank losing details of payments and foreclosing on your house. Then comes the planted drugs, and then comes the digitally manipulated photographs of you with the prostitutes, and then the police seize your house and find child pornography on your computer... and then, yes, all right, they appear outside your window and start trying to drive you mad by whispering sweet blasphemies, and controlling the mind of the one you love the most before turning her into a lascivious Lucy Westenra clone.

If you weren't an outsider before you started tangling with vampires, you will be by the time you've been tangling with the undead for any length of time. In the end, you may find that going on the run and behaving like a terrorist may be your only option.

When the Sun Went Out

Came a time when the dead ruled over the hearts and fears of the human race.

In a way, the dead ruled over everyone. Death was omnipresent. Now that the glory days of Rome were long gone, plague and war were realities for everyone. Grief was an everyday reality. The dead never really went away.

Perhaps it was this that created the fear of the vampire. A school of thought exists that suggests that any true tales of vampires date back to the Middle Ages, and that before this time they simply didn't exist, that somehow the collective human desire to regain contact with the masses of the dead called the ghosts of the dead back to earth.

But then, another school of thought says it's rubbish.

More importantly, more provably, in the year 536, the sky turned black. In the Byzantine Empire, the days grew short, and even at noon, the best light was as twilight. In Western and Northern Europe, crops failed; cold winds brought drought and famine. Chinese chronicles tell of a persistent choking fog that obscured the light. The empire of Teotihuacán, the fabled city of the Aztecs, collapsed under the weight of the famine and cold, as starving people ceased to obey the rule of law.

What happened? *How* it happened is simple enough to guess: a massive eruption took the top off Krakatoa, creating vast tidal waves and spewing so much foul air, smoke and dust into the atmosphere that the sky changed color. It had all the force that a small-scale nuclear war would have, and brought the same kind of ceaseless winter.

Why it happened is another matter. You could talk about geology and physics, but a fragmentary document held by agents of the Lucifuge active in Seoul and dated to sometime contemporary with the eruption includes a prayer for the darkening of the sky, an apparent magical ritual written in a Javanese script of the period, offering hints that its author was not a living human being. Most of the Lucifuge's scholars, the ones who have seen it, say it's a forgery. But what do they know?

Whether the volcano erupted because some vampire hatched a mad plot to extinguish the sun or simply because it was time for the volcano to erupt, the living world became a playground for the dead. Most human histories don't talk about it. They couldn't: the undead masters of the world held human affairs in too tight a grip.

And those who dared to stand against the vampires—the church, certain leaders among the Ummah, the ancient conspiracies, the tribal peoples who refused to be "civilized" by the failing imperial powers—faced the hardest centuries the world had so far seen.

The Ghûl Wife (799CE)

The Ghûl Wife

A virgin of surpassing beauty and grace came to Baghdad with her father, and he brought with him a handsome dowry. No one knew them, however, and the man gained no admittance to the homes of those who would marry her. But one night, a young man of good family named Nouman caught a glimpse of the girl, quite by chance, as she looked out of a window in her lodgings. It was enough for him to wish desperately to possess her, and the usual interplay of father and father, meeting and dinner and business deal commenced, and soon young Nouman and the girl, her name Amina, were married.

Victorian Folklore

Amina proved a dutiful and tender wife, but she exhibited some strangenesses of behavior. At meals, she would eat only a small dish of rice, one grain at a time, piercing each with a bodkin and carrying it slowly to her mouth. At other times she would eat no more than a handful of breadcrumbs, always one at a time.

And then a servant respectfully told Nouman that Amina stole out of the house every night. He did not know; she had always done so while he slept. One night, however, he feigned sleep, and when she left, he followed her. She traveled to a graveyard, and there Nouman saw his wife in conversation with a Ghûl, a frightful bloody-mawed creature accustomed to feeding on the dead, and then he saw her joining the Ghûl in sucking blood and marrow from the decaying limbs of a disinterred corpse.

The Ghûl Wife

The following day, as Amina dined on grains of rice, Nouman asked her if the rice was as flavorsome as rotting flesh. The woman, enraged, commanded Nouman to become a dog.

And he lost his mind. He became as Nebuchadnezzar, a pathetic creature akin to the beasts of the field. And while his faculties were absent, the woman disposed of his estate. She kept her husband on a leash, and fed him rotting scraps. And she seduced, corrupted or fed upon Nouman's servants and friends, all the time affecting the innocence of a young girl afflicted far too soon with a mad husband.

Nouman's plight would perhaps have been eternal were it not for a young woman of courage and perspicacity named Asha.

Asha is a somewhat enigmatic character. The tale as written assumes that Asha's exploits are known to the reader; it calls her a "protector" and a "shield-bearer." Presumably at some time these titles had some meaning in the context of the tale. Uncommonly, neither beauty nor breeding are attributed to Asha, as would be usual in stories of this kind.

Asha is said to have pursued the Ghûls of her country with a ferocity unequaled (the tale says that she was a "vengeance-seeker," but gives no clue as to what vengeance she sought, exactly). Asha had taken to haunting the graveyards of the region, and it was there that she saw Nouman's wife on her usual nocturnal jaunt, dining on blood and flesh.

Asha followed Amina home, and stealing into the house, there witnessed the horrors hidden behind the walls of Nouman's home, and the Ghûls who feasted there.

Asha engaged the Ghûls in conversation, pretending to share in their provender, and tricked the Ghûls into revealing that if their mistress is bade to leave using a certain order of words, then leave she will. She took her leave of the monsters, and found Nouman chained in the cellar. Asha knew a little magic, and with it she restored Nouman's faculties with a "prayer." Together, they confronted Amina. The sorceress tried to reduce Asha to the same state of animalism that Nouman suffered, but failed; Asha was in possession of a magical bracelet that protected her from such enchantments.

Asha bid the Ghûl-wife leave using the words the other Ghûls taught her, and she duly did. Nouman rallied the remains of his hired men, and with sunrise, they drove the Ghûls from the house.

The story does not end with Asha and Nouman being married, as one would expect. Rather, it ends with Nouman offering his thanks, and Asha moving on. One wonders about the context of some stories, and who Asha really was.

157

Story Hooks: Revenants

• **Obscure Weaknesses, Unusual Strengths**

Traditionally, vampire myth has more or less accepted the idea that vampires can operate in the daytime. It's only since Hollywood started making vampire movies that vampires in the media have burnt up in daylight. Obviously, most of the vampires that hunters face in the World of Darkness can't face sunlight at all. It burns them to a cinder. Which begs the question: where do the stories of vampires walking around in the daylight come from?

It might be a simple misunderstanding of the truth, one of those fatal, disastrous misunderstandings of reality that plague the Vigil. Or, it might be deliberate misinformation, fed into the pool of folklore by vampires who wanted to hide heir most desperate weakness.

In the bizarre story of Amina and Nouman, the Ghûl-wife has no issue whatsoever with daylight, freely using her blasphemous magical powers no matter what the position of the sun. More commonly, stories of vampires walking by day tell of how the vampires lose their powers in the daylight, becoming no more powerful than ordinary, living human beings.

Perhaps there *is* an element of truth in this. Of course, a vampire of the "default" sort bursts into flames when the sun shines upon him, but he isn't the only kind of vampire lurking in the night (note also that Amina eats human carrion, suggesting a slightly different order of the dead). Note also, however, that

Amina is under several obscure bans herself—she can only eat plain rice or bread crumbs, one grain at a time, and must lift them to her mouth on the end of a knife. She must leave and never return if told to do so in a certain way.

Perhaps it's a trade-off for having the power to walk by day. An "ordinary" vampire might be able to surprise our hunters with the power to walk by day, while having another, equally crippling weakness. Perhaps a vampire cannot cross running water under her own power and will be destroyed forever if immersed. Another vampire crumbles into dust after being pricked by a sprig of freshly-picked buckthorn. Another shares the werewolf's vulnerability to silver bullets.

The point is that a vampire's weaknesses—even those of the more commonly encountered social vampires—are by no means set in stone.

(**Hunter** players familiar with the other **World of Darkness** games may find it difficult to "play dumb" about vampires. By mining folklore and literature, the Storyteller can keep players on their toes with only one or two tweaks to an otherwise straightforwardly created vampire.)

• **Mind Control**

Of all the powers that the monsters of the night affect, mind control is perhaps their most defining—and some might say most diabolical— ability. Many vampires have some variation of the power to control minds or emotions. Some use direct mind control, exploiting the power of their will or voice to force people to do things against their will, and eventually to erode a victim's will to such an extent that he is unable to think for himself anymore. Some are more subtle, developing an aura that inspires others to fall in love with them. This kind of vampire doesn't make you do her will. She makes you *want* to do her will. Maybe it's a fine distinction, but it certainly changes the way that the vampire's dupes behave: they're not blank-eyed, slow-moving zombies—they're people who behave like, you know, people. Other vampires work on a similarly primal level, but instead instill fear in their victims. And other vampires still wipe memories or simply drive their victims mad. Amina had the power to strip away a person's faculties and make him no more coherent than an animal.

Whatever the specifics of the power, variations of mind control remain many vampires' greatest strength. Hunters should remember that. Making eye contact with a vampire (especially before you even know he's a vampire) could have lethal or worse-than-lethal con-

sequences. When your enemy potentially has control over the mind of any human being she meets, whom can you trust? Your spouse? Your children? Your friends? Your boss? The police?

Or even yourself? How do you know that the route you're taking is what you want to do, or what *they* want you to do? How do you know that in that last skirmish, you didn't get a bit too close? And what happened in those five minutes you lost on Thursday? Vampires are often very old, and know exactly how to use the powers they command to the most devastating effect.

A clever Storyteller should know how to sow the seeds of doubt, perhaps by giving players the evidence they need for the characters to uncover a sleeper agent, and then liberally scattering red herrings across the story. A good vampire story is always better with a bit of paranoia.

Saving the Maiden (1197... or Thereabouts)

THE MASTER OF DRACHENSTEIN

A shuddery tale of terror by VINCENT MOON

PART FIVE

SOMEONE died here tonight, Franz," whispered Partha Mac Othna, rising to his feet, wiping bloody fingers on his worn leather breeches. He set his face towards the corridor, its Acheronian shadows seemingly stretching cold fingers towards the grim-faced warrior. The man beside him, a small, blond figure swathed in a black cloak, nodded.

"See," he whispered, bringing his torch low, "A trail of blood leads...there." His trembling finger pointed into the reaching shadows.

"Someone dragged a body away. Perhaps... perhaps this is she?"

"Courage, Franz," said Mac Othna, placing a huge hand on his companion's shoulder. "The Master of Drachenstein wishes to make Drusilla his bride, not have her murdered in some moldy passage. I have no doubt that she is still alive." He paused. "At least... for now."

Franz looked up at his broad-shouldered companion and nodded. It had been three nights since Lord Yorak had seized Franz's betrothed and had taken her to the

glowering castle of Drachenstein; three nights of terror and peril since Partha Mac Othna, the lonely man from the North and West, his companion of many adventures, had shed his wedding-clothes and strapped on his sword, swearing to help his friend recover the girl or die in the attempt.

Now, having braved the wolves of the forest and the dog-sized sewer-rats that infested the region, the two doughty warriors found themselves in the vault of Lord Yorak's castle, prepared to face the Master of Drachenstein.

"We follow the blood," said Partha Mac Othna, grimly, his angular jar and heavy brows set towards the dark. Swords drawn, the two men crept into the dark. Franz would remember this night for the rest of his life: they tripped over the half-decayed, half-eaten corpses of men and women lost long ago. They skewered rats of uncommon size and aggression on the ends of blades that never rested in their sheaths. Eventually the dark subsided somewhat. They came to a corridor lit by sconces. A vile smell assaulted their noses. Six doorways, closed off with thick iron bars, revealed this to be a dungeon!

Mac Othna crept to the first of the doorways and raised his torch. A dried cadaver, loathly and covered with cobwebs and rat droppings, lay, still in the chains in which he had been forgotten. A rat scurried under the body, causing it to rustle obscenely. "Dead," grunted the huge Briton. "I'll warrant they all are."

As the two men stalked silently down the corridor, the sound of a rattling chain brought them to a halt.

"It seems not, my friend!" ejaculated Franz. He and his doughty friend approached the cell, cautiously. Indeed, it was true. In the last of the cells, there lay, coated with filth and laden with chains, a bearded old man. The emaciated figure looked up and his eyes grew wide.

"Have you come to kill me?" wheezed the old man.

"Nay," said Mac Othna. "Should we?"

"You are not Lord Yorak's men," whispered the prisoner, standing up. He walked to the length of his fetters and held on to the bars with grubby, twig-like fingers.

"What of it?" Said Mac Othna, threateningly.

"I mean that you are not here with the Lord's knowledge," replied the old man, his watery eyes narrowing. "Is that not so?"

"That is so," retorted Franz, curious despite himself. "Who might you be, old one?"

"I am Nicholas Hardestadt of the House Ventrue," said the old man.

"Lord Yorak's benefactor! But I heard you were dead these dozen years," exclaimed Franz.

"I am clearly not dead," smirked the old man. "At least, not wholly."

"Come, friend Franz," said Mac Othna in a low, impatient voice. "We'll not gain much conversing with this wretch."

"On the contrary, tall one!" cried the prisoner. "I can show you how to gain your revenge on the Lord Yorak. I know this castle. I know these passages. And I know Lord Yorak's Secret!"

It was as if the room suddenly went cold. Both men felt a sudden certainty that lightning had flashed outside, notwithstanding the hundreds of feet of earth and stone between them and the outside world.

"Speak," grunted Mac Othna, simply, his sword pointed at the prisoner's throat.

"The Lord Yorak is not a living man," said the old one. "He is a vampire, a ghost possessing a living man's body. He shuns the sunlight and thirsts for the blood of the innocent. He steals comely maidens from the lands around this castle and slakes his unholy thirst on them; having slain them, he makes them to rise into eternal living dead. They become his wanton brides, forced to exist as his eternal slaves, to lure the unwary into servitude, corruption and death..."

A cry of horror rose from Franz.

Nicholas Hardestadt turned to him. "I'll wager this is why you are here," he ventured, affecting the bearing of the lord he once was. "You seek a maiden."

"What is it to you?" snarled Partha Mac Othna, brandishing his sword once again.

"Free me, sirs, and I will lead you to the Lord and his victim. There may yet be time to save your maiden. I desire myself revenged upon Yorak for his theft of my lands and his disposal of my fortune, and any injury to him I would happily see. I will aid you in any way."

Mac Othna grunted. "I see no reason to do so," he stated, sullenly.

Franz grasped his arm. "Time is of the essence, my friend. If Sir Nicholas can help us, I say he should be freed."

Swayed by his friend's words, Mac Othna sheathed his sword in a smooth, simple motion. "Stand back, old man," he said, simply. The old one having done so, he took a few steps back and flung himself against the rusting bars. Three times he did this, each time creating a clang that must have rung out through every corridor of Castle Drachenstein, and on the third, the lock gave way and the bars threw open. It was a matter of minutes for Mac Othna to wedge his trusty poignard between a link of the chains, and, his massive muscles straining, sweat pouring from his sloping brow, to drive the iron open, and free Hardestadt from his fetters, if not the manacle, which still clasped the old man's ankle. Unfettered, the old man's back became straight, and he regained his noble bearing of old.

"This way, my friends," he uttered, an unwavering finger pointing to a junction in the endless underground corridors. "I know of a secret passage."

Hardestadt ran with a speed seemingly impossible for a man of his age, especially a man who had been only a few moments before chained, but the two warriors were too preoccupied with keeping up with the aged lord.

Eventually, Hardestadt came to a dead end in the corridor. Unconcerned, he crouched and began to feel in the mortar between the bricks with probing fingers, even as his two companions caught up with him.

Within seconds, a screeching noise ensued, and the wall swung back to reveal narrow, rising stone steps.

"From the depths to the heights, my friends!" said the

rag-clad Lord. He swung his hand expansively, and Franz and Partha were bound to enter, with Hardestadt behind them they traveled up a wide cylindrical tower, narrow steps at its edge, barely wide enough for one man at a time. The pit in its center grew deeper and deeper, darker and darker as they climbed towards what surely must be the highest point of dread-haunted Castle Drachenstein.

Partha Mac Othna suddenly stopped and turned. Behind him, Hardestadt was nowhere to be seen.

"Franz!" he whispered. Suddenly, a flurry of foul smelling rags and stringy muscle dove upon him from above. A twisted face, fangs bared, eyes blazing pushed itself towards Mac Othna's throat, even as the huge Briton's corded muscles pushed it away.

"You have brought me far enough," hissed the now-bestial Hardestadt. Your usefulness to me has passed!" He brought his fangs closer to the barbarian's throat. "I need your strength, huge one, if I am to be revenged on Yorak..."

A sudden blow turned the monster's face back; as the creature looked up, a dagger slid noiselessly into its eye. Hardestadt's hands rose to his face, and he shrieked. Partha shoved him with a massive hand, and the monster lost his balance. He fell into the pit, but caught himself, grasping a step with the fingers of a clawed hand. Mac Othna drew his sword and with a single blow, severed the hand from its wrist. Hand and monster plummeted into the pit, still shrieking, lost to sight, and then to hearing as the screams faded to nothing. Franz fancied he heard a small thud, far away, but he could not be sure.

He helped the huge barbarian to his feet. The big man did not thank him; the two men had saved each other's lives too many times for such an act to be anything other than the most natural thing. Instead, with an increased urgency, they took to climbing the stairs, heedless of the danger, covering three or four steps at a time as they climbed to their final destination, a brick arch with a single metal ring set on a cylindrical rod.

Franz twisted the ring and the bricks parted; the wall swung open. The men stepped into light, and a room.

The room was arrayed as a bedchamber, hung with tapestries portraying scenes of sensual excess, and lit with a hundred or more candles on candelabrae of solid gold. There in the center of the room on a rug made of bear fur stood a magnificently caparisoned bed beside a table on which there stood two glasses filled with the reddest wine Franz had ever seen. And there lay all of Franz' hopes and dreams—the maiden, as if sleeping, her face serene like an angel's, the fine, wispy silk of her gown only serving to emphasize her womanly proportions. Mac Othna put out a hand to stay his friend, but Franz would not be de-

layed. He broke his arm free of his big friend's grasp and with barely two bounds was across the chamber with the girl in his arms. He spoke her name:

"Drusilla..."

Her eyes opened, and her full, perfect lips parted in a dreamy smile. "Oh, Franz," she whispered, "Can it be you? Have you come for me?"

"I have, my love," said Franz, tears in his eyes. He held her close, not seeing the sudden cruelty of her smile, or the sharp white fangs that glittered in her mouth, fangs that even now prepared to bite deep into his throat...

TO BE CONTINUED!

DIG ME NO GRAVE!

"BUT IS THAT ALL?" I CRIED. "NO PROVISIONS AS TO THE DISPOSITION OF HIS FORTUNE, HIS ESTATE—OR HIS CORPSE?"

"NOTHING. IN HIS WILL, WHICH I HAVE SEEN ELSEWHERE, HE LEAVES ESTATE AND FORTUNE TO... MALIK TOUS!"

"WHAT!" I CRIED, SHAKEN TO MY SOUL. "CONRAD, THIS IS MADNESS HEAPED ON MADNESS! MALIK TOUS—GOOD GOD! NO MORTAL MAN WAS EVER SO NAMED! ...HE IS THE ESSENCE OF THE EVIL OF ALL THE UNIVERSE—THE PRINCE OF DARKNESS—AHRIMAN—THE OLD SERPENT—THE VERITABLE SATAN! AND YOU SAY GRIMLAN NAMES THIS MYTHICAL DEMON IN HIS WILL?"

"IT IS THE TRUTH." CONRAD'S THROAT WAS DRY. "AND LOOK—HE HAS SCRIBBLED A STRANGE LINE AT THE CORNER OF THE PARCHMENT: 'DIG ME NO GRAVE; I SHALL NOT NEED ONE.'"

- ROBERT E HOWARD, "DIG ME NO GRAVE" (WEIRD TALES, DECEMBER 1937)

Story Hooks: Lords of the Night

• **The Heritage of Dracula**

Dracula isn't the first vampire story. It isn't the best, not by a long way. But let's face it, it's the touchstone of the vampire legend. From pulp pastiche down to tarnished attempts at art, the tropes of the Dracula story, for good or ill, inform the vampire story as we understand it.

A group of desperate hunters. A vampire lord. A pathetic, deluded human minion. Wanton vampire maidens. An innocent in danger; another corrupted and destroyed. A bleak, cobweb-strewn castle, with a crypt. A desperate journey through the dark. Decay and blood, everywhere.

The elements are clichéd, sure, but sometimes a story can benefit from elements of homage. Over-the-top gothic melodrama can be difficult to pull off without it descending into farce (unless it's farce you want, in which case it's OK). But when it works, it can be a great deal of fun. It can be a straight horror story, or even a subversion of the genre.

• **On Literature (Of Variable Quality)**

Here's an interesting fact: in the World of Darkness, a number of vampires *did* lurk about Castle Drachenstein, in what is now Bavaria, and a pair of hunters *did* enter the castle in the year 1197 and *did* manage to destroy or drive away them. Or most of them, at any rate. The question is, how on earth did it end up as a horror story in a 20 cent pulp magazine? And as a fictionalized version of a real event, how much of it is truth and how much of it is, well, fiction?

It's something that has happened before. Both *Dracula* and its predecessor *Carmilla* are actual books which, in the World of Darkness, are about real vampires (*Frankenstein* is about a real monster, too, but that's not a vampire novel, obviously).

They're not the only ones. And it seems that the trashier the fiction, the more low-rent the movie, the more seeds of truth there are in the story. Who does this? Bram Stoker and J. Sheridan LeFanu were obviously human writers who must have stumbled upon some hints about the existence of real monsters. Both embellished and changed the truth for the sake of story (if not for the sake of some other influence) and both seemed to get away with it. Why did they get away with it? Was someone protecting them from the wrath of the undead? Or were the undead deliberately spreading misinformation?

The same goes for our current extract, found in a rare edition of one of the myriad pulps that existed back in the 1920s and 1930s. What does it mean? How much of it is true? And... *who wrote the story?* (Lightning flashes, dramatically as the question is asked...)

Imagine: while investigating a vampire incident, a group of hunters stumble across a dog-eared, falling-apart edition of *Eerie Tales* with one of the episodes of this story in it. As it happens, *Eerie Tales* folded before the December 1932 issue could come out, and so the last episode of "The Master of Drachenstein," which is the one that reveals the Lord Yorak's fatal weakness, was never published. But even so, the five episodes of the story before were published, and may reveal some truths ~ and some falsehoods ~ about the vampiric condition.

What about the hunters? Did they survive? Were they actually called Partha Mac Othna and Franz? (A clue: probably not.) And if they didn't survive as... living hunters, exactly, what *did* they survive as? What will our modern-day hunters do, having found and read "The Master of Drachenstein" when Yorak, Hardestadt or Drusilla turn up in their own city?

And what about that sixth episode? Just because it never saw print (and why did *Eerie Tales* close down? Did it fold because no one was buying it, or because someone or something wanted it closed down?) doesn't mean that the story is unfinished, or that that crucial final episode doesn't actually exist. The archives of the publishers, passed on through buy-outs or bequests, could be anywhere, but a really persistent scholar of the Loyalists of Thule, Aegis Kai Doru or Malleus Maleficarum may be able to find it... but can she find it before the vampires do? Or do the vampires have it already? And even if finding it is difficult, does it necessarily mean that the vampires don't want the hunters to find it—making our doughty heroes think that the fiction is valuable, and making it hard but not impossible to get is a great way of getting them to swallow it, inaccuracies and all, when they do get their sweaty hunter hands on it.

Storytellers with access to actual editions of old pulps—and many of them are not hard to come by—may find a wealth of vampire and ghost stories, all of them waiting to be retrospectively made "real." These lurid tales could well become handouts for players. Of course, they're most probably inaccurate, perhaps disastrously so, but then, that's the risk of relying on fiction. And even so, they're still probably better than the Field Projects Division Handbook...

• **Noble Heritages**

Blue blood is all over Europe. Old money and old families still control much of the world (even in the USA, in a way). Is it any wonder why the rest of us have often considered them to be a different species? So many vampire stories concern the nobility—them rather than us. In a way, those ideas about the ruling caste of the planet really being disguised lizard people from outer space tap into the same fundamental idea; *them* versus *us*.

The rarefied, secluded nature of the "nobility," however they're conceived, makes fighting the undead particularly visceral. Whether sporting heroes, fraternity boys from a military academy, corporate management, political wonks or actual royalty, the ruling caste have the power and the fame... and the distance. That distance adds to the alien nature of the vampire.

If you want, and your players are comfortable with it, you can use it to make a political point; it's a motivation in itself for some of the more radical members of the Union, for example. Members of other hunter groups with an interest in challenging power structures might also find a motivation in the elite nature of these undead. The iconoclast researchers of Null Mysteriis challenge the old-guard scientific and academic establishment: consider a scientific research facility staffed by prestigious and academically lauded professors, who research the synthesis of blood. The guerrilla film-makers of Network Zero thumb their noses at media elites: who moves in the background of that unattainable, shadowy world of agents, producers and backers? The feminist academics of Pi Alpha Kappa exist (p. 93), like the Union, because of a movement that came into being to challenge authority and preserve rights: imagine a Skull-and-Bones style society whose alumni now control the interests of all of the main political parties.

Fighting vampires who exist as the nobles of today only underlines the simple fact: they are not like us.

• **Perilous Alliances**

Our two doughty vampire hunters in the story form what ends up being an alarmingly short alliance with the vampire, Hardestadt. And some might say, therein lies a very important lesson.

Vampires look like humans, for the most part. Easy to trust. (Plus, pop culture has given us plenty of examples of vampires that play nice with humans— a tiny seed planted, but sometimes fiction resonates.) And some vampires really *want* to be human. They don't think themselves irredeemable monsters. They have enemies among their own kind. They might be willing to play nice with a hunter cell provided the hunter cell plays nice with them. And everybody lived happily ever after.

Yeah, no. The Hardestadt situation is something that might be mirrored in your story, albeit in a lon-

ger and less pulp-sinister capacity. A vampire, young or old, shows up to greet the hunters and offers his aid in tracking down their prey—perhaps even a nemesis of theirs is a nemesis of his. The enemy of my enemy is my friend, and all that. Maybe the vampire means it, maybe he genuinely wants to help. Or maybe he's planning to rip open their necks when the time is right.

Point is, the cell soon learns how perilous an alliance with the hungry dead really is. The vampire either finds his "good intensions" lost beneath a surging tide of blood-thirst, or he enacts his plan to off them after they've helped him get what he wants. Either way, their newfound friend is now a hissing fiend.

Discovery

With the Renaissance came a vast change in the world. The Reformation brought a time of questioning, and that strengthened a new flowering of science and the arts alike.

And with the new dawn of natural philosophy came the beginning of the end of the age of superstition. Even so, scientists and magicians were often almost indistinguishable. Paracelsus was as much an alchemist as a medical theorist; Isaac Newton considered his idiosyncratic works of theology and astrology as far superior to and far more important than his work on mathematics and physics. In this climate, the ascendancy of the vampire began to falter somewhat, as men who carried a twin belief in magic, a willingness to experiment with new techniques, and a new desire to rebel, to change the order of things, led the vampire hunters of this World of Darkness to become more proficient and more successful than ever. But the vampires responded. With the dogged persistence and ingenuity of the new breed of vampire hunters came subtlety and cunning for the undead, the like of which had never been seen before.

On the other hand, exploration into the East and West brought Europeans in touch with creatures they could not possibly have imagined.

The Lady of C'sejthe (1615)

One of a number of transcribed dialogues, recorded annually since the 16th century, this one only recently translated from the Italian, as recorded by one Fr. David Ezra, OSF in January 1615:

AB: A vintage to conjure with. I really must give you my compliments. Where..?

L: Perhaps better you don't ask.

AB: Ah.

L: To business, then. Lady Báthory.

AB: Yes. Erzsébet. Shocking business.

L: You knew her?

AB: A little. She gave tremendous parties.

L: You're not allowed to go to parties.

AB: Darling. Since when have you known anything about monastic rule?

L: Evidently, I know more than the Countess did.

AB: Touché.

L: Six hundred, was it?

AB: I believe so.

L: All virgins?

AB: Hah. A detail like that would interest you, mi Lucia.

L: You can talk. Drink your wine. There's plenty more where that came from.

AB: That's what I'm worried about.

L: Creative, too?

AB: Pardon?

L: Countess Báthory.

AB: Oh, undoubtedly. Do you know, she had a particularly cunning Iron Maiden. This one, rather than being a kind of spiked sarcophagus—you are familiar, I trust, with the workings—

L: Yes, yes.

AB: ...well, this one was more akin to an automaton, of sorts. It was powered with a clockwork contrivance. Its springs were wound by pulling its arms open. You could only do that if you were standing outside the grasp of the device. The Countess would place a young woman in the span of its arms and invite the woman to press a stud on its necklace. That released the spring, and the arms, which of course were spiked, would clasp shut with really quite agonizing slowness, pinioning the poor girl like a butterfly, who would then bleed to death.

L: And the Countess Báthory would drink it?

AB: Sometimes. Sometimes she preferred to bathe in it, or have it poured over her from above. Sometimes she mixed it with her cosmetics.

L: How charming.

AB: Quite. She seemed quite sick, by all accounts.

L: Really?

AB: Oh, yes. She had the most dreadful tendency to bite people.

L: Given that this is really your business, I don't find it all that surprising, Gio.

AB: The biting was really the precursor to a tendency to murder.

L: Again, I don't see why she should be considered one of mine any more than she is one of yours.

AB: She was a living woman. There isn't any evidence that she had anything to do with the leeches.

L: That is not a reason in itself, surely?

AB: Perhaps not. But surely, one would consider her to have something of the diabolist about her. Similar, one might think, to Gilles de—

L: Oh, not him again.

AB: I was simply offering a comparison.

L: I know, I know. But it's always bloody de Rais this, and de Rais that -

AB: If you're going to behave in this way—

L: Gio, Gio. My apologies. But you must understand—

AB: You are being quite—

L: Here. Sit down. Have another glass of wine.

AB: ...Yes. I will.

L: Merihem! Some wine for the good Father.

AB: Ah. I'll pour it myself, if you don't mind.

L: Good to know you're keeping up with your studies.

AB: You always knew how to charm me, mi Lucia.

L: There, now. So, the Countess. Please. More. I find her fascinating.

AB: Well, that she certainly was. She was...

L: Creative. As we have said.

AB: The Countess had a well-appointed torture chamber, as I said. She had, central to the chamber, a throne, and from there she watched the proceedings, invariably dressed in white.

L: Having the help do it. Oh yes. Now that's breeding.

AB: Well, to some extent. The practice was to find strong, tall young girls. They had to be between 12 and 18 years of age. They would be brought in and made to stand naked and bound before her. The

servants would customarily whip them until they bled. Having shed enough blood through this method, they would burn the girls with red-hot pokers, stab them with daggers, mutilate their maidenhead, and use shears to cut off noses and fingers. The Countess being a woman of some taste—

L: Obviously—

AB: —she couldn't abide screaming. If a girl screamed too much, the Countess would have her mouth sewn up. If the others didn't get the message, she'd do that to rest of them until they quieted themselves—

L: And died with some dignity?

AB: Apparently so.

L: How perfectly beastly.

AB: At some point, the Countess, having become somewhat... overwrought... by the sight of all this, would be walking among them.

L: "Overwrought?"

AB: Overwrought.

L: Pleasurably so?

AB: I... couldn't comment.

L: You probably couldn't. You've never even thought about women like that.

AB: I'm a man of purity.

L: Does young Brother Anatole know that?

AB: Hmph.

L: Please. Continue.

AB: Yes. Well, obviously, the Countess derived only so much... pleasure... from watching the torture. At some point, she would take a hand. Laughing. Crying out, "More, More!" And "Harder! Harder!" Until she killed a girl, at which point she... well.

L: Don't embarrass yourself. I know.

AB: I'm sure you do. Whore.

L: Catamite.

AB: Devil.

L: Hypocrite.

[Both spend a brief time laughing]

AB: Anyway, she had other contrivances. The Iron Maiden. And a particularly devilish cage. The Countess' maidservant, one Dorko—

L: Pretty name.

AB: It matched her looks, by all accounts. Anyway, this Dorko was the keeper of a cage, hung from the ceiling, under which the Countess was accustomed to sit. The cage was lined with knives. One of the inevitable girls would be brought in, dragged by the hair—this was apparently part of the ritual—and shut in the cage. Dorko would prod the poor girl with a hot poker.

L: And the girl would kill herself on the knives as she flinched? And the blood would fall over the Countess?

AB: That is correct.

L: I find this rather tasteless.

AB: You've done worse.

L: Never for vanity. Besides, I'm not alone in that, am I?

AB: Perhaps not. And then there was the freezing.

L: Oh?

AB: There is a winter night. The Countess gains an... urge. She calls one of the young women of her entourage to her carriage. There, she has her pleasure with the girl, which habitually involves biting and pricking with bodkins. She tires of the maiden, apparently, and throws the bloodied, humiliated girl out into the snow. She has the men force her to stand. And then they pour icy water of her. And it's so cold in a Magyar Winter—

L: The water freezes.

AB: And they leave the girl there, upright, all frozen and dead.

L: That I find most disturbing of all.

AB: It's unlike you to be squeamish.

L: I have an aversion to cold. Still, I fail to see why I should consider this woman as being among my problem rather than yours—

AB: The diabolism?

L: Ah. She did?

AB: Very much so. Enchantments, curses, spells, pacts with Satan.

L: As I said. Vulgar.

AB: And mirrors. Vast numbers of mirrors. She had one that was constructed with rests for her arms, so she could gaze at her face for hours without wearying. And others that she used for scrying.

L: I see your point. But still, her mania for blood was particularly uncommon.

AB: It was. The people at the trial reacted somewhat badly to the charges.

L: Were the charges true?

AB: I suspect some hysteria, if I'm to be honest. Still, a fascinating case, is it not?

L: And neither fully mine nor yours. Yes. Fascinating. So. More wine?

Story Hooks: The Bloody Countess and Others

• Vampires/ Not Vampires

Not all vampires are necessarily easy to categorize. Countess Báthory was undeniably human. She was a living, breathing woman. But she had a thirst for blood and an aptitude for black magic. And that combination makes her, in a way, as much of a vampire as the most revolting blood-drinking corpse.

In some respects, it's confusing. It certainly confused our two senior hunters, each of whom wanted very much to consider the Bloody Countess the other hunter's responsibility.

History tells us that Erzsébet Báthory's methods didn't work, but that doesn't have to be true, does it? An individual hoping to recreate such horrors might even become more successful than the Countess.

A human with a taste for blood and the right mix of diabolical rituals could become a human vampire, possessing vampire powers, becoming immortal... but being utterly bankrupt in terms of morality, a true monster who has to perform really dreadful things to maintain his perfect youth. There isn't any law that says a Storyteller can't apply a vampire's Dread Powers to a human Storyteller character's template.

Here's a high-ranking executive, a century-old CEO who disappears for a decade every so often and comes back as his son, and who seems to lose people who work for him remarkably easily. Hunters suspicious of him may find themselves confounded by his obvious humanity and lack of slasher traits... and when they discover the truth of his unique kind of vampirism (he drinks and bathes in the blood of the youthful and the beautiful), they may already be in his clutches.

Such a villain is terribly difficult to spot, easily confused when found with a slasher or a witch. In fact, there's nothing wrong with blurring the lines sometimes. In real world folklore the lines are nowhere nearly as clearly drawn as we sometimes present them in these games. Sowing a bit of confusion keeps everyone on their toes.

I Think of Erzsébet Báthory

I think of Erzsébet Báthory and her nights whose rhythms are measured with the cries of adolescent girls. I see a portrait of the Countess: the sombre and beautiful lady resembles the allegories of Melancholia represented in old engravings. I also recall that in her time, a melancholic person was a person possessed by the Devil.

\- Alejandra Pizarnik, "The Bloody Countess"

AN HISTORICAL NOTE

Real-world historians are fairly sure that Erzsébet Báthory was in fact largely innocent of the vast catalog of horrendous crimes attributed to her.

But then, this is not a book about the real world. When you're creating tales of horror and blood, myth is sometimes more useful than strict historical truth. This is one of those times.

• Torture and Mutilation

Vampires, whether living or dead, do really horrid things. Even the more humane ones go wrong now and again. Now this is partly because vampires have this supernatural compulsion that takes them over and turns them into unthinking monsters every so often, but actually, a lot of it is to do with the whole nature of their condition.

Drinking human blood is really a form of cannibalism. And the thing is, it's part of a series of increasingly awful things a person can do. True, drinking someone's blood might be a need... it might even be consensual, but there's a time when a vampire becomes jaded. She starts looking for other things to do, other thrills to experience. It starts with biting someone and taking a bit of blood. Then you stop asking. Then you start to take the blood from different places. Or making cuts just to see how the blood tastes.

It's conceivable that an epicurean vampire probably has ideas about which blood tastes best. Arterial blood, especially blood from the carotid artery, is richer and stronger to a vampire's taste than the more mellow, subtle and less immediately intoxicating venal blood. Blood from the wrist tastes different to blood from the throat, which is different again to blood from the inner thigh, or the shoulder, or the abdomen.

And what about the state of the victim when the blood is taken? Sure, if the victim is drunk or drugged, the blood is certainly different, but what about emotional states? Is blood taken from someone in the throes of orgasm better than blood taken from someone gripped by abject terror, or from someone in a state of trance?

How about betrayal? Or physical pain? And then, what sort of physical pain?

And then you start investigating torture. And at some point you stop looking at the people you're eating from as people. Suddenly they're food. And morally speaking, it barely matters to you at this point whether you're a gourmet or into fast food.

But you start playing with your food. You can't help it.

Often, it's useful to play the sort of game where the vampires are sympathetic, where, the players are encouraged to think long and hard about whether their characters' actions in hunting these creatures are right (and more on that a bit later). But sometimes, it is absolutely right to kill these things. And this sort of "play with your food" mindset is a good way to present the sort of monster that the characters *need* to destroy.

On the other hand, a Storyteller can easily spin it as a tragic thing. A creature tries to be noble. He tries to be good. But he's a monster, a broken mirror of humanity, and as hard as he tries, he just descends into ever more monstrous practices, hating himself all the more when he comes to his senses. Imagine a monster of this kind developing a sort of death wish, perhaps subconsciously laying clues and making himself vulnerable, all the better for the hunters to kill him.

• Annual Meetings

Who are these two odd friends, who have met every year for centuries, who have their conversations recorded by a monk who took a vow of silence?

Players and Storytellers who have been paying attention should be prepared to make some guesses. Hunter characters may be less sure of who was talking. At any rate, these transcripts are incredibly valuable documents, and if they fall into the wrong hands (and for that, read: anyone's hands apart from the archivists who keep the two copies of each that exist, one in Milan and one in the Vatican) both the Lucifuge and the Malleus Maleficarum will send agents to get them back—probably working against each other, with neither organization's agent or agents told what it is they're retrieving. Are the players' characters the wrong hands or the agents charged with getting the documents back (who could very easily become the wrong hands)? Anything could happen.

The Passion of the Demoiselle DeFay (1705)

From a journal attributed to the Chevalier Thélème:

Situation: Here, then is Chantal DeFay. And here is the Duc D'Assame. Favorites of society, certainly. Charming, elegant people, without a doubt. Acquaintances of the Sun King himself? No mean feat.

The life and soul of our Versailles parties? No. In that they have no life, and as for souls... that's a difficult thing to pin down with any certainty.

Evidence: Here is Mlle. Bernice Tillius. She is pretty. Rumor has it that she is somewhat profligate with her favors, but Rumor is a vicious conversationalist and I put little store in what Rumor has to say. She is seen disappearing for a walk accompanied by the Duc D'Assame and Demoiselle DeFay. She is not seen again for a few days. When she reappears she is solemn and quite ill-looking. In the evening, she spies the Duc D'Assame enter and she visibly blanches and leaves. Over the space of three weeks, she sickens and dies. She is perhaps the most visible example of this trend, but there have been others.

Evidence: Demoiselle DeFay and the Duc D'Assame's reflections are peculiar. They avoid mirrors, but in Versaille, reflecting surfaces are surpassingly common and these are hard things to hide. The Duc D'Assame's reflection is unusual in that even in the brightest light it is blurred and indistinct. The Demoiselle DeFay's is even stranger. Often, she has no reflection at all; when her reflection does appear, it behaves differently from the Demoiselle. Only last night I saw her reflection smile while she remained solemn.

Over the years I have become somewhat used to the way the most people simply do not see this thing until it is pointed out to them. They expect things to be as they were, and so that's how they see things. No magic is at work, nothing out of the ordinary. It is simply how people behave. I am not, I think 'people' and so I am privy to things others are not. If anyone has noticed the peculiarities that the two of them exhibit when reflected, no one has said. In part, this may be due to the Duc D'Assame's fearsome reputation as a duelist.

Still, it is of particular note I think that they never enter the Hall of Mirrors.

Evidence: The Demoiselle and the gentleman have, as far as I know, never been seen in the daytime. This is in fact, not wholly uncommon among the fashionable layabouts who haunt the court of the Sun King.

Evidence: I do not ever see the Duc and the Demoiselle eat or drink wine. But then, discretion in drinking is expected here, and many of the courtiers take food in their own homes and their own chambers.

Evidence: The servant. No one pays the least notice to servants, but the Duc D'Assame has a servant who seems unable to be noticed. I stare directly at the individual, and I am still unsure whether this servant is a man or a woman. And yet I recall meeting someone like this in England, a long time ago. It seems to be an occupational hazard with the ones who hide. In fact it may even be the same individual. I am fairly sure that if it is, he or she will not remember me. The undead have a curious blindness in this: they can't seem to understand that they may not be alone in lasting beyond normal human lifetimes.

Recapitulation: Did I say 'undead?' Why, I did, and well I should because this is the conclusion I have reached in my enquiry. The Duc D'Assame and the Demoiselle DeFay are clearly vampires and should be observed and destroyed, say I, for this is my duty. But the operation requires subtlety. One cannot simply drive a stake through the heart of a beloved courtier. This is not the way things are done in the civilized world. Let them do such things in the Americas; here we are not animals.

Development: So the Demoiselle comes to me, by night, of course, while I am in my chambers. I say: 'It was awfully careless of my valet.'

He is dead, and cannot be reprimanded, she says, her voice tinged with no more than the regret one might have if one had accidentally lost someone's handkerchief.

I maintain my dignity. Often it is all I have. 'I am at a loss as to why you pay me this visit Mademoiselle' I say, sitting up straight, my hands clasped in my lap atop the covers.

'There is no such place as Thélème,' she says simply. 'And if there is no Thélème, there can be no Chevalier Thélème. Your title does not exist, sir.'

'But there is no Demoiselle DeFay, either. You were never born. You never existed. Your name does not exist. The same would go for the Duc D'Assame, I'll warrant, had he not taken the effort to cover his tracks more thoroughly.'

'My visit here concerns the Duc D'Assame,' she says, sitting down at the foot of the bed and waving a small, graceful hand at me with an elegance and nonchalance that briefly makes me rather glad I have my hands clasped in my lap.

'Your friend? He has sent you here I suppose.'

'He has done no such thing, sir.' She straightens and looked away from me, her swan-neck swaying gently under the weight of her towering coiffure.

'You are here as a private agent?'

'If you like.'

'I confess myself intrigued.'

'You did not strike me as a man easily intrigued.'

'I confess, I am. Had you not murdered my valet, I would dress and perform my toilet, and make arrangements for a more formal consultation.'

'My apologies. It was... careless of me.' She licks her lips. I find the gesture faintly obscene. 'Anyway, here will have to suffice. Time is short.'

'I understand. I shall be direct, then. What is it you want?'

'I want the Duc D'Assame dead.'

I am taken aback. This is not a common occurrence for me, of course. 'This is unprecedented.'

'Perhaps.' She stands and places her hands on her hips. 'You should know that I was not always as I am now.'

'Surely, and please take no offense, Mademoiselle, this is evident. No one is born with your condition after all.'

'This is not what I mean, Sir,' she says, her lips making a slight move.

'Please, make yourself plain, if one of your beauty can ever be said to be plain.' It is not my best flattery, but it shall have to do.

'I did not have this name. I was not a woman of position and wealth. I did not know the ways of the court. I was a farmers eldest daughter. One night my family and I were murdered, by men who... killed. Who killed so much that they were not humans anymore. And that is all they did.'

'I know such men well.'

'The Duc D'Assame found my shallow grave and made me what I am. And then, over time, he made me who I am.'

'And—if I may be so bold—you never thought to question why he should be concerned enough with you to raise you or how he knew where to find the final resting place of a farm girl, even one as comely as your good self?'

'That is so.'

'And you have discovered that the Duc D'Assame engineered the murder of your family?'

'I could barely credit it. He had helped me to find the creatures who murdered my family, and we took pleasure in destroying them.'

'But you found them so very easily, did you not?'

'I did.'

'And who told you the truth?'

'I found it. I have... abilities. A moment of weakness on his part...'

'I see.'

'And you would have me kill him forever.'

'I would.'

Climax: I maneuver myself into situations where I will come into conflict with the Duc D'Assamei the Demoiselle: with nods, brief opinions and the flick of a graceful white neck, only offers fuel to our enmity. We jockey for precedence in court occasions. We collide in each other's choice of dancing partners. In a wager concerning the behavior of a young hot-head whose desire for one of the more worldly ladies at court leads him to humiliation and disgrace, I lose. I fail to pay. And when challenged, I insult the Duc and disparage his blood in the sight of three relatives of the King. And so the Duc challenges me to a duel.

He is a more accomplished swordsman than I... but I need only make eye contact. And then he is mine.

And under the arbor, I behead him and watch him crumble to ash before my eyes, and before the eyes of the Demoiselle DeFay. It is no triumph for her, and perhaps a warning of what will come.

I expect that she will meet with my blade herself one of these nights. For now, though I must leave her alone.

Story Hooks: Treating with the Dead

• Factions and Enmities

One of the things about the vampire condition is that it's essentially predatory. If vampires form a society at all, it dissolves into factions. They can't help it. They have to jockey for position. They have to engage in the one-upmanship. They have to fight amongst themselves.

Even vampires who are closely tied together often end up hating each other, even when they love each other (which makes a twisted sort of sense—the old cliché about love and hate and the two sides of the same coin and everything comes to mind here). When you spend your entire existence emptying the life from people, you find that betrayal comes easy, too.

Of all the social monsters that hunters are likely to meet, vampires are perhaps the most likely to enter

into their own very small, limited kind of civil war.

Given that, an enterprising, foolhardy or confident hunter may think about using that to his own advantage. It's about the most dangerous game a hunter can play: not only does it involve attempting to get to grips with the labyrinthine, subtle and often hideously violent business of vampire politics, but it means picking a side to ally with—or manipulate—and knowing when to get out before the monsters try to suborn you (...or have they already? How can you tell? You may not even know they control you...) or dispose of you. You can't trust them. They can't trust you. The inimitable Chevalier Thélème did rather well out of his alliance with a vampire lady... but then, he has a lot of good reasons why he's "inimitable."

Remember, vampires are masters of the double-cross. And they're at least as smart as you. Double-crossing *them* before they double-cross *you* is a really difficult proposition. It may well be advisable to plan your betrayal before you even start working with them; they almost certainly have a dozen or more plans in reserve for occasions such as this.

Beware when the vampires approach you for help in their struggles. They might bang on about how you've impressed them with your courage and your mettle, but let's face it, a supernaturally strong walking corpse who can snap your neck with a flick of her wrist doesn't really think of you as an equal. Maybe you're a really dangerous animal to her, but it'll take a lot before you're feared enough to really get any respect. No, they just want to flatter you. If they ask for your help, the chances are that that they simply want to use you as a deniable tool. And a disposable one.

Approaching them, on the other hand, is suicide unless you have something they want. A source of blood? The discovery of an enemy's headquarters? Something else? Don't even think of tracking down a vampire partisan if you don't have something to give and something to offer. Something they want. Something you're preferably not holding in your hand. Because if they can see it, they can and will take it off you.

Of course, you don't *have* to ally with anyone. A hunter who finds out that there are factions or enmities, even if he doesn't have their names, is hugely dangerous to the undead, since he can, if he's clever or careful, create situations where the mayhem he causes is thought by one

SULHA

The exceptions to all these dire warnings are the Ascending Ones, whose modus operandi has for centuries included the practice of *Sulha*, the Arabic mode of shuttle diplomacy. Boiled down to its basics, *Sulha* concerns the resolution of conflicts through an impartial observer traveling back and forth between offended parties. He carries with him the markers of the two parties and bears a responsibility of truth.

It's not a violent means of dealing with resolution, but who says that every hunter necessarily *has* to kill all the monsters? Well, apart from us.

Vampire wars cause, as we said, collateral damage. Ending one with some sort of agreement may be the best a hunter can do.

Groups of Ascending Ones in the larger cities have for centuries memorized ancient forms of greeting and long-honored symbols and marks. An Ascending One who sees a supernatural war appears bearing the symbol of a ruling clan or faction. The vampires see the signs, hear the forms of address and recognize the hunter as an Ascending One and a qualified figure to handle this form of democracy.

Or that's the theory. One problem is only the older vampires necessarily recognize these old symbols. That bunch of '80s throwback *Lost Boys* rejects may laugh, shrug and eat you when you turn up with the thees, thous, wherefores and hails. Even if the vampires do recognize the formal signs, who says they're going to accept the hardest-looking homeboy, even if he does know the ancient words?

faction or the other to be the work of the opposition. In the past, hunters have started supernatural wars with a few well-placed and anonymous attacks. Then they've sat back and watched the mayhem... well, in theory. The problems with vampires going to war are that they're primarily urban (and dependent on there being a large number of humans on whom they feed) and don't naturally consider real people to be as important as they are. The result is "collateral damage." People get in the way. Innocents die. Escalate a vampire war, and you can all but guarantee that someone innocent will die.

The Perils of Attending the Theater (1877)

From Judy, or the Essence of London, *a popular satirical magazine of the era, dated September 22nd, 1877:*

OUR REPRESENTATIVE MAN.

(After a Visit to the Lyceum and Opera Comique, He Reports to the Editor, and Throws in a Little Theatrical Intelligence Gratis)

Our Highness, a piece by MR. VINCENT MOON, or a piece founded on a novel by MR. VINCENT MOON, demands attention from Your Representative. By whom The Adventures of a Dead Man in the Land of Malkavia has been dramatized for the Lyceum is not stated in the play-bills; therefore there is an additional interest in the production, on account of it being mixed up with No Name.

The author of the novel, we are however informed, had given his "express permission" (a somewhat ebullient way of expressing it) for somebody—our friend with No Name—to transform his work into a play. The Adventures of a Dead Man in the Land of Malkavia was by no means a good novel; its adventures were uncommonly dead. In fact, it had hardly any life in it from the first. Although its subject matter should have made an appallingly lurid tale of blood, wantonness and death, it became by its very unrelenting detestability, uncommonly dull. It might have furnished some material for a melodrama, surely its material was not sufficient for in itself for true dramatic purposes.

Still, although the action was overwrought and possessed of too many words, even for Your Representative, the play was well-presented.

The event in Act I where MRS HAWTHORNE (JANE MASTERS) pleads with her husband's corpse not to leave the grave and travel to the mythical land of Malkavia is well-performed. A thrill of horror adds depth to the actress's voice, and the entire audience wills the corpse to accede to her wishes. Alas, he does not.

A brighter child than "TINY MICHAEL" has seldom been seen on the stage. He represents a boy of four, and speaks like one, indeed. The audience received him with great enthusiasm.

MISS SARAH ARMSTRONG as the maiden deserves plaudits, but her costume left something to be desired, Nevertheless, her death was most convincing, as the Dead Man left her pale and lifeless on the road to his non-existent destination. MR. CHRISTOPHER STACEY, too, as a Mephistophelian Devil, gave the performance of a lifetime.

The presentation was top-hole. One might even consider the deaths of extras and the creation of a miasma of darkness at the central point of the final act to be quite spectacular examples of the scene-maker's art. Concerns, I know, have been raised by some more hysterical members of the theater-going public as to the less-than-healthsome implications of these no doubt entirely mundane but chill-making effects.

Stories of individuals fainting and developing diseases of the blood in the darkness are no doubt exaggerations. I may venture that if they were feeling sick, it may only be because they had experienced Mr. Moon's prose beforehand...

THE EXPERIENCE OF EMPIRE

Behemoth or Bogey? Awful Apparition or Sorry Show? Colossus of Roads and Realms, Over-Stepper of Deserts, Over-strider of Mountains, Floorer and Framer of Faiths, Extinguisher of Nationalities, Absorber of Empires, Disposer of Manifest Destinies, Defier of Magnificent Distances; or Immensest of Impostures, Darkest yet Dullest of Diplomatic Deceptions, Shallowest of Shams, Biggest of Baubles, most Barefaced of Bankrupts, Gelatinous of Giants, and Weak-kneed of Warriors? The most far-seeing and far-reaching Power that ever pursued a settled purpose of Universal Dominion through centuries of shifting circumstances; or the most monstrous mushroom-growth of empire that ever struck root in corruption, to swell to deceptive dimensions, and thence dwindle into swift decay? Thou canst not be both. Art thou either—or neither?

-*Punch*, or the London Charivari, July 1877

Story Hooks: Gaslight and Greasepaint

• The Theater

Vampires don't show up so well on film, but even so, they have this urge to art. Art controls hearts and minds. Performance and demagoguery is a means of control as much as political power. And what better place to pursue art than the theater?

Vampires have been dramatists and stage actors for as long as the stage has existed. Fragmentary accounts from Imperial Rome tell of stage actors who killed their fellows and drank their blood. Greek tragedies describe murder, incest and betrayal. Legends of traveling theatrical troupes composed wholly of the undead have circulated for centuries.

Other ways to control people exist. A stand-up comic can change attitudes more subtly through making people laugh than any dramatist. A torch singer or an alternative protest singer has the power to make people desirous or angry.

And of course, if you're on the stage, you have a glamour about you. You inspire admiration. People want you. People come backstage, attend after-show parties. People throw themselves at you without thought for the consequences.

People disappear at backstage parties. People die on stage. People get sick when the lights go down.

• The Fog of Empire

In a city, it's easy to get lost. The nooks and crannies, the alleys and avenues. Now imagine that expanded into a vast urban empire. The British Empire was called the Empire on which the Sun Never Sets, since somewhere in the world it was day; but it could just as easily have been the Empire on which the Sun Never Rises, since if it was always day somewhere, it was always night somewhere, too.

And it was easy to get lost. Lines of communications stretched around the world. Mass transport and telegraphs made the British Empire smaller and yet more complex than any Empire that yet lived.

Empires still exist. They're not quite the same. The American Empire is more economically based than militarily, but even so it keeps those lines of communication alive, and creates the cracks through which a monster can vanish. Business Empires stretch across international boundaries. The Catholic Church makes its problems vanish on a regular basis.

And more than that, vampires are, on a conceptual level, fundamentally imperial. They are obsessed with control. Control over minds, over money, over the future. They represent the stranglehold of the past. They are the dead, unable to let go. Small wonder then, that in the business of Empire, vampires thrive in the high places as well as the low. Vampire factions can spread across the world in some respects. So why haven't they taken over?

Vampires are paranoid. They're prone to in-fighting. More than that, they're agoraphobic. Empires are not continuous things; they are islands of influence, and between islands of influence, spaces exist. In the islands, the vampires have the power. In the spaces, less so.

What this means is that while vampires won't follow a hunter from city to city, what they can do is spread the word, so that their counterparts in other countries—who, being vampires, might actually hate their supposed allies—are ready for the dangerous mortals.

The Speed of Things

The world ground to a halt at the beginning of the 20th Century, and millions died in a war that had no apparent meaning. Since then, things sped up. The human race began to eat itself, developing new technologies of creation and destruction at a terrifying rate, accelerating toward a critical mass.

And behind it all, the hungry dead waited. In the times of death, they profit from the carrion. In the times of peace, they gorge themselves on a choice of meals they have never before seen the like of.

Goodbye to All That (The Somme, 1916)

9th October:

Gas attack today. Each time it seems more like hell. I don't know which circle. It's a smaller one each time, I suppose.

The smell of chlorine or whatever it is, the steam. The way your hands shake as you try to get those damned stupid masks on, so the more one desires to get it on one's head, the more difficult one finds the process.

And then the glass steams up and one can hardly see a blessed thing through the mist and the smoke. You crouch in the cold and the filth and the mephitic smoke, and around you all the distorted snouts and the glass circles like the faces of devils, from a *Hieronymus Bosch* painting.

One of the men, a new man, one I didn't know, I am ashamed to say, hadn't put his mask on quickly enough. He began to flail around, and then he started to choke. He panicked, and of course then the poor chap was lost. It was all the men could do to stop him from bringing down the shelter on top of us.

He curled up in a ball. We watched him choke, and cough up pint after pint of blood and froth. And then he was dead. We watched him die. What could we do?

I will never get used to seeing men die.

10th October:

Today has been the strangest, and the worst, of all possible days. I rather think I would like to have dreamed it. Perhaps if I write it down, and tear the pages from my diary, I will forget it as one would a fevered dream. The dead man (Pvt. Owen, George. He was only 16) was not the only casualty of the attack. Three others died: Pvt. Jones, Rhys John; Cpl. Jones, Rhys Owen; Pvt. Holme, Timothy). But here is the most peculiar thing: they died with their masks on.

Each man showed no sign of having choked. There was, according to the Sergeant-Major, nothing that anyone could tell was wrong with the gas masks. But they were dead.

I met Sassoon at the field hospital's mortuary; he said that we should see them. The three men who had died with their masks on, they looked so serene. Pale like alabaster. They looked for all the world like the people back home think that all our young heroes look when they die.

Young Owen's body was markedly different: still bloodied, still twisted.

"Like a devil's face. A devil's, trapped in hell. Sick of sin and unable to escape it."

That was Lt. Sassoon. The men, I found out not long ago, call him "Mad Jack." He is prone to acts that an observer who did not know him would consider the acts of a hero. But of course, he hates this. He is no career soldier. He simply wants an end to the war and his part in it. He wants to die.

We stood in silence, for a time. He spoke again. "Captain Graves," he said, "I do not think it was the gas that killed these men."

I looked at him, somewhat quizzically, perhaps. "They were clearly not shot," I said.

"I did not say they were shot." There was a quaver in his voice. "I saw something last night. I cannot expect it of you, but I wanted to ask you if you would accompany me once more tonight." He set his jaw. "I wish to face what I saw."

I nodded. "Of course," I said. "But shouldn't we tell the men?"

"No," he said. "No. At best they'd think Mad Jack had lost his mind completely. At worst they'd believe me."

And with this he said little more, and bid me adieu. I saw him again after dinner. He said nothing. He nodded. He was carrying his gasmask, and bade me take mine. Slung over his shoulder he had another satchel. We went outside into the drizzle, and went backwards into our lines, leaving trenches altogether at points. I prayed some sharp-eyed Allemand wouldn't pick me off; Lt. Sassoon made no sign that he was at all frightened.

We came to a branch of the trenches I had not seen before, and ducked under a shelter I would have considered rickety even by the standards of our own men's work.

Here, by electric torchlight, Sassoon showed me the contents of his bag. Three Very flares and the gun from which to launch them.

I asked him where he had got them. "The Signals Corps weren't using them," he said, simply. I saw a look in his eye, and held back on asking him what on earth he would use this for.

He told me that we must wait.

And we waited without a word. Although the cold had begun to seep into my bones, and Sassoon's animation was disturbing, to say the least, I found this place strangely comfortable. There were no men here to concern me. And the sounds of guns and shells seemed strangely distant. I began to fall asleep, but was jolted from my reverie by Sassoon, who clutched my arm and hissed silence at me.

A figure had appeared in the far side of the trench. Its face was wreathed in shadow. It—he—was wearing a colonel's uniform. He turned. He looked like a corpse. His skin was pale and greenish, as if he had been killed by gas. His eyes were black pools of shadow. He was far too young to be a colonel.

"I know you're here," the apparition said, matter-of-factly. "You should come out. I won't harm you."

Neither Sassoon nor I made the slightest move; and the newcomer approached the shelter.

He peered into the pitch darkness that shielded us. "I know you," he said. "You were there last night."

"I was," said Sassoon, suddenly.

The man with the greenish skin suddenly vanished from sight before my eyes; the next thing I know, I felt a cold, steely grip around my neck, an impact and then a strange, dreamy sensation took me. I saw eyes, felt a pressure on my neck, and then once more I jolted out of it.

Sassoon was beating the green-skinned man with the butt of his revolver. I shook my head and drew mine; my hands shook and I was slow. I looked up to see the man swat Sassoon to the far side of the trench. He hit the wall so hard that clods of earth dislodged and fell on him. The corpse-faced man, snarling with a mouth full of teeth like sewing needles, was almost upon me when I shot him in the stomach. He paused and looked down at the hole in his tunic, and then he looked up and cocked his head at me. And then he smiled with those terrible shining teeth, and he stepped towards me. I shot him again, and again the bullet had no effect.

Then there was a terrible bang, and the monster screamed and thudded into the earth wall beside me; I covered my face and dived as far away as I could as the glow of a flare in the monster's back lit up the shelter and burnt away the corruption that—I know Sassoon was right—had killed my men. And the fire died down and we were in darkness. With our electric torches, we surveyed the shelter. Apart from the smoldering remains of a stolen uniform, there was nothing here but ash. I looked down at those remains and felt a chill run down me. Not because of what I had seen, no; because I felt nothing as I looked at it.

Sassoon spoke. "Are you all right, old man?" He said.

I put a hand to my neck, felt the raised edges of something bloody and slightly sore. "I think so," I said.

Sassoon sat down on the earth beside me. He handed me a hip flask. I took a deep draught, handed it back.

We were quiet for a long while. "That wasn't remotely the worst thing I've seen," said Sassoon.

"No," I said. "Does that bother you?"

"It does, rather. You?"

"Yes. Yes it does."

A machine-gun started to go off over our heads.

Anthem for Doomed Youth

• War

What better place for a vampire to feed than in a war zone? There has hardly been a year since 1900 where there hasn't been a war going on somewhere in the world. The Great War changed the way that wars were fought in a way that has made it easy for the undead to flourish. True, the socialite and the conspirator have little to manipulate in a world where social structures have gone to hell, but they're not the only kind of blood-drinker out there by any stretch of the imagination.

A vampire on a battlefield may be able to vanish into the earth, or vanish in plain sight. The wounded don't fight back. When chemical weapons get deployed (and they do still get used, sometimes), a vampire is not usually affected. What use is poison gas against a creature whose existence does not depend on whether it breathes or not?

A group of soldiers cooped up in a base or barracks make easy prey for a monster. Notwithstanding Hollywood's depiction of soldiers trapped in difficult situations, soldiers are *not* the most resourceful people out there. In fact, most military training depends on getting soldiers to lose their initiative enough that they follow someone else's order. Which is the only way in a situation where teamwork and following orders keeps you, your pla-

DREAMERS

Soldiers are citizens of death's grey land,
Drawing no dividend from time's to-morrows.
In the great hour of destiny they stand,
Each with his feuds, and jealousies, and sorrows.
Soldiers are sworn to action; they must win
Some flaming, fatal climax with their lives.
Soldiers are dreamers; when the guns begin
They think of firelit homes, clean beds and wives.
I see them in foul dug-outs, gnawed by rats,
And in the ruined trenches, lashed with rain,
Dreaming of things they did with balls and bats,
And mocked by hopeless longing to regain
Bank-holidays, and picture shows, and spats,
And going to the office in the train.
- Siegfried Sassoon.

toon, and (hopefully) any nearby innocents alive, but no good at all when a monster is picking off your friends one by one in your own base.

Although shells and heavy-duty explosives may be able to deal with the undead, guns don't really work. Bullets *do* have an effect on vampires—but it's a tiny effect, and it takes a lot of bullets to kill one (and they have to be close together, because a vampire can heal a bullet wound in seconds).

Penanggalan (1955)

NOFORN **ORCON**

VALKYRIE STEERING COMMITTEE EYES ONLY
DEPARTMENT OF WAR
Washington, DC

TOP SECRET

December 1st 1955

From: GSP
To: DDE
Subject: Incident in Malay "Emergency"

The following memo was sent by a British operative in Kuala Lumpur and intercepted by our man in Hong Kong.

We thought it expedient to take a copy for a number of reasons, not least the subject matter. More interesting, perhaps, is the implication that the British apparently have a counterpart to TF:V, referred to in the document as DRU, also as MI18. Which leads us to presume it is tied to British Military Intelligence. Our British contacts and CIA records officially list MI18 as an unused Military Intelligence designation.

Note the reference to Loke Yew; this refers to the so-called "New Village" in Kuala Lumpur. For those of you unfamiliar with the term "New Village," it refers to fenced and guarded townships in which British troops have resettled large numbers of (mostly Chinese) Malayans, the intention being to prevent the locals from aiding or being propagandized by the Communists.

The second and third pages of this memorandum comprise a copy of the British document.

From: Barton, B.
TO: K / DRU
RE: Recent developments in Loke Yew

NOFORN

1. On the night of ~~scribbled out~~, a squad of Gurkhas under the command of one Sgt. Davies, W, were alerted to a disturbance at the northern extremity of the settlement; residents had found an hysterical and incoherent elderly man sitting with the bodies of his wife, his son, his son's wife and his four grandchildren. A large amount of blood was found at the scene; much of this appeared to belong to the old man, who had received wounds on his throat and arms similar to those one might receive from an attack by rats. The bodies were exsanguinated. According to Cpl. Agong, Sgt. Davies' number two, the amount of blood on the scene, although not inconsiderable, was not enough to account for the blood lost by the man's dead relatives. The old man, described by locals as senile and harmless, was unable to explain what had happened, beyond the repeated word: "penanggal." Several of the Gurkhas made repeated note of an acrid smell reminiscent of vinegar, although Sgt. Davies was unable to understand why this should be so significant.

2. My assistant Milligan, in his survey of the week's reports, caught the reference to a "penanggal" two days later. I was able to survey the scene, then, on ~~scribbled out~~. Although the bodies had been removed and the blood cleared up, the scene still smelled of vinegar. However, there was little else to learn. I resolved to interview some of the locals.

3. A Penanggal or Penanggalan is a particularly bizarre variety of vampire native to the Malay Peninsula. It takes the form by day of a woman. By night, however, her head detaches itself from the body and flies where it may, dragging its glistening lungs, heart and entrails behind it. She feeds on blood; those on whom she is unlucky enough to feed upon and survive contract a wasting disease, and soon die (the old man had followed his family by the time I managed to get around to investigating).
The Penanggalan is always followed by the smell of vinegar. Her preferred prey are infants, but she will feed from anyone if necessary.

TOP SECRET

ORCON

4. Having absorbed the local folklore, my only option appeared to be to locate the creature's hunting grounds. I instructed Milligan to look for any further incidents. Over the space of a month, we discovered three more in‡cidents, all within a three‡mile radius of the first assault.

The thing to do, then, seemed to be to set up camp in the area. Taking three Gurkhas with me, we spent the night shift patrolling the region. After four nights of this (and one more incident that we could not, regrettably, prevent), we perceived a smell of vinegar, and shortly afterwards saw the creature, exactly as reported by locals.

One of the Gurkhas, Pvt. Mathuram, proved to be less sturdy than I had expected. His screams and attempts at flight attracted the monster, which took hold of him with innards that proved to be rather more useful than the superstitions might suggest, and tore his throat out. The other Gurkha, Pvt. Foo, opened fire, accidentally killing Pvt. Mathuram, but doing what seemed to be very little damage to the creature.

The creature dropped the first man and grasped the second, dragging him at a considerable but not impossible to pursue speed along an alley (it seems that its strength was not enough to lift the man from the ground, although its grip around his throat was enough to immobilize him). I took chase, in‡structing the other Gurkha to follow at a distance, so that if anything hap‡pened to me, he might give support or escape to get help.

I pursued the creature to one of the better‡maintained homes in the dis‡trict, the home of a well‡regarded local midwife known to my companion, her name Zohary Badawi.

The creature dropped the second man, having exsanguinated him appar‡ently on the move, and attacked again; this time we fought her off with our parangs and shortly after lost sight.

Cpl. Zamri, the third man, suggested that we make entry into the house. I agreed.

An open cellar door led us to an underground chamber. A wooden bath which proved to be full of vinegar sat in one corner; the headless naked body of a woman sat upright in a chair, hands folded in her lap, in the opposite corner.

The walls were lined with bottles, half of vinegar, half of surgical spirit and disinfectant.

Cpl. Zamri, showing remarkable self‡possession, suggested that we smash the bottles. He ventured that the broken glass should be placed within the cavity of the woman's body, this being a foolproof way to kill a Penanggalan. He ex‡plained that the glass would irreparably damage the entrails, and could not be removed. I accepted this as reasonable and this done, we vacated the house.

5. Two days later, we staged an arson attack on the house.

We took control of the local press in the matter; The SIS boys have sent around their own information through usual channels: the story goes that the accounts of the vampire have been reported to the locals as the work of commu‡nist agents, seeking to stir up discontent by playing to local superstition.

Stranger things have happened.

The attacks have ceased.

The next of kin of the two casualties have been notified. They are listed as having been killed in action by insurgents. Cpl. Zamri has been transferred to Sarawak.

6. Please find attached my application for transfer.

Page 3 of 3 pages   Copy 1 of 1 copies

Story Hooks: Intelligence Agencies and Other Horrors

• Facing The Unexpected

Not all vampires fall under the basic categories of vampire.

We've already seen the Arabic *Ghûl* and the Malaysian *Penanggalan*.

In ancient Babylon, the *Ekimmu*, insubstantial spirit of an unburied man, rose to feed upon the blood of the living. The *Yara-ma-yha-who* roams parts of the Australian Outback. He has a vast mouth and suckers on his hands and feet through which he sucks the blood of his victims. The *Asiman* of West Africa is ethereal, and hides inside human bodies. It leaves its unaware host body at night, appearing as a glowing figure, or as a ball of light. The Chinese *Ch'ing Shih* is deadly white and has long curving talons on its fingers. It flies at terrifying speeds. The vampires of India have back-to-front feet. The Filipino *Aswang* appears as a revolting old woman with oily holes in her armpits. She kidnaps her victims, and creates replicas of them from rubbish which go home, sicken and die. When the victim's funeral is over, she eats her prisoner.

Some of these may be variations of the more common vampires known to the dedicated hunter. A lot of this folklore may be arrant nonsense. But some of these vampires are doubtless unique.

A lot of the powers these creatures have don't appear to be covered by the existing Dread Powers, but that's an illusion: systems are abstract, and two monsters that look completely different can use the same powers with different effects. A vampire's feeding simply causes damage; what difference if the vampire takes the blood through a bite or through his fingers?

The inchoate *Asiman* and *Ekimmu* could be treated as ghosts with vampire Dread Powers tacked on. The *Aswang* is a witch, so why not let her have magic like a warlock?

In the end, you don't actual need formal systems to include these creatures in a game. The appearance of a bizarre vampire and its powers and weaknesses are really just window-dressing.

• Task Force: VALKYRIE's Counterparts

Task Force: VALKYRIE can't be the only world government agency out there that has put two and two together concerning the undead. It doesn't work like that. But the question is, who are they? In 1955, Britain's equivalent was, apparently, MI18 / DRU. Are they still going? And what does "DRU" stand for? It does stand to reason that the Americans might want to know about them: conspiracy lore has it that secret agencies in the UK and US don't trust or respect each other.

It stands to reason that China, Russia, India and Israel at least have comparable agencies, of varying efficiency and resources. In the 1970s, rumors abounded that the Soviets had managed to train up their agents with psychic powers. If a Russian conspiracy existed, it stands to reason that its endowment probably includes some sort of psychic powers. On the other hand, it might be massively corrupt and more or less run by oligarchs or mobsters, or it might be desperately honest but operating under a crippling budget crunch.

A Chinese conspiracy could have access to all sorts of mind-control techniques and drugs, but at the same time probably works on a culture of paranoia among its agents.

MI 18 AND MI 13

In the second World War, British Military Intelligence divided up its various duties into numbered departments, from MI1 through to MI19. The only ones that weren't used were MI18 and MI13. After the war, all except MI5 (now the Security Service) and MI6 (now the Secret Intelligence Service) became defunct.

Military Intelligence supposedly let MI13 vacant because many intelligence agents were superstitious enough that few would work for an agency numbered 13. In a business where even the slightest hesitation can lead to the deaths of millions, even a trivial factor like mild triskaidekaphobia. But why skip from 17 to 19?

Real-world conspiracy theorists have long believed that MI18 was in fact a department that intercepted and analyzed radio signals from the Americans (which is why they could never admit that it existed). On the other hand, some have even suggested that MI18 was in fact responsible for investigating and covering up extra-terrestrial activity.

But what if MI18 really existed, and still exists today? And for that matter, what about MI13? What would they investigate? Would they know about each other? Would they even have good relations (consider the fabled rivalry between MI5 and MI6)? What would be their aims? And what benefits and risks would come from working for them?

If MI18 / DRU really exists it has access to gadgets based around supernatural surveillance, things like scanners and detectors that pick up ghosts and vampires. The Israeli agency's masters would keep its agents under a close watch. The Holy Land keeps secrets under its ground, and those secrets are best used by the right people.

Whatever the case, these other agencies are probably intensely curious about what goes on in the US, and would be very interested indeed in finding out what VALKYRIE knows. Agents who find themselves going abroad in pursuit of monsters may find themselves the subject of interest for more than monsters.

Lovebirds (2005)

From an interview, held by George Roberts, representative of the Barrett Commission, Early March 2006:

RANDOLPH: We fell in love the night Katrina hit. The bar was falling down. She pulled me out of the way of a sign that the wind had ripped down and she let me stay at her place. Love at first sight. Me and Janie. We managed to get by together. Patched the apartment together, went out in a rowboat we found and salvaged stuff. No electricity in the apartment. Gathered up fallen branches from the trees for firewood. Traded all these crates of whisky we had. Newspapers did a thing on me and her. "Katrina Lovebirds" too. We were on CNN one time. Tale of survival and heroism. Me, I thought we were just getting by,

ROBERTS: Then what happened?

RANDOLPH: Real life got in the way, I guess.

ROBERTS: Go on.

RANDOLPH: She got me a job at the bar she worked at. I was a bouncer. The boss said I was "eye-candy." I took advantage of that, I guess. I wasn't exactly faithful.

ROBERTS: No?

RANDOLPH: No. Pretty faces turned my head. So we started to argue some. Then we had to leave the apartment. We got behind on the rent. We moved into a new place next to the voodoo temple.

ROBERTS: The voodoo temple? Did that—?

RANDOLPH: No. It wasn't the temple. It was the storm.

ROBERTS: The storm.

RANDOLPH: Yeah, the storm. It was like something was all shook about when the storm came. It wasn't just a storm. It was something else. The owls. I kept hearing owls everywhere I went.

ROBERTS: Owls?

RANDOLPH: Yeah. They'd be hooting and screeching all night. Came to the point you couldn't get a night's sleep. So I took to drinking. And then I took to cheating on Janey. And then we took to fighting.

ROBERTS: And she said she was going to throw you out. The landlord and your boss both corroborate this.

RANDOLPH: That's right, yeah. She told the superintendent that my name was coming off the lease. And I told Wayne she'd told me she didn't want me around no more.

ROBERTS: What made you kill her?

RANDOLPH: The booze. That's all it was. The booze. Nothing more than that.

ROBERTS: And then you—

RANDOLPH: I strangled her. And then I fucked her. I was drunk out of my mind. It was the owls. It was like there were a flock of them outside the window and I don't know what I was doing. And while I was fucking her, you know what? She started moving. She started smiling and whispering my name in this creepy voice, and touching me back.

ROBERTS: She came back to life.

RANDOLPH: You don't believe me.

ROBERTS: I believe you, Mr. Randolph.

RANDOLPH: It wasn't her, though.

ROBERTS: How did you know?

RANDOLPH: She stopped eating. I mean, she went out of a day, and she went to work—

ROBERTS: She went out by day?

RANDOLPH: Yeah.

ROBERTS: OK. So what did she do?

RANDOLPH: She made me do things. Really terrible things.

ROBERTS: Worse than killing your girlfriend and violating the body, you mean?

RANDOLPH: I was drunk! And I was going mad! Can't you see that? Can't you see?

ROBERTS: What, exactly, did she coerce you into doing?

RANDOLPH: She made me bring her people. Girls, boys. She'd make me screw them and she'd watch. And then I'd hold them down and she killed them. And she drank their blood. Like a vampire.

ROBERTS: Like a vampire.

RANDOLPH: And then she said she got bored, and I... did what I did.

ROBERTS: She told you to... do that to her?

RANDOLPH: She was bored, she said. She wanted to move on. So she used that voice on me and lay down. And I got out the knife...

ROBERTS: I don't need to hear it again.

RANDOLPH: She was dead again. And the owl... the owl sat on the windowsill and watched the whole time. And then I cooked the pieces... Everything I've ever done, I failed at. The army, gettin' a job, love with my girl. Everything I am. I failed.

ROBERTS: You expect me to be sorry for you?

RANDOLPH: No.

ROBERTS: You know why you're here?

RANDOLPH: No.

ROBERTS: Good. I think that's going to be all. Here.

[SOUND OF SOMETHING BEING PLACED ON TABLE]

RANDOLPH: What you want to give me that for?

ROBERTS: I don't think you'll use it to escape. Be a man, Joe.

Media Studies (2009)

From a talk given by Howie Greenaway at ClamCon IV:

The Patterson-Gimlin Bigfoot film changed everything. You know that. It revolutionized Fortean film-making. It brought the weird into the mainstream. Those were simpler days. We live in a world where any idiot of the street can buy a handicam and film-editing software. And that's a good thing and a bad thing.

It's a good thing because the more opportunities there are to film something, the more chance there is of catching something amazing.

And it's a bad thing because there's so much crap out there. And it's so easy to make a convincing special effect. Every year, it gets harder and harder. Have you got a Fortean phenomenon or a frat-boy pulling a fast one? The amount of stuff you have to look through is vast now, and the signal-to-noise ratio is phenomenal.

Still. Sometimes you find stuff. Some film clips here I want you to look at.

OK. This is from a videoblog. Outside broadcast. Street scene, evening, pretty crowded, camera focused on the girl in front. She's actually talking about politics. Nah. Not worth listening to. OK. And...

There. See there on the left? That blur? I'm going through frame by frame now. See? It's moving. It's moving like a guy. See? Behind that guy there... in front of the woman there... and pause again... right. OK. Craig? Could you blow that up a bit?

Right. Now. Even though we got hold of the original recording before it got You-Tubed, the resolution isn't great there. But this is what I want you to look at. First, notice that while this guy is blurred, this guy right here who's about as far away is about as crisp as you'd expect him to be. And so's the woman the blur is walking in front of. And you see the gaps in the middle here, under what you'd think were the arms? You can see the woman perfectly clearly. Most people who'd make an image like that wouldn't bother with that sort of detail. It's not hard to make a blur that's really definite in some places and not in others, like there... but why would you?

Notice also that the blur has this weird quality where it appears to be translucent, like it's only lightly on the image... in fact, it's an illusion. It's opaque. Look, see? There's an image behind the blur... and we'll go on a few more frames... and look. You can see that it's the same image behind the blur, which doesn't reflect anything else, anywhere in the film. So what you've got here is a blurred, superimposed image... on top of another blurred image. Two blurs. And no image underneath it.

But what it is not is a blur on top of an image of a man in the street. Because the image underneath is also screwed up. Which seems too thorough.

Now supposedly, you could insert a figure there, right, but why take so much care to have this blur walk through the street in and out of people. A few more frames and now he's in front of someone there and about to go behind of this guy here... and a few frames more and he's gone. It takes him maybe three seconds to get from one side of the screen to the other behind our presenter, who has no idea he's there.

So what gives? Sure, there isn't a single thing on here that you couldn't do with CGI, but the question is, why would you? What on earth would possess this woman and her friends to undercut their politics rant with a special effect worthy of ILM?

Story Hooks:
Photographic Records

One common, well-known characteristic of vampires is that they don't show up in mirrors. In some versions of the story, they don't have shadows, either. In modern iterations of the story, they often don't show up on film, whether still or moving. And in some versions, you can't even hear them over the phone. All this is actually true of a very few vampires.

But most of them do come across just fine on the phone, and *do* show up in mirrors and on film... only in a very limited way. Sometimes, it's a curse: it limits the ways in which they can communicate, and is a dead giveaway as to their supernatural nature... but only if people think that there's something up. And in this age of absolutely convincing special effects, people are more willing than ever to avoid thinking about the consequences of weirdness in film: it's just CGI.

Even so, sometimes a film comes up that can't be explained: Howie Greenaway's film, for example has no really compelling explanation. Mechanically, it can be explained, but what was the motive? The problem is, motives, or the lack of them, are pretty slippery things. And they're hard to prove or disprove.

Many vampires have the talent to make their images appear—temporarily—clear. Imagine a character who sees an image change from being blurry to being clear... only to find it's blurred again the next time he tells someone. As frustrating as it may be, it raises other questions. Why should a vampire allow someone who's on to him to see his face?

Who's pursuing who?

When you've been in the same line of work for a long time, it's easy to get jaded; for the policeman, the firefighter, the doctor or the paramedic, you have the added danger of becoming callous, of being hardened to the horrors to which you are subjected day and night. You stop caring about people; see them as statistics and challenges. Because the alternative is to go mad. People die in violence in every second of every day; if we bore the burden of the grief of every bereaved soul, we would all be crushed.

Consider a man who has taken upon himself the detective's vigil for longer than he can remember, for longer than anyone he knows (with one exception) has been alive, who has lived under a false name for so long he has forgotten the name under which he was born. His only confidante terrifies him. The only home he names never existed.

Why, then, does old Mr. Thélème love his work so much? It's almost unseemly to take such joy in these things, and yet he derives an intense private amusement from things that sicken or drive mad the most hardened of his fellow hunters.

On occasion, people have challenged him on this point. His only explanation: *Well, you have to laugh, n'est-ce pas?*

"You made a mistake. I could snap these like they were... made of paperclips."

"Ah. I see."

"Let me go now and I won't kill you."

"I rather think I have lost the key. Sorry."

"This is your last chance."

"Ah well. You shall just have to break the cuffs and kill me."

Mr. Thélème pulls up a chair and sits in front of his captive, a young black man in a cheap suit. He steeples his fingers and gives the young man in front of him a small, sardonic sort of smile.

"You think this is funny." The man in the chair suddenly snarls; his eyes redden; his teeth become needle-sharp; he lunges forward, his mouth aimed for Thélème's throat. The old man doesn't flinch or move in the slightest as the captive's chair, still handcuffed to him, flips forward with the motion, casting its occupant onto his face with a sickening crunch.

Mr. Thélème allows his captive a moment for reflection. Then he gets up and effortlessly rights the chair. "I do, rather."

"Ow," says the captive.

The vampire in the chair's nose is broken and bleeding; several of his razor-teeth are broken. He sticks out his tongue and licks at the stream of blood coming from his nose, which straightens itself and stops bleeding; he licks at a broken tooth. It grows back.

"There now," says Thélème. "All better." He pulls out a handkerchief and dabs the excess blood away.

The vampire strains once more against the handcuffs.

"I find, in my line of work," says Mr. Thélème, "that it is useful to know the tensile strength of handcuffs. Have you ever found that?"

The smooth-skinned youth in the Top Man suit stares at him.

Mr. Thélème is unperturbed. "Also, observation is the key. Now, with the older examples of your kind, one finds they are unpredictable. They have little to prove, and it in point of fact suits them to keep their capacities secret, to some degree." He leans forward. "On the other hand, a

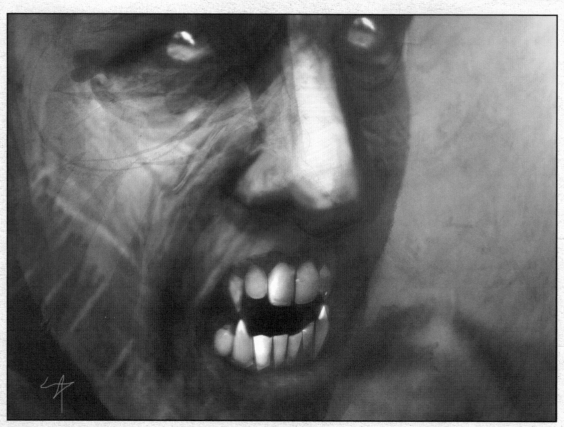

younger, newly-made vampire, particularly a young Eng-lishman like yourself who is already prone to a certain bra-vado, does not hesitate to demonstrate what modest powers he has, for he is delighted to have them. Indeed, one might think they were his primary delight."

"So?" The vampire is looking down now.

"So one only needs to watch a young vampire such as yourself for one, maybe two nights before one has a fairly accurate idea of exactly what the quarry can do. And this," Mr. Thélème gestures gracefully towards his captive, "is why you are here. For it did not take long to ascertain that while possessed of certain doubtless impressive capacities, you are not endowed with the ability to break a well-made pair of handcuffs."

Mr. Thélème's captive glowers at him.

"Of course, this is not the reason I have you here."

"Thanks for clearing that up." It's a challenge, but the boy's voice wavers, as if he has a presentiment of exactly what Mr. Thélème is prepared to do with him.

Mr. Thélème is silent for some time. He rubs his chin. "I want to talk about this: a chain of factory farms of which your masters are clients."

"What?"

"The blood. You are buying blood. You and your friends are buying a lot of blood."

The young vampire looks nonplussed. "Yeah."

"From the farms."

"Dunno where you got that from. It's from blood banks, innit?"

"Ah. Of course."

"What?"

Mr. Thélème stands up and walks behind his captive. "What is your name?"

"Marvin." The vampire's bravado is fading.

"Marvin, it strikes me that you know very little. How-ever, I think I shall tell you what I think is happening, and you can tell me whether or not it is borne out by your expe-rience. Is that agreeable?"

The vampire is silent, watches him as he paces around the cellar.

Mr. Thélème continues anyway. "Good." He sits back down and leans into the vampire's face. "I think that your friends are stockpiling. I think there is something that they are scared of happening. Either they are worried about something, or expect their chances of hunting to be cur-tailed. So, they are gathering resources; hence the increased demand on the blood farms. Or from wherever it is you think you are buying the blood. Does that make sense?"

"I suppose."

"But this of course means that there must be some-place where the blood — if this is the only thing you are stocking up — is being kept."

Again, Marvin is silent.

"I think you know where that is. You do not want to tell me this."

Mr. Thélème holds out the palm of his hand; he spits a gout of cold blue flame into it, where it stays. Marvin, eyes wide, makes a small, high-pitched noise. He shrinks back, as much as he can, and his arms strain at the cuffs.

The old man has had a great deal of practice in its appli-cation, and it is perhaps no surprise that Marvin tells Mr. Thé-lème exactly what he wants to know in less than a minute.

Mr. Thélème leaves behind Marvin's headless body, his skull reduced to smoldering ash on a rotting corpse (he is not an old vampire at all), still tethered to the chair.

He can always buy another pair of handcuffs.

⚬━✦━⚬

In the alley behind the Tesco supermarket in East Ham lurks a monster, watching the people pass by on the pavement, walking in the dark and cold of an early February evening. He leans nonchalantly against the wall back, incongruous between the wheelie-bins. He's vast, a huge greasy bulk in a leather apron, picking at obscene, stained teeth with a cal-lused, pudgy finger. He shifts his position, and leaves behind a faint covering of mold on the alley wall; he brushes against the steel wheelie-bin, preparing to move on; a second or two later, the paint begins to peel. He licks at warty lips with a tongue, appraising a young man who has stopped at the end of the alley to light a cigarette. He steps forward, his grace bely-ing his bulk, and he reaches out a hand, and then a man behind him makes the quiet, theatrical sound of clearing his throat.

The huge thing spins around, withdraws into the shadows.

And the voice says, "Hello, Andrew."

"By the Virgin's munificent cunny! I thought I was well rid of you." The monster's voice is a rich Cockney ten-or. He forms every vowel and consonant with exaggerated movements of those hideous lips.

"I had thought much the same of you, my friend," says Mr. Thélème, straightening his scarf and tucking an end into the col-lar of his overcoat. Do you remember the last time we met?"

"I had you by the throat. I would've slit you from gul-let to gizzard if you hadn't slipped my clutches."

"That is not strictly how I remember it."

The beast leaps at Mr. Thélème, the thick fingers tipped suddenly with jagged black talons. His grace des-erts him, however; something has his ankle, and he topples to the ground, face first. The cobbles beneath him develop a thin coating of algae and slime. As he gets up, it concen-trates beneath his hands, spreads out in every direction.

"Truce," says Mr. Thélème. The monster looks up at him.

"I'll not treat with the likes of you, Frenchie."

"Have it your way. I only want to talk."

"I could flick a wrist and you're a smear on the cobbles."

"You are not doing very well with that, are you?"

The creature does not move.

"You are aware that your awakening has caused some consternation among your friends, hein?"

"They can shit their britches for all I care, the cunts."

"In this, at least, we are in accord."

"Say your piece and I'll let you go, Frog."

"For tonight."

"For tonight."

"There is something of which the others are more scared than even you, Andrew. They are stockpiling blood and finding places to hide in light of a coming storm. Does that not interest you?"

"Nah. I seen it through before, and I'll see it through again."

"You have seen it through! Yes. This is exactly why you are so important, and why they are so frightened of you. They believe that you are connected to it."

The man and the beast regard each other.

"So what," says Mr. Thélème, "did you see?"

⚬━✦━⚬

Mr. Thélème leans against Marx's tomb. He's looking at his nails.

"That's not terribly respectful." The speaker is a middle-aged man; he has just come from the overgrown area behind the tomb.

"Still holding a torch for the International, Gerry?"

"Nah. I'm just holding a torch." He is. He shines it in Mr. Thélème's face. "God almighty. You haven't aged a day."

"I think I have probably aged a day. Or two."

Gerry puts down the torch. "I must confess, I wasn't ever expecting to hear from you again. When was the last time we were here?"

"Highgate Vampire, wasn't it?"

"Yeah. Of course, it wasn't in the end. Still got the bastard, though."

"Good times."

"Great days."

"Or nights."

"Or nights, yeah." Gerry leans against the monument beside Mr. Thélème. "So what's going down, Mr. T?"

"I obtained what you might think of as a tip-off. We are to go to the Circle of Lebanon. I am given to understand that we may see something there."

"That's the other end of the bloody cemetery. Why meet here?"

"Old time's sake. You are still part of a union, after all."

"Renew my membership every year. Still paying the dues. Marx would have understood."

"I don't think he would have, you know." says Mr. Thélème, as they set off. "He had no sense of humor. I don't think he ever bought the drinks."

⌁

"What are we looking for, exactly?" says Gerry. They pick their way over gravestones, some better-tended than others.

"I am not sure. I think we shall know when we see it. Or hear it." Mr. Thélème is, as usual, sanguine. An owl hoots overhead. Another replies. And another. And a fourth.

"They're out in force tonight," says Gerry.

"They are the spirits, the low spirits and melancholy forebodings, of fallen souls that once in human shape night-walked the Earth and did the deeds of darkness, now expiating their sins with their wailing hymns or threnodies in the scenery of their transgressions.'"

"What?"

"Owls. Thoreau."

"Oh."

"You know, in ancient Rome, they thought that owls were vampires, who sucked the blood of children."

"Yeah? Were you there too?"

"No. That I read in a book."

They walk on. The to-and-fro of hoots and screeches becomes deafening.

"I've never heard anything like it," says Gerry. "I can hardly hear myself think."

"It is very odd, yes." Mr. Thélème stops and grasps Gerry's shoulder. "Look."

Two men are carrying something long and heavy towards the crescent-shaped monuments that comprise the Circle of Lebanon. A third follows.

"Bet you a fiver that's a body," says Gerry.

"No wager," says Mr. Thélème.

"Please yourself."

Gerry and Mr. Thélème crouch now, taking a more circumspect route towards their destination, in the hopes that they have not been seen. They arrive at the edge of the circle.

A man — young, tall, blank-eyed — keeps watch at one end of the Circle.

Gerry nods at Mr. Thélème, and the older man walks away some distance, to double back. They've done this before. Gerry pulls a set of brass knuckles from his coat and puts them on. And then he gets as close to the watching man as he can without being seen.

Mr. Thélème walks straight up to the sentry. The man pulls out a carving knife and advances in a jerking, clumsy fashion, as if very tired. At which point Gerry grabs his shoulder, spins him around and gives him a face full of metal. The man crumples, giving Mr. Thélème the chance to put his scarf around the man's neck. Gerry keeps pounding until the man is out. No one makes any sound that could be audible over the hooting of the owls.

And then the owls become louder. Gerry and Thélème look around the corner. The other two men, as sluggish and blank as their friend, unroll the bundle.

"I claim my fiver," whispers Gerry as the figure of a man rolls to the ground. The screeching and hooting of the owls rises, until both Thélème and Gerry have to cover their ears. Then it stops, abruptly, instantly. And the body gets up.

"It wasn't a corpse after all," says Gerry.

"No. I think you're wrong." Mr. Thélème is shaking, clutching his chest. "This is bad, Gerry."

"What?"

"I *know*."

The body looks in their direction. His eyes reflect the light at certain angles. He opens his mouth, and makes a sound at the moon, like the sound of a man's throat trying to approximate the screech of an owl.

Mr. Thélème looks up. Standing or crouching on the walls of the monument, looking down on them, are more men and women, their clothes stinking and ragged, their eyes luminous; among them more dull-eyed, blank-faced men.

⌁

Two old men are running through the graveyard, as fast as they can, as young corpses and their young slaves gain on them.

"The gate!" calls Mr. Thélème.

"The gate's locked! Why are we running for the gate?"

"I never come alone," says the Frenchman, as he punches a dull-eyed thrall in the face and vaults over a teen-age girl like a man a fraction of his age.

The body looks in their direction. His eyes reflect the light at certain angles. He opens his mouth, and makes a sound at the moon, like the sound of a man's throat trying to approximate the screech of an owl.

Gerry's knuckledusters are slick with blood, some of it truly vile-smelling. His torch, too, stopped working but has made a more than adequate club, the black rubber covering coated in blood that drips over Gerry's hand.

Every turn they make, every trick they try to lose their pursuers in the cemetery, they come face to face with more of them. They beat in faces with stones lifted from ill-kept graves; they push; they kick; they go for throats and breasts and groins. Mr. Thélème now has a carving knife relieved from one of the creatures' thralls.

The monsters, for their part, are not well-served by their dazed, clumsy slaves. Gerry sees one, in frustration, ram a vicious blade through one of the thralls' throats rather than be obstructed again; others trip over gravestones. One falls in front of Mr. Thélème, who can hear the sickening crunch of a breaking neck even as he leaps over the prone man.

But the shrieking doesn't stop, and this wears on the two men. And they are old.

It comes to this: Gerry and Mr. Thélème, exhausted, their sides burning, reach the gate, and it is, as the Frenchman promised, open. Gerry catches sight of something small and neither birdlike nor batlike flying around the gates; a foul smell wafts briefly across his nostrils.

And then they are surrounded. A dozen screaming men and women with light-reflecting eyes, and a dozen more of their sluggish followers now surround the two men, and the possessed corpses are shrieking, their mouths wide, their teeth razor-sharp in the moonlight.

The circle contracts. Mr. Thélème and Gerry stand close, circle each other back to back.

"My apologies," says Mr. Thélème, over his shoulder.

"Oh, I don't mind, Mr. T," says Gerry. "Let you into a secret, actually. Got cancer."

"Oh? What kind?" The shrieking makes it hard for them to hear each other.

"Testicular."

"Ouch."

"See. Better ways to go than that." The monsters are nearly within reach. A clawed hand swipes at Mr. Thélème, who ducks back.

"Gerry," says Mr. Thélème. "I am going to do something, and when I do, I want you to run. Do you understand?"

"Yes. All right. What?"

Mr. Thélème calls out: "*Allons-y!*" Something swoops down from the gates and circles both men three or four times, faster than Gerry can see in the dark. The monsters back off slightly, and suddenly it seems as if Mr. Thélème's hands and face are wreathed in fire and light; the Frenchman launches himself into the crowd. A gap opens.

Gerry runs for the gates, and does not look back, and does not stop running until he gets to his car.

⚔

The following night, Andrew the Tanner awakens from his daily slumber in the mold-covered abattoir cellar, licks wart-covered lips, and squints in mild surprise.

He puts a vast hand to his forehead, and pulls off a Post-It note.

Written on it in fountain pen ink, the handwriting exquisite, only this:

I do not appreciate being misled. The next time I come, you will never know that I was here. –T.

What's at stake when hunting vampires? For one hunter, it's the satisfaction of vengeance, to know that the monster that destroyed your family and stole away your wife is now just a smear of grimy ash on a warehouse floor. For another hunter, it's knowledge—vampires are ancient, and have minds that are labyrinthine with secrets. The struggle against the nocturnal fiends does not take one form, and every cell, compact and conspiracy has its own approach to stalking the night.

Cells: Everyday People

You send the husband away on the bus to stay with his buddy in Reno. He's an accountant. He's fragile. Not like you. Not like the other girls in the cell. The pit boss at the Cadillac Casino, he's on the leash of a blood-sucking motherfucker named Carson. They've been messing with people for too long. Who knows how many bloodless corpses are buried out there in the desert? How many working girls and cocktail waitresses have to die? The desert's about to have two more bodies. And then it's over. At least until the next one... and the one after that...

Story Hooks

• When the new gang moved onto the block your cell knew something had changed. They hung around convenience stores at night, terrorizing the customers and smashing the windows of the shop when the owner (a man named Maple) asked them to take their business someplace else. Then one night one of them threatened an old woman with a knife and Maple lost his temper. He took the shotgun out from under the counter and told the punk to get lost. The ganger charged Maple and got shot. Both barrels. The old lady had a heart attack when the ganger got back up. Maple told you the 'banger smiled at him, showing a pair of mean fangs before limping out of the store. Now Maple has come to you, asking for help. That smile keeps him up at night. It was a promise of things to come.

• Every morgue has stories about a corpse that got up and just walked out. Everyone knows the stories are bullshit...except when they aren't. Your cell has heard rumors about a morgue where more bodies go in than come out. The word is that whenever vampires get into a scrape and have to play dead, they get taken there. A couple pints of blood and a change of clothes later, they're back on the street.

• The creatures of the night do not appreciate scrutiny. Soon as a hunter cell starts poking around a vampire's business, the vampire starts poking right back. The doctor the cell visits when they have injuries but no explanations suddenly ends up dead—or worse, now he's on the vampire's pay-

You don't understand me. You are not expected to. You are not capable of it. I am beyond your experience. I am beyond good and evil, legions of the night, night breed, repeat not the errors of the Night Prowler and show no mercy.
—Richard Ramirez, Serial Killer

roll (or worst of all, suckling at the creature's bloody teat) and wearily sells out the cell as soon as he gets the chance. And it doesn't stop there. One hunter thinks his wife is acting weird. Another hunter finds a message written on the mirror of his child's bedroom: two eyes drawn with lipstick and the letters ICU beneath it. Some of this stuff is real. Some of it may not be. Vampires are masters at fucking with one's head, and they're deliriously talented puppetmasters. Is the cell mired in its own paranoia? Can they separate truth from fiction and stop the vampire before it dissects the hunters' lives?

The Enemy

To the everyday people that encounter them, vampires aren't romantic figures of dark passions and striking pale looks. Vampires aren't creatures of interest, problems of national security or a riddle to be solved. No, vampires are monsters—plain and simple. They are fiends that destroy lives and shatter families. Small hunter cells sometimes form in the aftermath of an atrocity committed against family or friends... a little girl found bloodless in her bed, a wife stolen by the hypnotic allure of a dark stranger, a neighborhood plagued by a gang of cackling bloodsuckers.

Why is this enemy so terrifying to the average hunter cell? Consider it. For the most part, vampires look human. They can walk amongst us, and because they only do so at night, any signs of their damnation or death (yellow eyes, pallid faces, dark striations in the flesh) lay concealed beneath shadow. They're a parasite, a disease; like ticks and leeches, they hide, bite and *drink*. Perhaps worst of all, this disease is contagious. Vampires represent an infection, and whether it's a biological phenomenon or a purely mystical one doesn't much matter. No, what matters is that should a vampire so choose, the young teen daughter he drinks dry could wake up the next night as one of Them. Where once a man had a daughter with good grades and a nice boyfriend, he now has a mockery of his little girl, a fiend who wears her flesh and has her memories but hungers for blood above all else.

Plus, reliable information on how to hunt and kill vampires isn't easy to come by. Public libraries don't carry books with titles like *Vampire Killing for Dummies* and any information easily obtained on the internet should be considered highly suspect. Most of the knowledge everyday people have about vampires comes from TV and movies or popular myth.

This works to the vampire's benefit. Some poor schmuck that expects a vampire to cower in fear at the sign of the cross is in for a big surprise when the vamp in question laughs and shoots the would-be hunter in the face with a .38 snubnose (then laps at the wound like a hungry dog). Partial understanding of the truth can be just as dangerous as complete ignorance. A cell that manages to take down the vampire stalking their local bar that believes they are safe in their homes because vampires have to be invited in won't last 'til sunrise if more vampires show up looking for payback.

Worst of all, vampires aren't just blood-hungry predators. They're manipulators. They're parasites that have wormed their way into society's *brain*, and from there they can control a great many things. Police reports go missing. A hunter's bank account is suddenly devoid of its already meager funds. The head of the neighborhood association no longer blinks, and is happy to issue an eviction notice with that blank stare and a blanker smile. This is Invasion of the Body Snatcher-type stuff, right here. From their positions in towering penthouses and black-windowed boardrooms, vampires work puppet strings in their gifted hands, virtuosos of Getting What They Want. It's bad enough that they can leap high, run fast, and rip a signpost out of the ground with some kind of infernal strength. But it goes so much deeper than that, and a lone hunter cell trying to combat a vampire's considerable physical and social presence is in for the fight of its life.

The Response

Times of tragedy and crisis bring out the both the best and worst in people and hunters are no different. Consider the following scenario. A vampire has taken up residence in the basement of a college dormitory. He sneaks up the stairs at night to feed from sleeping or drunken students and is eventually caught in the act after causing a death. A group of students band together to fight the creature, forming an impromptu hunter cell. Operating with the best intentions for everyone (human at least) involved, the hunters could descend to the basement during the daytime to track the vampire down and kill it. Without sure knowledge that vampires are totally comatose when the sun is up, this is a fairly dangerous course of action that might lead to casualties among the hunters. Alternately the cell could disable the sprinkler system in the building and pull the fire alarm during the daytime, just prior to setting the place on fire. Hopefully the fire alarm would allow everyone to get out of the building before it burst into flame, but it's still likely some innocent lives would be lost. Even though both solutions are liable to be equally effective, one places the hunters in harm's way to protect their fellow students, while the other puts innocent lives at risk to protect the hunters.

A first tier cell combating a vampire or its influence must always make choices, choices that have no easy answers. What's the approach? Is it physical? Do they attempt to outright destroy the vampire? Sure, stakes are readily made from any solid piece of wood, combustible materials are as close as the nearest gas station and slashing or stabbing weapons are easily bought from hardware stores. Shotguns can do the trick if they are loaded with the kind of buckshot that might blow a vampire's limb off at the joint. Explosives can also be effective, but they're not exactly legal to own or make, for the most part (not to mention the fact that *big boom* will draw a lot of attention).

The reality is this: first-tier hunters hoping to go toe-to-toe with a big bad vampire are going to end up very dead, very fast. Smart hunters watch, wait, and come to recognize that vampire society seems predicated on some kind of pyramid scheme: at the top, the vampire. Beneath him, lesser creatures, including other vampires. One layer down lurks the human servants of the monsters, and further down are the ignorant "human resources"—those individuals who unwit-

LIKE DOMINOES, TOPPLING

That's the thing about vampires. You fuck with the wrong one, and next thing you know, the world around you is falling apart, one domino at a time. None of it seems directly attributable to the creature of the night, of course, but isn't it a spooky coincidence that the phone company turned off your phone for late payment (even though you just paid)? And that your position at your bank is suddenly forfeit, and the cops are investigating some money that you "stole" (but you didn't, of course)? And now the wife is seeking a divorce, and although you don't see any bite marks on her neck, you *do* find a dark bruise right over her carotid artery...

tingly provide work and services for the creature in question. Whether the vampire heads a brutal gang of thugs or sits in at a desk in a locked room of a banking conglomerate, the idea is still the same—the gang head has his lackeys and 'bangers, the corporate monster has his assistants and account managers. The smart hunter works at the pyramid from the bottom, removing one brick at a time. The not-so-smart hunter starts at the top, and doesn't live to see another morning.

Of course, the vampire response to hunters can be of equal measure—a hunter often has his own little pyramid, too, except those who support him might be co-workers, friends, even family. A vampire might start knocking *those* bricks out one-by-one, as well, whether by a sharpened fingernail across the throat or by a hypnotic command whispered into a sleeper's ear...

Compacts

Although they lack the gadgets, advanced weaponry or paranormal abilities of the conspiracies, compacts *do* have access to a broader range of information and support than a confused cell trying to hold back the night with a half-empty shotgun and a sharpened chair leg. Membership, as they say, has its privileges. Each compact views vampirism in a different light and their response to the threat varies based on that viewpoint. The one thing they can all agree on, though, is that vampires are a threat not to be underestimated.

Ashwood Abbey

When Jon announced, after several rounds of absinthe, that he was going vampire hunting, you laughed and figured the green fairy had got the best of him. You humored him and slid into his Escalade along with a couple more of Jon's wealthy, ne'er-do-well cronies. After a short drive down to a particularly derelict section of the warehouse district, the SUV came to a sudden halt and Jon pointed to one of the others. The designated crony jumped out of the vehicle and hadn't taken more than two steps before the shadows seemed to twitch and blood from his severed head spattered against the vehicle. With a shout, Jon leapt from the vehicle and let loose with the biggest fucking handgun you'd ever seen. What looked like a homeless man staggered out of the shadows, clutching at his chest, except no homeless man should have fangs or gory claws protruding from his fingers. Suddenly, the idea of vampire hunting seemed a lot less funny.

Story Hooks

• You've tasted the forbidden fruit of vampire blood once too many times and now you can't stop thinking about your undead lover. And you wonder if others in your compact have the same problem. Thing is, that lover? She wants to know the names of other Abbey hunters. Oh, not to hurt them, not according to her. Will you give them to her? Is it betrayal—or are you doing them a favor by nudging them into a mesmerizing adventure?

• That judge the Abbey had been eyeing as a prospective member has suddenly starting hanging out with the wrong crowd. Everywhere he goes he's seen in the company of a pale, attractive young man who whispers in his ear. It could be the judge has finally come out of the closet, but when he sentenced an Abbey member to jail time for a minor possession charge you now suspect differently.

• This is what you've heard: across town, the Bowling Green Boys (another Sybarite cell) has admitted a pair of vampires into its little club. Artists, you hear. A supposed brother and sister in the blood, whatever that means. It all seems well and good until corpses start showing up only a few blocks over—of course, these *artiste* vamps claim it wasn't them, oh, no. What do you do? Could they be right? Or must they—and the hunter cell that hosts them—be destroyed for what they are and what they do?

The Enemy

It didn't take the Ashwood Abbey long to verify that, yes Virginia, there really are vampires. The first member to claim the head of a vampire was compact founder Rev. Ogilvy. Ogilvy had heard rumors about a blood-sucking creature that stalked the city streets of Edinburgh by night and, in true Sybarite fashion, immediately organized his inner circle for some "sport." The well-heeled hunters descended on Edinburgh festooned with garlands of garlic cloves, ornate golden crosses (borrowed from the Reverend's church) and wooden stakes. Ogilvy carried his trusty elephant gun into battle, a cavalry saber and a hip flask full of holy water. When the hunt ended, several Abbey members were dead, but so was the vampire, a stake in its heart and its head removed after several enthusiastic slashes with the saber. Ogilvy had the head preserved, mounted and hung as a trophy in his den. Apart from confirming the existence of vampires, this historic hunt taught Abbey members that brute force and a bit of tenacity were more reliable weapons for a vampire hunt than smelly herbs or questionable faith.

Shockingly, the Abbey does have reasons for hunting vampires other than just the entertainment value. Vampires have a tendency to muck about in the affairs of politicians, judges and other figures of the high society to which most of the Abbey belongs. Finding out that the mayor is in thrall to an undead leech when he was *supposed* to be "owned" by the Abbey is both embarrassing and irritating. The Sybarites regard high society as their own personal playground and view the efforts of vampires to muscle in on their territory with a mix of disdain and fear. Truthfully, more than a few Abbey hunters are elitists—snobbish, by some measures. Vampires aren't even human. They're filth, really. *Fun* filth, sometimes, but not deserving of the laurels heaped upon them by high society. Sometimes, it's important to remind such creatures of their place.

It doesn't require much imagination to picture vampires as a whole like an undead version of the Ashwood Abbey. Both groups enjoy hedonistic pursuits and neither group is overly burdened with pesky morals. It is the choice of victim that separates vampire from Sybarite. Vampires are happy to feed on whoever comes their way, predators reveling in a world of prey. Every life ended by greedily sucking mouths diminishes the mortal community in some way, even if the effects aren't immediately obvious. Worse even than death is the parody of life vampires inflict on humans that replaces true emotion with base need and hollow desires. Vampires don't love, they possess. They don't feel joy or happiness, only swiftly-fading satisfaction. Even the hatred or anger felt by a vampire is a cold, dead thing fueled by spite rather than passion. The leeches exist in stasis, replaying their memories of humanity night after night like bad actors in a poorly scripted play. Better by far to be dead than locked in a world of singular sensation and eternal hunger. The Sybarites relish in the thrill of life—and by proxy, the thrill of the hunt. The destruction of a vampire and the rush that comes from pursuing them is life-affirming to the Abbey. Every blow against the undead is another crack in the dark mirror the vampires represent to the Sybarites and a repudiation of the stagnation for which they stand. Though they would object vociferously if accused of good intentions, deep down in their soiled souls the hunters of Ashwood Abbey know their actions, strange as it may seem, actually serve the common good.

The Response

Not every vampire is Public Enemy Number One, of course. Many are quite interesting. They remember things. They can pull strings that Abbey hunters cannot. Those creatures of the night with a modicum of good table manners and impeccable dress are worth keeping around, at least for a time. At least until they grow dull or reveal themselves to be the true monsters they are.

Whenever possible, the Abbey invites vampires to its parties. The antics of the undead provide for a certain grim amusement and it gives new Sybarites a chance to get a close and personal view of vampiric behavior. It would be rude not to offer a guest refreshment and so the Abbey even encourages vampires to feed from willing members, both for the spectacle and for the pleasure. Proof that no detail is too small, the Abbey even decorates these parties with their guest's special needs in mind. Long, fancy tablecloths hide the fact that all the tables are cheaply constructed from sheets of plywood with four (solid) wooden legs glued in place. If the hunters grow bored with their guest, they flip over the tables and wrench the legs free from the plywood. They tussle. They bludgeon. They stake the poor creature and, where appropriate, enjoy a taste of the fiend's blood.

Many Abbey hunters agree: the taste of vampire blood is an excellent high that every member must experience at least once. Of course, some of the dilettantes want more than just one taste and start hanging around in places known to be frequented by vampires looking for more. The Abbey doesn't really understand the properties of vampire blood, other than the euphoria it produces, which has lead to some problems for them in the past. They have a vague understanding that the blood can be addictive, but so can anything: sex, drugs, food. Sadly lacking is the knowledge that repeatedly drinking blood from the same vampire can lead to more than just addiction. The Abbey does realize that members who spend a lot of time around vampires seem to grow inordinately attached to them and sometimes go rogue, feeding information about the compact to the vampires that feed them. Worse yet are those few members for whom simply tasting the blood of vampires isn't enough. A Sybarite-become-vampire is an unholy threat not only to the lives of Abbey members but also to their place in society.

Once a year, around mid-summer, the Ashwood Abbey chapter in Seattle conducts what they call a "Charity Drag." For a month or two before the Charity Drag, the Abbey focuses its attention on the lower income areas of the city, looking specifically for signs of vampiric activity. All the facts, rumors and suppositions are gathered up and the entirety of the chapter spends a weekend in the slums, hunting and killing vampires. The Seattle chapter piously states that the Charity Drag is solely for the benefit of the poor, underprivileged citizens that live in the decaying neighborhoods and always seem surprised when the other hunters in Seattle are less than impressed with their civic pride.

The Long Night

You wanted to believe her story that the marks on her wrists, feet and by her ribs were really the stigmata, that she'd been blessed by an angel of God for her conviction. You wanted to believe, but every night she got paler and paler from loss of blood and you never found so much as a drop of it on her sheets. So you told your pastor about her visitations. The pastor visited your home and examined the marks. He took you aside and explained the truth. Now you wait outside her room with the pastor and other men from your church, holding weapons to destroy the Devil's bride. Your soul burns with righteous fury and you feel a fierce joy that you will soon be able to prove your dedication to the Lord through word and deed.

Story Hooks

• "Come along with us; let's lie in wait for someone's blood, let's waylay some harmless soul..." *Proverbs 1:11.* Your cell has managed to capture a ghoul, a blood slave to a vampire, and you are attempting to both save her soul and get her to provide information about her master. The problem is the addiction. Without regular infusions of vampire blood the ghoul is beginning to age with increasing rapidity. Are you willing to let her die and face God's judgment? Your cell *really* needs the info only she can provide. Are you willing to feed her craving just to get at her master? Will God forgive your transgressions?

• "Do not harm the land or the sea or the trees until we put a seal on the foreheads of the servants of God." *Revelations 7:3.* Everywhere you look you see the signs of the End Times approaching. The land suffers under war, drought and natural disaster. The seas are polluted and grow uneasy with the melting of the polar caps. The trees are felled in their thousands to make way for encroaching civilization or for worldly riches. The signs are all there even if most people are too ignorant to see them. The last vampire you killed had a seal on his forehead. Literally. It looked like it was made from a mixture of blood and wax. Thing is, you couldn't see the seal until he was nearly dead. This blasphemy must have a reason.

• "In His anger against Israel the Lord handed them over to raiders who plundered them." *Judges 2:11.* You hear it all the time: "It's the liberals who are to blame. Their bleating about equal rights for minority groups and their open embrace of godless heathens or false gods has created a modern day Sodom and Gomorrah. God has turned His face from us and let loose the beasts of the Apocalypse to punish us for our crimes." This kind of sentiment is all too common among modern Christians and no small number of Long Night hunters. Your cell has recently come into contact with a newly formed cell of Long Night hunters and it seems to you that *all* of them walk and talk like fundies. They've had success dealing with vampires and they believe that their success proves the truth of their small-minded bigotry. Your cell could clearly use their help battling vampires you've uncovered, but by accepting their aid are you adding fuel to the fire?

The Enemy

Other hunters might believe that vampires are simply monsters that feed on mankind. The Long Night knows better. Vampires are one of the plagues of the End Times sent to cleanse the earth of one-fourth the population. Vampires are demons that have escaped from Hell and walk the earth in these times of sin. Vampires are the vanguard for the armies of the Anti-Christ, preparing the way for his thousand-year reign. Vampires mock the sanctity of the holy cup and the blood of Christ that grants eternal life, offering instead the cold blood of a corpse and eternal damnation. Vampires are more than just simple monsters; they are symptoms of the twin diseases of blasphemy and heresy that grip the world.

The Long Night quickly established the fact that vampires aren't even slightly afraid of holy symbols and suffer no ill effects from holy water or stepping on holy ground. Far from dissuading them that vampires are the spawn of evil, this open display of contempt for the works and symbols of God makes the Long Night even more certain the undead are willing tools of the Devil. The fact that the kiss of a vampire brings pleasure to their victims hearkens to tales of succubi and incubi and further lends credence (in their minds) to the fact that vampires are devils sent to tempt the weak and reward the wicked. On the rare occasion that one of the Tribulation Militia is seduced into joining the ranks of the undead, the rest of the cell mourns the loss of their brother before setting out with stake, sword and flame to put his soul to rest. It isn't uncommon for the Long Night to stay the killing blow until the lost sheep has asked Jesus for forgiveness, even going so far as to imprison an ex-

member and purify their body with the scourge and the cane. Some people might call this treatment brainwashing, but the Long Night knows that no earthly punishment compares to the eternal torment found in hell.

The Response

The total redemption of most people that have given themselves over to the plague of vampirism is beyond the abilities of the Long Night. The greatest success with the salvaging of damaged souls is that of Long Night members turned to grim unlife, and even then the recovery rate isn't encouraging. The Long Night has had some success in convincing individual vampires to seek absolution in the forgiveness of Christ. They urge vampires willing to listen to spread the word of God's mercy to their fellows and beg for His forgiveness. Vampires that are willing to be saved are granted God's mercy and the Long Night prays with them in an all-night session. As dawn approaches, the Long Night hunters might even tie the vampire penitent to a post, waiting together, hunter and vampire, for the sunrise. The Long Night figure that a vampire that dies repentant, in the cleans-

ing light of the sun and through means other than suicide, has a fair chance of actually achieving redemption and ascending to heaven. It takes an individual of extraordinary faith to willingly take part in a ceremony that ends in final death (though some Long Night hunters argue that this is what they themselves do—by hunting monsters, they have committed themselves to death one way or another, but they have also reached for salvation). By and large, the most common result of confrontation with an undead menace is to meet it in holy battle and free what remains of its soul to face heavenly judgment.

The Long Night believes strongly in trial by fire and by their doctrines, that suffering makes them worthy of Christ. Just like Jesus bore the pain of the lash and the agony of the cross, the Tribulation Militia bears the pain of wounds suffered at the teeth and claws of vampires to prove their dedication. They fight with holy zeal and steadfast righteousness, willing to become martyrs to the cause. They truly believe that Armageddon approaches and are willing to carve their way through a sea of demons to stand at the right hand of Christ in that final battle. Hunters that think the End of Days has already come are even more fanatical about their war on vampires. It's as if they can hear a ticking clock in their heads, beating out the scant remaining time they have left to prove their devotion to the Lord.

"Zealot" doesn't translate to "suicidal idiot," though. The hunters realize they must stay alive to continue the fight. Though frontal attacks against overwhelming odds have a certain crusade-like appeal to hunters of the Tribulation Militia, they know for a fact that dying at the hands of a vampire is the *best* possible outcome of a losing battle. Being taken alive by a vampire is a fate far worse than death and one that could imperil their immortal souls. Hunters know the flesh is weak and shudder at the thought of becoming a blood slave to the vampires or worse, of being turned. The Tribulation Militia chooses its battles with care and remains willing to flee if the fight turns against them. After all, the Lord helps those that help themselves.

The Loyalists of Thule

You've gone deep. You look at the leash around your neck. The chain that connects you to the vanity. She thinks you're hers, now. But you've mastered the techniques. Breathe in, breathe out. Picture something outside you: a picture of a loved one, a Sudoku puzzle, a sink full of dirty dishes like the one you left behind. It's enough to push past the brainwashing. You find her phone in the vanity drawer. You send a text message to your cell—who you haven't seen for months. It's short. But you tell them everything. And now it's done. You have to get out of here before she comes back—are those footsteps you hear?

Story Hooks

• The grand old Loyalist the cell reports to has gone missing. If that wasn't bad enough, his filing cabinets, full of information about God only knows what, have also vanished. The only clue your cell was able to find after searching his office was a hastily scribbled word in Greek, written on a piece of paper that was stuffed into the seat of his chair. You looked up the word, *vrykolakas*, at the library. It means vampire. Below that was a hastily-scribbled street address from the worst part of town.

• You've managed to get hold of a hard drive owned by one of the vampire's human blood-junkie servants—but things got weird even before you hooked it up. Something was rattling around inside. Opening it up, you found a handful of dead scarabs. You put the thing back together and tried to hack into it, but the encryption's tough—some occult cipher keeps the thing hidden. Can you crack it in time? When will the vampire figure out that you've taken its data?

• Those German geriatrics that run this compact call it something that loosely translates as "The Listing," but your cell calls it "Dracula's Directory." The Listing is a series of logbooks chock full of reports on vampires that list names, locations and other useful information that could be put to good use. *Could* being the operative word. Instead of actually using the information, the geriatric trio sits on it and doles out bits and pieces of info like it's made of gold. Your cell's requests for release of information about a vampire in your town have been repeatedly denied with no explanation, leaving you with two choices. Attempt to deal with the vampire on your own or go to Munich and "appropriate" the files for yourself.

The Enemy

The threat that vampires pose to humanity is ancient, with roots stretching back further than recorded history. Every society has legends about vampire-like creatures from the Greek *vrykolakas* to the Malaysian *bajang*. Translations of stone tablets thought to have originated in Thule speak of monsters that hunted the night for blood. The Indebted record and disseminate as many of these legends as possible (including more recent urban myths), to give them a thorough grounding in the appearance and habits of vampires.

Vampires are walking, talking storehouses of dangerous occult information—truly *verboten* knowledge lurks in the undead minds of creatures who may have been walking around since the concentration camps opened their gates, if not before. Hell, some of the human thralls of vampires were guards at the camps or were occult archaeologists working for the Third Reich, but have long subsisted on the blood of the ancients and frankly don't look a day over thirty. Growing to such an age wears down the mind; any reliance on human morality winnows to bare slivers, and for some such an ethical code may not have been much to begin with. Couple that with awful occult knowledge (blood magic, grotesque biological experiments, freaky Fascist mesmerist tricks) and a penchant for killing folk to get at their blood, and it doesn't take long for a Loyalist to realize what a threat the vampires truly represent.

Even if they're not that ancient or aren't repositories for damaging occult know-how, vampires still represent an erosive social influence. Vampires are more than a little fascist, at least in the eyes of the Indebted. It seems that most cities suffer under the rule of some kind of blood-sucking autocrat (sometimes called a "Prince," other times a "Prefect"). Such autocrats—with help from their cabals of like-minded monsters—gladly quash any dissension and ask that the lesser creatures support the rule of the greater. The vampires represent a grim and seductive influence and often remain concealed behind layers of obfuscation and occultation. The Loyalists cannot abide the rule of authoritarian monsters, especially since their monstrous rule often unwittingly extends to the human populace. It's all too often that the Loyalists find that the tendrils of vampiric influence wind around all aspects of human society—corporate records, building inspections, fraud, organized crime, the weave and weft of high society, and so forth. Like any invasive plant, the roots of evil must be torn free from the ground. And burned, whenever possible.

The Response

The Loyalists of Thule are rarely found in the thick of the fight, preferring instead to provide backup and advice to other vampire hunters. They feel, possibly for good reason, that they can cause more damage to vampires by using their brains than their brawn. More than one cell survived first contact with the enemy as a direct result of information given to them by the Loyalists. It can be difficult, at times, not to reveal the source of their information, especially when confronted by hunters that think they know more than they do. The Indebted don't rely on word of mouth alone to spread their knowledge either. See, here's the thing: vampires have secrets, and they guard those secrets with eternal determination. Any time the Loyalists can get a hold of any such secret, they don't keep it to themselves. They share it—*widely*. They'll tell any hunter cell that will listen. They'll

post it on flyers and hang it around town. They'll disseminate it across the Internet. It seems that the vampires thrive on secrets, and hide behind them. Remove the secrets and you've removed their armor. It exposes them.

Of course, getting hold of such secrets is easier said than done. Even the lowliest creature of the night zealously guards such information. As soon as a Loyalists comes sniffing around, the vampire is likely to react—some are patient and might destroy parts of the Loyalist's life over the course of many years, but younger monsters are more impetuous, and are likely to come hissing, fangs out, ready to tear the hunter limb from limb.

How do they do it, then? How do the Loyalists uncover the forbidden secrets of vampire society? One way is to penetrate the monster's society somehow—the Penitents of the compact may offer themselves as addicts or slaves to the vampire's wishes, hoping to push past any brainwashing long enough to steal knowledge and get it back to the compact. Other Loyalists—like members of the Advance—strive to play power-games on par with the vampires. The creatures of the night are puppet-masters, so, hunters of the Advance set themselves up as the same: they establish themselves as competitors and endeavor to place themselves on equal footing. It doesn't always *work* that way, of course (some hunters fail to see just how deep the rabbit hole goes when it comes to the influence of vampire society), but notable gains have been achieved through this methodology.

Some hunters seek to expand the knowledge of the compact by delving into musty old crypts or by seizing the libraries and other written works of the vampires. They go armed and prepared for the inevitability of conflict with stakes, blades and guns (vampires might not mind bullets, but their blood slaves sure don't like being shot) to complement their knowledge of the foe.

A not-small contingent of the Loyalists are actually quite obsessed with understanding the origins of vampirism. Discovering the origins—which surely go back all the way to Thule, potentially due to some accursed transgression of humanity—might help them quash the plague of vampirism that runs as a rampant and parasitic strain through society. Whatever the occult origins of the vampire, the Loyalists view it like a puzzle to be solved. Once solved, can the curse be unraveled? The Indebted certainly hope so.

Network 0

Paige worked for the local free press, taking pictures of charity and social events, along with the odd political fundraiser. It was while developing film from a fundraiser for the mayor's re-election campaign that Paige first noticed the blurred figure that showed up in her pictures. She checked her equipment and her film for problems and, finding none, decided it must just have been some kinda freak occurrence. Later that month Paige took some shots at a charity dinner for the historical museum. There, in the picture, the same blurred figure—same smeared face, same hues and colors. Frowning, Paige looked over the notes she took to match faces to names and found the same name corresponded to both sets of pictures and both blurred images. Just then her cell beeped, alerting her to a text message. The message was from a number she didn't recognize and it read, v knows about pix. v is coming 4 u.

Story Hooks

• Someone has hacked your passwords. They've been posting videos under the name of your cell. And these videos are righteous garbage. Faked to the gills. It damages your already shaky cred, and only weakens your ability to disseminate the truth. All the fake videos, too, have to do with vampirism, loudly touting authentic "VAMPIRES R REAL" footage— it's clumsy, and now they've changed *your* passwords so you can't get back in.

• Some cocky rich prick in the compact has put out the call: he'll give a cool fifty-thousand dollars to the first Network 0 hunter that provides him with proof— video and audio *proof*—that vampires exist. Of course, he won't give his name. All you have is a codename ("Overholt") and a post office box. Problem is, capturing a vampire on video has proved just about impossible. And who is this guy, anyway?

• You know a girl that makes her money by doing nude netcam shows. Lately there haven't been any new shows and you haven't heard from her. The site says it's down for maintenance and in the one video playing on loop in the background you can just barely make out what looks like puncture wounds on her inner thigh.

The Enemy

Hackers say that information wants to be free and even the non-hacker members of Network 0 can sympathize with that mindset. Sharing information about the monsters that hunt humanity is the best way to open people's eyes to the truth. Realizing they would be outnumbered a million to one, the monsters hide the truth and no creature is more adept at hiding than vampires. Their whole existence is a lie and they spread further lies to conceal their activities. It might be a gross oversimplification to say that the struggle between Network 0 and vampires is one of truth versus

lies, but that idea encapsulates the core of the matter. With their inability to reliably capture an image of a vampire on film, vampires pose the biggest challenge to the Secret Frequency in their battle to expose the truth.

Vampires are masters of propaganda. They lurk behind countless false fronts and fake identities and it's from behind these curtains that they reach out and victimize the innocent. It's bad enough that they're monsters that harm, kill and enslave humanity. But to the hunters of Network 0, the biggest crime is their manipulation of information. Fake headlines? Classified ads that work as bait to lure victims into a vampire's abattoir? Stock prices "adjusted" so that the little guy gets poor and the monster's coffers swell? It's a gross injustice. Whistleblowers go missing. Secretaries end up brainwashed or drugged. Those desperate to belong think they're joining some self-help group and instead end up in some kind of blood cult that grows more and more insular, bound to the fat spider that twitches in the center of its web. (Some hunters grow mad with paranoia, assuming that every word they read or sound-bite they hear over the TV has been supplied by Our Benevolent Undead Masters. Others can't hack it, and just retreat from the world, finding a cabin in the mountains with a shitty Internet connection so they can monitor the downfall of humanity.)

The hunters of the Secret Frequency aim to expose this—to kick over the log and reveal to the world what squirms beneath. Of course, that's practically a Sisyphean task, isn't it? Not only do the vampires work overtime—with the benefit of being immortal—to conceal all their piles of dirty laundry, but they don't even show up properly on video. This is daunting for some Network Zero hunters. But for others, it's a boldfaced challenge.

The Response

The primary weapon of Network 0 against the things that go bump in the night is largely useless against vampires. Video or pictures of vampires never shows anything more than an indistinct image of the creatures, almost like the camera lens refuses to focus on them. It's hard to scare people with a blurry image. The compact is used to having people dismiss their videos as hoaxes and charges of fakery become even harder to defend against when the main attraction is a shadowy blob. At first Netzo posted the videos online anyways, hoping that someone would at least see something familiar to them and maybe make a few connections. When that didn't work, some members turned their attention to easier subjects, the rest decided to change tactics.

The Secret Frequency began taping their targets using a variety of different methods intended to highlight the differences between the hazy figure of a vampire and the clearer images of the people around them. They experimented with Kirlian and aura photography and incorporated the results into videos that explained and showcased the differences between human and vampire images. They used thermographic cameras and made thermal videos that showed heat "dead zones" where the vampires were standing. The compact took pictures and video using infrared technology that succeeded in eliminating some of the blur, albeit with an unusual side effect. Infrared shots resulted in pictures (or video) that highlighted the bone structure of the creatures, almost like in an X-ray. Even though the picture produced from infrared failed to capture detailed images of vampires, Netzo used the X-ray effect to point out the over-developed canines and other... skeletal oddities. Null Mysteriis is sometimes happy to partner with Network 0 in this capacity, working with one another to put together an intensive study. On the other hand, Task Force: VALKYRIE is happy to "partner" with the Netzo hunters, too—usually by just stealing their equipment and footage and offering a small stipend of cash in return.

While some members searched for a way to film vampires, others began to compile information about the undead by cross-indexing instances of hazy images with crimes committed. Network 0 hunters and their accomplices collected video from security cameras, cell phones, on-board cameras in police cruisers and any other source they could beg, borrow, steal or hack from. They plotted the results on interactive online maps hosted by Netzo secure servers and slowly began work out patterns of activity around the vampiric hot spots (called graveyards or just GY). Once they were reasonably certain their data was concrete, the Secret Frequency began to send emails to other more confrontational hunter cells containing links to the information they'd uncovered and to videos starring blurry vampires.

A local subset of both the Secret Keepers and the Army of Truth has been accumulating information on vampires for the better part of ten years, now. They won't share it with *anybody*—and that includes other hunters. No, these guys are deeply afraid that everybody could be compromised, so insidious is the influence of the creatures of the night. Their goal? As soon as they've reached some kind of breaking point (a point only they can determine, presumably), they intend to go "live" with it. Of course, going live with this information means assaulting a local news affiliate station with arms to bear, kicking down the doors and taking over the airwaves for *just* long enough to transmit the "truth" as they see it. It's an admirable plan, or would be if their information wasn't equal parts truth and lunatic conjecture.

Null Mysteriis

The vampire thought they must be crazy. He'd noticed them following him around town a couple of nights ago but hadn't decided what to do about it yet. Then one of them approached him at the club. The girl they sent was young and a little overweight but that didn't account for the way she was sweating inside the air conditioned confines of the building. Stammering slightly, the woman told him that her colleagues (not friends, colleagues) had identified him as an individual that suffered from some disease with a name ten miles long, more commonly known as—she bent forward and whispered the word—vampirism. He arched an eyebrow at the woman and said nothing. With hesitation, she offered him a business card and asked if he'd agree to an examination. Finally irritated, he locked eyes with her and told her to leave. After they were gone he picked up the card she had dropped and slid it into his pocket. At least they'd be easy to find.

Story Hooks

• Your cell has been approached by a guy that knows about your research with an offer to sell you vampiric blood, *sans* the vampire. While he wouldn't reveal the exact location of the stuff, it turns out a local medical research facility has *liters* of the stuff in cold storage. Why they have it he doesn't know, but he says he can get you some if the price is right. Of course, it might be better to just get the address, but he's not willing to share *that* piece of data.

• Anyone that watches TV these days knows that bodies go through a set process of decay after death. Putrefaction sets in and the bodies release all kinds of fluids and gases, most of which have a pretty awful smell. It stands to reason that vampire bodies, existing in a perpetual half-life state, would discharge trace amounts of the same gases and fluids. Obviously these trace amounts don't register to the basic olfactory sense, but it might be possible to construct a mechanical "sniffer" that could. At least that's the theory one of your colleagues has been working on. He's willing to share the credit for his discovery with your cell if you can find a way to install the test devices in specific locations around the city that are rumored to host vampire gatherings.

• While paging through a scientific journal you found an article that discussed the use of microchips for tagging animals in the wild. Like with a dog, the chip can be implanted in the ear (or for the truly advanced, into the stomach lining). The chip sends a signal, and those with an RFID reader can track the signal. The only real drawback to the system (which keeps it from being widely employed) is the short 50 yard range at which "animals" can be tracked. A local Null Mysteriis cell either wants the hunters to help them install the tracking device in various vampires across the city... or they've already done it, and they fucked it up, and now the creature's after them.

The Enemy

Vampires aren't really the enemy to (most) members of the Organization for Rational Assessment of the Supernatural. Vampires are a phenomenon to be studied, quantified and rationalized. They aren't a blight of evil sent from some theoretical God-figure to punish humanity for its sins. Vampires follow their instincts, just like every other creature, it just so happens that their instincts urge predation upon humanity. A vampire that kills someone while drinking their blood isn't any more evil than a lion that attacks and kills a human for food. Both creatures are predators following their natures.

That doesn't mean Null Mysteriis are vampire apologists; far from it. A lion that attacks a human should be put down and vampires that routinely kill their prey should be treated in the same way. But killing is only a temporary solution. It's far better to behave proactively, divine the source of the problem and figure out how to fix it. Rather than waste all their time and energy simply fighting the symptoms of vampirism, these hunters search for root causes and a cure. They hold fast to their belief that science will overcome.

It is true that vampirism is a sticky problem to solve, but if the solution were simple the problem wouldn't exist. A serious obstacle to pursuit of the solution is the, often contradictory, myth and legend that has come to be associated with the word vampire. Every society that tells stories about vampires offers different explanations to the cause of the affliction, possible cures and methods of fighting or discouraging the predators. Holy symbols, garlic, and use of wooden stakes are fairly common but so are the beliefs that vampires can't cross running water, pass into a home uninvited or travel during the day. Sorting the fact from the fiction is a serious challenge and so the compact runs experiments, records their findings and experiments again.

Unlike some compacts, the information discovered by Null Mysteriis scientists is disseminated to its members through private journals, newsletters, and protected websites. Of course, because nearly any theory is given credence, a great deal of misinformation (or incomplete information) ends up disseminated amongst the ranks. Most information verifies some scientific angle (say, for instance, a 30-page paper tying hemophilia to "early stage" vampirism), but often fails to account for the social angles of vampire society. Regrettably, Null Mysteriis often treats vampires like a species of animal or disease pathology rather than a society to be studied.

The Response

The membership of Null Mysteriis is divided into three camps on the question of how best to deal with vampires. Unsurprisingly, the camps fall along the same lines as the three major divergent philosophies in the compact: the Rationalists, the Open Minds and the Cataclysmicists (see **Hunter: The Vigil**, p. 121).

The Rationalists want to continue with current studies of the phenomenon before making any hasty decisions. They argue that the slow and steady due process of science will eventually crack the mystery of vampirism and will dictate the most logical direction for the compact to follow. These hunters prefer to conduct controlled experiments on vampires, both in the wild and the lab, and record their observations. The Rationalists believe that vampires are just humans that suffer from some sort of disease and most of their work is focused on identification and treatment of that disease. They reject the findings of the Open Minds as quasi-scientific nonsense at best and dismiss the warnings of the Cataclysmicists as paranoia.

The Open Minds theorists question the effectiveness of applying standard scientific procedure to a problem that is decidedly non-standard. Although they don't believe that vampires are in any way supernatural entities, these hunters openly question how many times vampire blood needs to be tested before the researchers are willing to admit they aren't finding anything new. The Open Minds prefer to work up close and personal on "live" subjects so they can better gauge the results of their experiments. These Null Mysteriis scientists bombard the bodies of vampires with radiation to observe the effects, they isolate vampires and feed them only animal blood or plasma to see how the creatures respond, and experiment with hypnotic suggestion while employing a plethora of other methods that range from merely unorthodox to truly bizarre. Rumor has it that a few members of this branch have even gone so far as becoming the blood-addicted slaves of vampires (or, by some stories, vampires themselves) to better study the condition. The Open Minds find the staid scientific efforts of the Rationalists too pedestrian to be worthwhile and though they might ally with the Cataclysmicists from time to time, generally consider the latter group to be alarmist.

The Cataclysmicists are the group least likely to conduct their own experiments on vampires, instead relying on their studies of work done by the other groups to form their opinions. Originally, this group acted as a peer review board for research publications produced by other members of Null Mysteriis. As time went by the hunters couldn't help but to notice a definite upswing in *Homo Haemophthisicus* activity and began to voice their concerns that the problem was reaching a point of critical mass. Instead of continuing in their accepted role, the Cataclysmaticists began to suggest more direct methods be taken to nip what they saw as a serious crisis in the bud. They began to print their own literature filled with graphs and estimates and started to produce their own theories. The theory that gained the biggest momentum in the group was that of divergent evolution; namely that vampires weren't human at all, but were a completely separate species. The Cataclysmaticists adopted the name *Haemophthisicus Sapiens* to refer to vampires and began to clamor for mass extermination of the threat or at least a systematic quarantine. The group likes to point to Neanderthals as an example of what happened to the last group of humanoid creatures that existed in competition with a superior species. This branch of the Organization believes that both the Rationalists and the Open Minds are moving too slowly and lobby for research dedicated to ending the threat.

OBSERVATION POSTS

Null Mysteriis often dots the city with what it refers to as its "observation posts" (or, cynically, "duck blinds") intended to study vampires from safe distances. Such a post might be a black van parked in an alley while the hunters within use listening equipment to try to mark vampire habits, while others are more "in-the-field"—like the cell that sits the Vigil every night in the light booth at the local nightclub, watching the vampires and their "migratory and feeding patterns" at a seemingly safe distance.

The Union

Vampires are tough to kill. They shrug off bullets like nothing and you don't want to get close enough to 'em to use a blade. Eddie's boss gave him keys to the machine shop years ago and now he puts in a little overtime working with scraps from the junk yard. The things he makes resemble bear traps in the same way a butter knife resembles a machete. Vampires are tough to kill all right, but once they lose a foot to one of Eddie's traps they die—or die again—a whole lot easier.

Story Hooks

• Someone dropped off a list under your door. It's got twenty names on it. All of them, bigwigs in the neighborhood. A county commissioner. A VP of research at the pharmaceutical company where half the town works. The head of the PTA. The list is typed, like on a typewriter, but at the bottom is something else. Something written in blood. It reads: "PUPPETS."

• "First taste is free." That's the word on the street. You thought it meant drugs—why wouldn't it? And in a way, it does. Truth is, a vampire's moved onto the block. And he's making the rounds, giving everybody a taste of the dead blood in his veins. They love it. And now they love *him*. And they'll do anything. People you thought might be your allies—or, at least, pigeons who'd rat—now won't come near you. Like roaches running from the kitchen light. By the time you've heard of it, the addiction has already spread far and wide. It's time to clean house. But how?

• The abandoned warehouse was always a haven for junkies and drunks, and lately it's become home to a different brand of scum. Your cell is positive that the warehouse is vampire lair, but going in and cleaning house is out of the question. During the daytime the place is guarded by the same junkies and drunks that always lived there, only now they work for the vampires. At night your cell would face both vampires and their human watchdogs. Still, something has to be done.

The Enemy

Vampires like to think they are superior to the herds of humans that surround them. They use and abuse mortals for their own benefit and sometimes just for entertainment. The members of the Union have seen it all before. They've seen it in the way the fat cats use their employees to line their own pockets, living in multi-million dollar homes all the while piously claiming the company can't afford to pay for health insurance.

They've seen it in bosses that try to pressure their secretaries into sleeping with them or middle-management fucks that run their departments like petty tyrants. Vampires are just one more example of how someone with a little bit of power can make the lives of honest working men and women that much harder.

Vampires aren't only a threat to the lives of Union hunters and their families, they are a plague that effects whole communities. Vampires spread disease, they lower property values with the violence they commit and their political machinations rarely benefit anyone but the vampires. Vampires also fight dirty. If they learn the identities of the group of humans that has been hunting their kind, they will use skullduggery to make the lives of those humans a living hell. The undead have their fingers in all kinds of pies and it doesn't usually take much effort for them to get a hunter fired from his job or even to orchestrate the temporary shutdown of a entire facility for "environmental hazards." Loss of income is no laughing matter to most members of the Union and vampires know they can curtail the activities of working class hunters by messing with their livelihood.

The biggest problem suffered by the Union in its struggles with vampires is their decentralization. Union members are scattered all over the United States, Europe and, increasingly, other countries. They share message boards and private forums over which they offer suggestions and observations about vampires with other members, but no real effort is made to organize the info in a coherent fashion and the usefulness of search functions are limited. Stickied FAQs give some tips and hints that can be useful for vampire hunting and solid, practical information does exist on the boards if you know where to look. Like any often used message board or forum, however, the important stuff is hidden in the middle of multi-page threads filled with random chatter and off-topic observations. People that have to deal with mandatory overtime, spouses, children and God knows what else just don't have the time to read every post in every thread and have to make do with whatever info they can find.

The Response

Other compacts, cells and conspiracies might have alternative objectives that factor in to how and why they hunt vampires. Some groups want to harvest from them, some try to redeem them and some might even seek to emulate them. The hunters that form the membership of the Union have no such pretensions. They hunt vampires for one reason and one reason only: to destroy them. The way the Union sees it, the only good vampire is a truly, really, honestly dead one. Most of

the undead that come to the attention of the compact have done something that forces the hunters to take notice. Whether it's feeding from their children, enslaving their friends or threatening the livelihood of a member, a vampire that finds itself hunted by the Union has usually provoked the fury of the hunters through its own arrogance. Underestimating poor and middle class families is a mistake that is easy for vampires to make.

The bosses used to underestimate the little guy, too. That stopped when the little guy got together with ten or one hundred or thousands of his fellows and told the bosses where to stick it. The people have the power, don't forget it. When the people work together they can shut down whole corporations and squeeze 'em till they holler uncle. It's no different dealing with vampires. One on one, a human isn't much of a match for one of the undead. Vampires are stronger, faster and just plain tougher than any Ordinary Joe or Jane. A group of humans is a different story. Armed and ready to fight the "lords of the night," a group can kick some ass and piss their names into the ashes that remain. Sure, humans will take their share of whacks in a fight with a vampire no matter what the numbers are, but they'll *win*. That win makes the next one a whole lot easier.

Direct combat isn't always the best or most viable solution, however. If vampires have taken up residence in a condemned house, entering the house and attempting to kill the vampires within isn't the safest of activities. Rather than confront the vampires directly, the Union can use the strength of its numbers to petition the city to demolish the house. If vampires are taking advantage of a dark alley to ambush passersby, the Union can ask for streetlights to be installed to take away that advantage. Politicians, policemen or other authority figures that the Union discovers are controlled by the undead can be forced from their positions through activism rather than bloodshed. (See the "Lobby" Tactic, p. 129.)

Information about how to kill vampires that is easily gleaned by scanning Union boards and forums usually amounts to a few solid facts. Vampires can be immobilized by a stake to the heart, edged weapons do more damage than guns and hunting them by day is the safest bet. Characters with extra time on their hands that try and delve deeper into the forum archives can attempt to locate useful information by making a research extended action (see the **World of Darkness Rulebook**, p. 55). The number and type of facts uncovered is left for the Storyteller to determine but is unlikely to contain any complete information about vampire society. A lot of hunters don't really care about that stuff—they'd just rather kill the damn bloodsuckers and drive their slaves off the block.

That's not exactly true for hunters of the Political faction within the compact, though. No, these hunters feel that working politics against politics is the only way to put the boot on the vampires' necks. These hunters found grassroots cells that are concerned as much with staging violent protests against vampiric interests (say, a bank whose money ends up in the pocket of one such monster, or a nightclub frequented by a cabal of the Damned) as they are with actually destroying the creatures outright. They see the oppression brought on by the vampires—killing individual monsters is great and all, but it always seems that the fiends replenish their numbers easily enough. Better to eradicate the platform on which they stand—and that might mean whistle-blowing on a local business or just blowing the whole damn building into rubble.

The Conspiracies

For the most part, the hunter conspiracies have been around a long time—hundreds of years, if not thousands. And while this has given them access to inestimable resources, resources that the compacts cannot access, it has *also* supplied them with no end of enemies. In the case of the accursed vampires, these enemies are a stone's throw from eternal. For as long as the conspiracies have been operating, they have seen the hungry shadows move at the ring of the firelight, a gleam in the eyes that signals a growing bloodlust.

Aegis Kai Doru

You always knew that vampires were immortal. That's their game. Thing is, you didn't realize just how immortal, did you? When Lydia showed you the skull with the curved fang canines, you figured it was just another Relic. You asked her what it did, and oh boy, did she show you. With her two front teeth she nipped at her own finger and squeezed a blob of blood into the skull's mouth. It didn't take long. The skull toppled over. The jaw started clacking open and shut, open and shut—fangs snapping against fangs. It only lasted for a few minutes. But it taught you a lesson, didn't it?

Story Hooks

• The characters must retrieve a Relic from a private collection. The Relic lies behind heat sensors, in a room filled with pure nitrogen at night. Only a vampire can retrieve it, and the characters know just such a vampire. She's even willing to do the job for them. But the price she asks is that each character take a drink of her addictive blood. How far are the characters willing to go to retrieve this ancient, precious Relic?

• "Get this. We have a secret basement below this complex, where we keep a bunch of staked ancient vampires. No shitting. Every now and then, right, someone takes one of them out of storage, yeah, feeds it, pulls out the stake and questions it for what it knows. I didn't believe it either till that crash the other day. Van overturned in the car park. You didn't hear? It was carrying a bunch of boxes filled with blood bags. True. The cleaner's brother told me."

The Enemy

Archaeological evidence suppressed by Aegis Kai Doru, dating from before the official dawn of civilization, suggests that vampires have walked alongside humans since before known written history. They have moved with the human herd as it followed the retreating ice caps, settled where people settled and farmed humanity the way humans cultivate livestock.

Thinking this through, one may reasonably conclude that if vampires have stalked humans for so long, they have had plenty of time to study these humans. Some hunters forget, to their cost, that all vampires were human, once. Some vampires have forgotten that, too.

To hunt vampires is to hunt an enemy that often knows Man better than Man knows himself. Vampires are a true apex predator, often presenting a savvy and socially aware façade that enables them to blend in with the crowd, wolves in the fold.

All that being said, in the eyes of the Aegis Kai Doru, vampires don't pose as great a danger to humanity as that posed by werewolves and witches. That's not to say that the Guardians just accept the vampires' presence in society unchallenged, however. Or that the vampires leave the Guardians alone.

Guarding Relics

The Aegis Kai Doru maintains assets all around the world. They not only have powerful and unique Relics, such as the purported square inch of Mary Magdalene's skin held in a shrine in Ephesus, or the scrolls purportedly written by Simon Magus which they keep in Boston. They also count as assets the groups of scholars studying those Relics and, occasionally, the worshippers blindly venerating them.

Occasionally a solitary vampire may take an interest in these Relics or their support groups, and interfere with them. He might seek the power that the Relic's capabilities could offer him. He might simply want to own the artifact for study, or to wear it as a pretty adornment—or destroy what he perceives a symbol of god, or godlessness.

Another vampire might suborn the studying group, or turn the worshippers into her devoted blood slaves, milking them for money and blood with equal ease. The Guardians cannot abide such callous manipulations, especially when it involves their bread and butter.

Preserving Memories

Even indirectly, vampires' actions might bring them into conflict with the Guardians' interests. Bloodsuckers don't like to leave clues which might lead humans to become aware of their existence. As such, most cities have dedicated cabals of vampires whose mission is to go around "cleaning up" scenes of supernatural incidents. This includes using Dread Powers such as "Alter Memory" (p. 169) on witnesses to cloud their recollections of events.

As Guardians prize knowledge, some of which is stored in the memories of witnesses to supernatural incidents, they frown upon anything that occludes that knowledge and erases evidence. This goes double for evidence of vampiric interventions, including documents, sites of unusual activity, discarded corpses and blurred photographs of the vampires themselves.

Sometimes it's not an individual vampire that steps on the Aegis' toes, but a whole accursed coterie of them—even the vampires' equivalent of a compact or even conspiracy, such as the Victorian pseudoscientific vampire cult that occasionally tries to interfere with an Aegis investigation. When the local bloodsuckers begin taking a collective interest in the Aegis Kai Doru, the Guardians band together to fight back in order to preserve their assets. And their necks.

Brokering Knowledge

Vampires also raise the interest of the Aegis Kai Doru in another way. Some of the oldest beings in the world are bloodsuckers, and these centuries-old beings have access to knowledge, secrets and skills the Guardians would kill to get a hold of. At times, Guardians have even traded knowledge, information and even offered service to vampires in exchange for vital and reliable knowledge, such as the locations of Relics once thought lost.

The one thing the Guardians will *never* do, however, is trade, give away, sell or even simply loan the Relics themselves. Their services don't extend to renting use of those Relics, either. (At least, not as a conspiracy—certain Guardians over the group's history have been caught doing just that. Most of them were never seen again.)

The Response

The conspiracy's reactions to vampires span a wide range, from alliances of convenience to outright hostilities.

Sometimes, a local Aegis group finds that it needs the aid of a faction of vampires to fend off attacks from witches or werewolves; aid for which it pays with service. Often, the Aegis find that it's a devil's deal, suddenly discovering that they're irretrievably entangled in the monsters' Byzantine schemes.

In other parts of the world relations between the Aegis and the vampires are considerably cooler, due to some perceived (or misperceived) diplomatic slight—and the Guardians are right on the front line of a war against immortal fiends who want their literal blood.

In fighting vampires, the hunters of the Aegis Kai Doru have learned to be subtle, and fight with knowledge rather than rely upon the power of their trinkets. Many a Guardian has found to his detriment that the power of their Relics only goes so far: and that, stripped of his Relic, a Guardian is just another human morsel to a hungry vampire.

The Scroll

Of the three factions of the Aegis Kai Doru, the Scroll has the most to gain from an alliance with vampires, as well as the most to lose. The Scroll are the keepers of lore, protectors of their greatest treasure—knowledge. This knowledge includes detailed information and histories of ancient vampires and their schemes past and present; knowledge which they can use as leverage to buy the vampires' services in fighting the Guardians' other enemies.

Many of the older vampires are prone to long periods of torpor, in which their thoughts and memories become polluted with dreams of grandeur and paranoid fancies. This is where the Guardians step in, offering such a vampire a way to bolster their shaky recollections and confirm pertinent details. Some even have Relics that help someone sift real memories from nightmares. Some such ancients are more than willing to negotiate to earn such favor, hoping to put their hoary old minds to rest about what's real inside their heads, and what isn't.

Of course, some ancients are happy to tear through the local Aegis Kai Doru chapter, ripping flesh from muscles and muscles from bone until someone gives it what it wants. The Guardians recognize that dealing with the ancients can sometimes be on par with juggling old dynamite. Some think the risk is worth it.

The Sword

These Guardians protect the interests of the conspiracy as much as they play an active role in exterminating the supernatural. When the Aegis perceives that a threat to its assets comes from vampires, the Sword is quite happy to demonstrate to the bloodsuckers that their edge is just as sharp on undead flesh as it is on the flesh of their usual prey.

When The Sword fights, it attacks with knowledge. They discover the vampires' weak points, the flaws in their schemes, the vulnerable linchpins on which their conspiracies hang ... and the Sword strikes deeply to destabilize their power structures.

The coroner who suppresses vampire activities gets fired as his drug problem comes to light; the bloodsuckers' media puppet suddenly runs a news special on the vampires' blood cult; the sanguine resonance of their sacred sites becomes corrupted, warping their arcane blood witchery and leaving them vulnerable when they least expect it. The Sword doesn't attack wantonly. It makes targeted strikes against the power structure's table legs, hoping to collapse it, if only for a time.

The Temple

When The Temple hears that a potent Relic has fallen into a vampire's hands, it will do its best to relieve her of her treasure. The Temple organizes elaborate stings, robbery attempts, and assassinations to secure a Relic that has fallen into a vampire's cold grip. Of course, some vampires are willing to give up such an item without a fight—for the most part, the accursed monsters only want the Relic for its value as an artifact or because it looks nice draped across one's heaving bust-line. That's not to say they'll give it up for *free*—but they might relinquish it without it coming to swords and shotguns.

When they do manage to procure such a Relic from a vampire, they keep it locked away nice and tight. Most of the Temple's hidden caches are protected by at least one Guardian at all hours of the day and night—and, should that Guardian fall in his service, most caches are also rigged to alert another when a body enters the cache whose temperature is well below the human norm.

Ascending Ones

The other hunters, they don't get it. Since the days the desert was a verdant valley, we've been fighting the darkness—and since our brothers disappeared way back when, we've been left alone. My daughter, this fight has been eternal. The darkness comes every night, and it comes hungry.

Only we've been in this fight for this long. Only we can recognize the true trappings of evil. Just two nights ago, we found Jamal dead. Do you know what we found on his hand? Carved into his palm? A sigil. A sign. Of a long dead cult, a cult that used to be a part of us. Do you know the name Seth? Typhon?

Story Hooks

• Sulha. It worked for a time. The vampires had worked out a tenuous peace agreement with the help of the local Ascending Ones. But now it's broken. And *those* Ascending Ones are all dead. The vampires are warring, and evidence is coming up to suggest that hunters—from some other conspiracy—are the ones making trouble. They want to shatter the peace. But why? Can they be stopped? Who's responsible for this fuck-up?

• "Those bloodsuckers we've been after are in the basement of the abandoned brownstone on the corner of Third. Mom and my sister Shara lived there, with Aunt Naaila, till the landlord turned everyone out to make room for these bastards. They're peddling. They're competition. Can't have that. Story goes that they got a whole chain of horrors and it goes to the tippy-top of their pyramid. Anyone wanna go down there just after dawn tomorrow and 'evict' them?"

The Enemy

Knowingly or not, vampires inflict suffering on whole neighborhoods with their presence. When they move in, they *interfere* with the place. If the block has any kind of neighborhood watch scheme, for example, that's the first group the parasites hit.

Why? These are the people most likely to notice when locals start to disappear. They're the ones who realize when the vagrants, streetwalkers and illegal immigrants, whom no one else is going to miss, go missing. Forget about the cops; they're on the payroll of the city's big players. And without someone to keep an eye on the human criminals, all the scum move in and take over. Oh, the vampires don't go killing all the neighborhood's watchmen—that only draws further attention. No, they... seduce them. Play with their minds. They grow to own them, body and soul. The guardian angels become servile demons. And the vampires laugh.

Poor and immigrant neighborhoods are perfect feeding grounds. Self-isolating, often full of illegals and generally ignored by the police, a leech setting up shop there would have the run of the block and, providing he kept his feeding to the locals, nobody outside would lift a finger to stop him.

These are the people the Ascending Ones protect.

The Response

Of all the conspiracies, the Ascending Ones are most closely connected to the grassroots level hunter and human communities, in particular the disenfranchised ethnic communities who have no voice to speak for them. This brings them into direct conflict with the vampires who prey on those silent masses.

The Brotherhood of the Southern Temple

Alchemy, the Brotherhood would argue, isn't just the science of cooking Elixirs for the conspiracy's front line troops. No, alchemy is the purification of the human soul—the "transformation of lead into gold," meaning the soul's symbolic change from base lower awareness to Higher Consciousness. "As above, so below," the saying goes, meaning that human souls ("below") tend to want to evolve, to reach upwards to find Unity with God ("above").

If vampires have souls, they cannot be changed or improved. The vampire's soul is a rotten thing. To paraphrase a Sufi notion, if the soul of an ordinary human is a stone, and the soul of an Ascending One a stone that has been polished to a ruby reflecting God, the soul of a vampire is a worthless slag of metal, base and unchangeable. It reflects nothing.

Oh, but here's the thing that sticks in the craw of many brothers within the Southern Temple: vampire blood is not human blood. It is something... *more*. And that's strange, because it certainly begins as human blood, but as soon as it's tossed into the crucible that is the undead body, it changes. It transmutes to another substance, which is of course a key principle behind alchemy and behind the conspiracy's own Elixirs.

Many within the Brotherhood seek to study the properties of vampire's blood, pondering its use in Elixirs. So far, any Elixirs formed of the blood of the Damned certainly *works* on some level, whether it's to provide preternatural strength or gift the hunter with a measure of a vampire's hypnotic command. Problem is, even when the Ascending One transmutes the supernatural blood in his *own* body, it still remains the blood of a monster: sweet, terrible, and ultimately addictive.

A CURE FOR VAMPIRISM?

Rather than try and tackle vampires individually, some within the Brotherhood seek a solution to vampirism itself. They are after a cure, and most of all they know that the cure is going to have to be a mystical one. Many poisonous draughts have come and gone.

Of course, the key issue is *testing* such concoctions, which necessitates vampiric trials. And since most Elixirs are at best potent drugs and at worse deadly poisons, this has been a point of contention amongst the hunters of the conspiracy. Vampires are certainly far from innocent, but some Ascending Ones argue that they cannot help what they are. And even if they can, is torture really the answer? It is forbidden by elders within the conspiracy. But still, is it possible that some within the Brotherhood are testing unbidden and unseen?

The Knife of Paradise

The inner city Imam. The Rabbi, leading a community of Hasidic Jews. The Anglican priest and student of the Gnostic texts. The Freemason with ties to the local police force, and the Tantrika running New Age female empowerment classes out of the local YMCA.

The Knife of Paradise wears many faces, from Anglicans to Hindus, Sufis to Sikhs; and, in the fight against vampires, their task is to protect the communities under them from being ravaged by the bloodsuckers. Fortunately, the Knife of Paradise can call upon those communities for help.

See, vampires surround themselves with a "human shield" of criminals and thugs, hangers-on clinging to them like lampreys, doing their Masters' bidding and fending off threats. The Knife knows that by fostering community spirit and communication between cultures, they can work together to drive off these parasites, stripping the protective layers from the vampires and leaving the parasites vulnerable. (This isn't always perfect, of course: religious issues can be painfully divisive, and this is even true within the conspiracy itself. The Knife of Paradise ostensibly puts all that aside, but that's a "perfect world" scenario.)

It's a tricky line to walk: the Knife doesn't care to make community members aware of the existence of vampires—that puts them in danger, and when the herd is spooked, it reacts, often violently. But, they *do* want to point out the corrosive influence of such creatures, even if they're framed as "human parasites" rather than supernatural ones. If the community can work to oust corrupt officers or put money together

SULHA

The Knife is the most likely group to practice diplomacy with vampires.

If trouble's brewing between individual vampires, or between bloodsucker factions, hunters of the Knife often approach the key players and offer their services in brokering a peace settlement.

Typically they approach the servants first, dealing with the factotums to gain the confidence of their paranoid masters.

The other Ascending Ones factions regard these diplomats with incredulity, even scorn. The diplomats consider it pragmatism. They'll do everything they can to keep the monsters away from their people. Even if it means risking their necks to talk to the bloodsuckers in the middle of *their* territory.

to save a local library or athletic center, the human herd grows stronger and the monsters in the shadows grow weaker.

The Knife will help local hunter cells, though, particularly to fight the insidious menace put forth by power- and blood-hungry vampires. Whereas a lone first-tier cell is vulnerable to a concerted attack by vampires, a cell The Knife protects is more likely to survive—even if that protection is anonymous, in the form of windfalls of cash or gifts of medicine or supplies.

The Jagged Crescent

Sad reality is, vampires are competitors. One moves onto the block. Starts peddling his own blood as an addictive panacea, some kind of uber-heroin that you only need to drink, and profits go down for the Ascending Ones. The Crescent's grim and unpleasant business is how they fund the Vigil for the rest of the conspiracy. They don't care about protecting the addicts—anybody who'd bother poisoning themselves deserves to be poisoned. But the cash flow can't be interrupted. So, they take the war to the vampires because these are *their* streets, and *their* customers.

It's like a game of Go, with street corners as the places on the board. You put your guys on the corners to keep their guys off them. In this game, though, if you're not on top of the dung-heap at the final reckoning, you're gonna get buried beneath it.

The Cheiron Group

You think you know about vampires, but you don't know shit. We had one on the slab, right? Two nights earlier, thing was up and walking around but here it was, cold and dead like any other corpse. Gideon and Sheppard couldn't find anything—body had its blood, and splitting open the chest revealed no stake or wood splinters in the heart. Then Gideon checked the guts. They started pouring out. Maggots, but little and red, with heads like black shiny pins. I'll make a long story short. I got out of there. We had to close off that wing of the facility and burn it. I remember running. Hearing Gideon and Sheppard first screaming, then laughing. We re-ran the security tapes, watched it happen. Maggots on the skin, then beneath it. The two surgeons... both in terrible pain. But then they smiled. And their images went blurry, like someone smeared a gob of Vaseline on the lens. Jesus. So let me reiterate: you, me, all of us? We don't know shit about shit when it comes to vampires. Throw your handbook away.

Story Hooks

• Cheiron doesn't really like to make it known, but they have various "infectious materials" labs dotting both Europe and North America. Home to potent diseases both supernatural and mundane, the conspiracy claims the need to keep such caches for "research purposes." And then comes the night when one of the labs goes dark and drops off the grid. The last transmission from one such remote location is from some Cheiron tech: "There's a whole goddamn nest of them, they're killing everybody, and three of them—" *Static*, transmission ends. What do vampires want with infectious diseases? Dangerous blood? And who leaked the location to some goddamn bloodsucker? Cheiron wants this cleaned up. The corporate chopper's waiting.

• The military doesn't make its own rations. It doesn't design the pharmaceuticals its soldiers take to "stay frosty." Who does? Well, take a guess. Cheiron hit the bid, and offers the military a wide variety of products. The 'Hercules' energy bars, for instance. Or the pills soldiers pop to combat PTSD (called "the red pill" by many, since it's a horse-pill capsule filled with cloudy crimson fluid). They don't like to talk

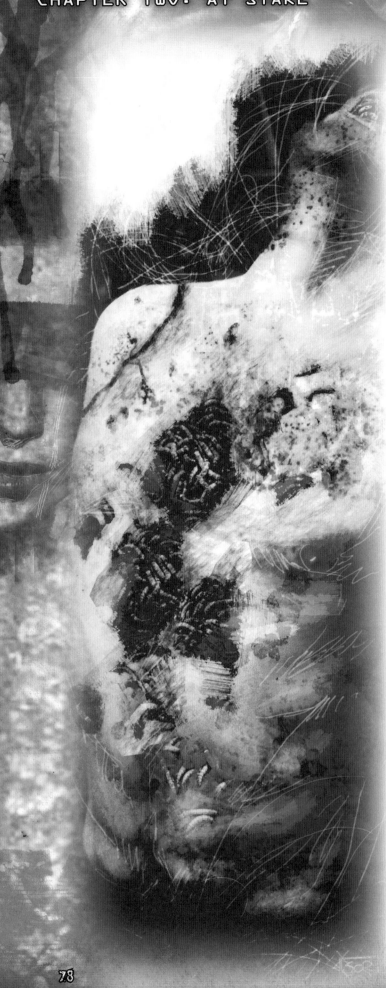

about the side effects: sure, they make you happy, strong, fast. But nobody'll admit they're addictive. Or how some of these products make 'roid rage look like a mild tantrum. And nobody—*nobody*—will talk about exactly how Cheiron makes these products. But some suspect. Some have heard the rumors of a whole lab filled with caged bloodsuckers, a dozen tubes running out of each one. The cell hears of it. They ask a superior. And boom, they're offered bigger money and better, safer hunts. Of course, they only have to keep their mouths shut...

The Enemy

Cheiron doesn't like to rule anything out. When it comes to vampires, it's important not to dismiss them out of hand. Sure, they're monsters, yes, of course, they're awful. But they're valuable. And they're a stone's throw from human, except for that whole "being dead" bit. Cheiron likes to be flexible in its dealings with the society of the night. It looks at vampires as one of three things:

First, as resources. Vampires have what Cheiron wants, in many cases. Cheiron likes money. They like insider secrets. They like supernatural blood. If they can use the vampires to get these things, so be it. Send a cell out to pilfer a draught of a unique elder's blood or maybe just steal all the folders in his safe, and Cheiron wins.

Second, as customers. Vampires want. Their desires sometimes overwhelm them. That's a great place for Cheiron to work its magic. A vampire wants the heartsblood of another of its kind, an enemy of great power? Maybe the bloodsucker wants some kind of unguent that helps her more easily mimic life or some pharmaceutical bezoar that helps her digest human food? Cheiron is happy to make an offer. Sometimes, money is good enough. Other times, a new price must be negotiated. If a vampire is willing to sell out a compatriot—maybe even get him staked and in a box and sent to one of the Big Pharma buildings in Philadelphia—then that'll work just fine, thanks.

Third, as allies. Most within the throngs of restless dead are weak, dumb, young. But some of them are smart. Savvy. Cheiron loves to have investors from among this 'higher order' of vampires (their bank accounts are practically as eternal as they are), and doesn't care to make competitors of such elder creatures. Better to make friendly. Cooperation is king. Of course, it rarely lasts forever—one side usually betrays the other (and if the lower Status hunters in the conspiracy ever found out that they're hand-

BIOLOGICAL WEAPONS RESEARCH

Cheiron remains forever interested in new diseases and infections. Vampires, being undead, particularly fascinate TCG because if they are dead, what can harm them?

What about blood-borne parasites such as malaria and trypanosoma (Sleeping Sickness), or West Nile virus or HIV? What if blood from a parasite-infected vampire got into a human host, such as a blood drinker?

The Cheiron Group have developed some interesting strains of the above diseases; but one disease stored in the Utah facility, designated SYRIA-3, is feared by human and vampire alike. SYRIA-3 is a strain of Yersinia pestis cultivated in vampire blood, a septicemic plague bacillus that destroys vampires' blood and can send them straight into torpor. Of course, it's earned the nickname "Extinction" because at present the strain remains wholly fatal to humans, with an infectious vector that promises wholesale eradication of the human species in like, two weeks. Needless to say, Cheiron keeps this one under wraps until it's... working properly. Maybe SYRIA-4 or 5 will do the trick...

shaking deals with centuries-old monsters, that could be a public relations cataclysm), but Cheiron is usually prepared to deal with such loose ends. That's why they have hunters, after all.

The Response

On a general level, Cheiron doesn't bother with the ground-level vampires all too much. They're all the same, for the most part—so what's the point? If an old or unique specimen comes along, then cells are encouraged to make the capture—or make the kill, if enough of it can be harvested.

Field Research Division

In business, it pays to stay one step ahead of the competition, always. The Company sends Field Research agents to infiltrate the companies and holdings infiltrated by vampires. Posing as janitors, temps and secretarial staff, they ferret out as much dirt on these companies as they can, bringing it home for other people to sift and turn into grounds for hostile takeovers. These experts never strike immediately, preferring to cover every legal base before acting.

TCG agents are the best infiltrators money can buy. Their resumes are spotless, their acting skills flawless and their devotion to Cheiron ruthless. Against vampires, these company men have a weapon that is as simple as it is devastating: publicity.

Vampires can't stay in the spotlight long; they flee before people notice that their reflections don't show up clearly in mirrors. If a company suborned by a vampire became the subject of a messy IRS tax fraud investigation, or the INS dropped by to have a word about the illegal labor in the back room... well, that's trouble for the fangs, isn't it? Lesser vampires cut and run. Of course, more powerful vampires play the game right back, but that's fine. Cheiron enjoys a shadow war in the trenches of commerce, as long as it doesn't cut into profits.

Recruitment

Vampires' servants are coveted potential recruits to TCG's Field Projects Division. The drawback is that most of them are bound to their masters by ties of addictive blood. The loyalty they feel is nigh unbreakable; and it's compounded by the revelation that if they come off vampire blood, they age very rapidly in a short period of time—meaning that the oldest, most powerful servants depend on vampire blood for their existence. But that's okay: Cheiron likes an agent who depends on them for his very life. It makes them perfectly loyal.

Problem is, they need a reliable source of vampire blood that doesn't addict or enslave anyone. Manufacturing the blood hasn't yet worked (though some fascinating... side effects have occurred, including strange half-vampire creatures whose mindless devotion to feeding is second-to-none). Rumors exist of whole "black site" prisons where vampires are kept, fed, and then bled. That blood is then given as payment to those blood-addict hunters that operate under Cheiron's corporate aegis.

Of course, once Cheiron has offered the gig to a blood slave, it's all or nothing. If the thrall refuses to rebuff his master and take a regular paycheck, well, Cheiron can't just let him walk away. Seeing how their organs tend to age rapidly when removed from the body, "Renfields" don't even provide useful implants for Thaumatechnology. Thankfully, the genetically modified pigs in TCG's DNAlogy Life Sciences Laboratories don't mind the occasional odd taste in their feed, do they?

Retrieval

Again, for the most part Cheiron doesn't bother retrieving vampires for "processing." Why bother? Obviously, if a cell finds that one's giving them a hard time, bring him in. Cheiron surgeons can always use the blood for some purpose or another—it makes a strong anti-clotting agent, for instance. And it can help critically-wounded hunters heal a little more easily (yes, by making them subservient to the blood itself).

Still, some men of vision within the company have an idea. Championed by Burkhard Charteris, the vision is one of... drum roll please, "anti-aging products." A low grade version (heavily diluted) would go over-the-counter for the masses, and a full-strength high-test version (selling at or above $100 grand a shot) would only be available to society's elite. You know, sports stars, politicians, movie moguls, pop singers. (As Burkhard put it, "Madonna isn't getting any younger, but if we can crack this secret she won't be getting any *older*, either.")

Problem is, Cheiron doesn't have the mass quantities of blood necessarily to fulfill Charteris' vision. If his vision does come to pass—and it's working its way through the choking tangle of red tape right now—then Cheiron cells should soon expect the word to come down from on-high: Bring. In. Vampires. *Any* they can find.

The Lucifuge

I don't know who told them about me. But there they were, waiting on my doorstep one night, a slavering pack of undead fanboys. They'd heard that I had the Devil's blood in me, and they were part of some cult that worshipped Belial and Baalphegor and blah blah blah. Oh, and the one boy said I was "hot." Right. Great. They asked me—begged me—to come down to their rat's nest off the Interstate and partake in a ritual, and would I be so gracious as to let them have a taste of my blood? Pretty please with a pitchfork on top? I went. And I brought my own friends. Listen, I genuinely feel bad about it. Fire hurts them so dearly—all that shrieking and running about. They don't mean to be what they are, but they should try to make the best of the blood within them. We do. They didn't. Sorry, boys. At least you'll finally get to meet your masters.

Story Hooks

• Some Lucifuge perform what's known as the "Duty." A vampire grows tired of his damnable existence and wants out. A hunter of the Lucifuge will destroy the creature with as much mercy as can be mustered. One particularly powerful elder no longer wants the blood of countless on his hands and begs them for a merciful death—seems he's found God, an irony given that he's coming to the Devil for mercy. Two complications arise: rival vampires who want to drain their client of his heartsblood and gain his powers, and the client's own inner beast which refuses to die, which means the elder runs the risk of a truly maddening frenzy. Still, though, the cell has its Duty—what must be done, must be done.

• The Devil must be recruiting. All the vampires in town have suddenly found the joy in some Satanic Baal-cult. They've broken their society's own rules, and they're waging open war on their own kind and on the mortal herd. The Lucifuge is way outnumbered

---

HUNTER: DEAL OR NO DEAL

Here's an idea for a **Hunter: The Vigil** story. You usually think hunters are about killing the monsters, right? Or maybe investigating them, even redeeming them. Not an unrealistic expectation. But a hunter can just as easily be "hunting" deals for his cell, compact or conspiracy (Cheiron, above, is a likely target). A cell of socially-savvy hunters whose purpose is to broker deals, negotiate treaties, even outline the terms of war... well, that's a whole different kind of **Vigil** game, isn't it? One night, the cell's helping negotiate a deal between two vampires on the price of a valued blood slave. The next night, they're on the run, trying to grab a cell signal or internet connection long enough to fix a contravention of territory before wholesale war breaks out across the streets. A week later, the "broker" cell is caught between a rock and a hard place: one compact of hunters wants to take to the streets with shotguns and Molotov cocktails in order to bust up what's been a relatively peaceful coven of vampires.

Thing is, with this kind of game, hunters walk a weird line between selfish and selfless—on the one hand, by making deals and keeping things calm, innocent lives might very well be saved. On the other hand, there could be big rewards on the line: information, cash, allies.

here, which means they have only a couple options: either partner up with some other hunters, or partner up with the besieged vampires who don't want these demon-loving upstarts to burn their precious hunting grounds and carefully-cultivated schemes to cinders.

The Enemy

The Devil has sympathy for vampires, it seems—or, at least, the Devil's Own Children do. The Lucifuge generally looks upon vampires with a conflicting mix of empathy and disdain. The empathy comes from understanding having one's cursed blood shackle you to a lifetime (or more) of service. The disdain comes from the fact that most vampires refuse to actually buck the chains, and end up giving into their foulest, most reptilian of desires. The hunters of the Lucifuge have managed to rise above their vile blood, so why can't the vampires?

For the most part, they approach the Damned with scrutiny. The children of evil are not necessarily evil, and measures must be taken to ensure one's genuine monstrousness before going off and slaying every night-breeder that walks. In fact, many Lucifuge don't so much *hunt* vampires as much as act as counselors and confessors to the undead. Knowing that they have so much sin in them, weary bloodsuckers are often grateful for any chance to unburden to a mortal who, alone among the herd and uniquely even among hunters, is willing to *listen* to them without prejudice. Both share secrets, too, that dare not be spoken. It can create a bond, if a tenuous one.

Still. Some Lucifuge hew to the idea that vampires are basically corpses with demons bound to the flesh—folklore is sometimes quite clear that vampires are creatures of Hell itself, and certainly some of the Children of the Seventh Generation can see the reasoning. For those zealous hunters, the only option is to destroy the vampires. Mercy may still come into play, but it comes at the end of a wooden stake and a can of petrol.

The Response

Official policy from Milan notwithstanding, each agent has her own personal take on vampires. The following are just general guidelines: as befits the children of the First Rebel, each Lucifuge agent is encouraged to think on his feet and put the dark impulses of his heart over any sort of Official Doctrine. How the factions informally deal with the fangs can be found immediately below.

Blood Canvases

For all that their creative spirits are damaged by undeath, many vampires still appreciate art. Some vampires *create* art.

The Lucifuge Herself runs a small private gallery in Milan, where she collects art created exclusively by vampires. Much of this is ordinary: night scenes (they're *always* night scenes) of empty, dark landscapes, or hellish nightmare landscapes reflecting the vampires' tormented daytime thoughts.

Some portraits are special. Created with pigments into which the vampires have added their blood, their eyes don't just follow you across the room. These portraits *talk*, whispering dark secrets.

According to the rumor, in exchange for telling the paintings some of her own secrets, the Lucifuge coaxes these images into divulging some of theirs. What she knows about individual vampires might be nowhere near as interesting as what those paintings know about *her*.

The Denial

It's odd to some that the agents of the Denial are about redemption. But they are. They know that some marked by evil can still turn away from evil, and vampires represent this possibility perhaps best among all creatures. They didn't have a choice (well, some did, but such specimens are rare). They are driven to sin by the cruel blood, and so many can build up a tolerance against the blood, thus allowing them to do good things—or at least be kept from committing evil deeds. Those that refuse to find some kind of redemption—however small—must be dealt with in some fashion. Some among the Denial kidnap such reluctant creatures and torture them into turning away from evil. Others stake them and bury them—perhaps later, a stronger and wiser agent can urge them off the iniquitous path. The final solution is, of course, to let the light of the sun burn out the evil within. Permanently.

The Reconciliation

The Devil provides Castigations to the Lucifuge's agents for a reason: to punish sin, without exception. Vampires often personify sin, by acting on the darkest impulses of their withered souls. Their vices are siren songs in their unbeating hearts that they cannot deny, calling them to commit acts of wanton lust, gluttony and greed.

Among the Reconciliation are those Lucifuge who believe that vampires are in some way demonic—not metaphorically, but literally creatures possessed by or in service to demons. This puts them at odds—sometimes, violent—with the hunters of the Denial.

The Truth

Those hunters following the Truth have taken upon themselves a truly frightening task: to pursue the oldest of the vampires and to learn from them. Truly ancient vampires are hard to come by (and often they slumber, protected by hordes of lesser fiends), and so it's sometimes best instead to track down the writings and artifacts of such creatures, or even their progeny and thralls. The goal is to discover truths about the Lucifuge's own origins. Yes, sometimes the fiends must be destroyed, but every ancient vampire destroyed is like a thousand books thrust upon a burning pyre—the loss of knowledge is terrible. Many among the Truth go mad pursuing this knowledge, or end up in service to the eldritch creatures they seek.

Malleus Maleficarum

They took my beautiful Theresa from me. We'd had some success, you see. Father David, Mullins, Theresa and myself... we'd really been making a dent. The saints had been kind to us. Someone had left us a map marked with the havens of the dead, and we took to burning them. But their revenge was insidious. They took Theresa. They made her like them. And then they set her upon me. Now I've got her bound to the bed.

Her face changes. Sometimes I see the soft beauty and grace, but other times it's a twisted rictus, pinched with hunger for the vein pulsing in my neck. I grab the hammer. I grab the sharpened chair leg. I love you, Theresa. God bless.

Story Hooks

• The characters have just finished a long night's hunting. It's been tough, but they figure that they can rest easy, now that they've taken on a particularly nasty vampire and won. Except... nobody's picking up the phone at the chapterhouse. When they arrive there, they first see the police vans and cars, and the reporters and TV crews parked outside. Everyone's being hauled away in police vans, and worse, their names just flashed up onto the screen as fugitives, wanted for questioning in connection with an investigation into a "child prostitution ring" they were tipped off to. What now?

• A vampire approaches under the auspices of peace. He says he is a man of the cloth and has the vestments to prove it. He explains that the city is home to a number of heretics and heathens within his own kind—witches of the blood whose depraved acts and human sacrifices are purposefully done to spite God. If the characters will spare him and his church, he'll show them where these other monsters lair, and will even help in routing them. Can they trust him? If they do, will their own superiors come down hard upon them?

The Enemy

Since the founding of the Malleus Maleficarum, their operatives have been indoctrinated into believing that vampires are Christendom's most implacable, insidious and deadly threat—the tools of Satan, sent to Earth to corrupt the world and make it more like His dark Kingdom.

It didn't take long for the vampires to recognize the growing threat posed by the rising star of the Hammer of the Witches and respond accordingly. While they found it impossible to get rid of this threat as easily as they could eradicate a lesser hunter organization, they could still alleviate that threat by strategically undermining their strengths. This they did through guile, treachery and working through their rich proxies at the time: bankers, princes, kings and even a corrupted pope or two.

The conspiracy responded to the vampires' moves with countermoves of their own. Rather than attack the bloodsuckers directly, they began to work on *their* holdings, sending mundane inquisitors and witch hunters in to break up their little cults, disrupting lines of communication between key vampires and taking advantage of the vampires' one true weakness: their pathological sense of competitiveness towards one another.

The war between the sides became a war of attrition, and to this day, the moves are still being played out on the streets of Rome, London, New York and Cairo. Nowhere is free of this great game, as agents of the Shadow Congregation fight bloodsuckers and their cults on the unsafe night-lit streets of Eritrea, Basra and Sarajevo.

The vampires of the Old Country learn to keep their heads down in the run-up to Easter because at this time of year, not only are the nights getting shorter but the power of the hunters' Benedictions waxes stronger with the approaching Christian festival, culminating during Holy Week with the Malleus Maleficarum at their metaphysical strongest. It's not been above agents of the Hammer of Witches to capture individual vampires, hold them for "prolonged interrogation," then stake them and leave them for the sun just before Palm Sunday. As long as their quotas are met before the end of Lent, everybody's happy.

The Response

Generally, the vampire hunters of the Malleus Maleficarum live simple, Spartan lives. When possible,

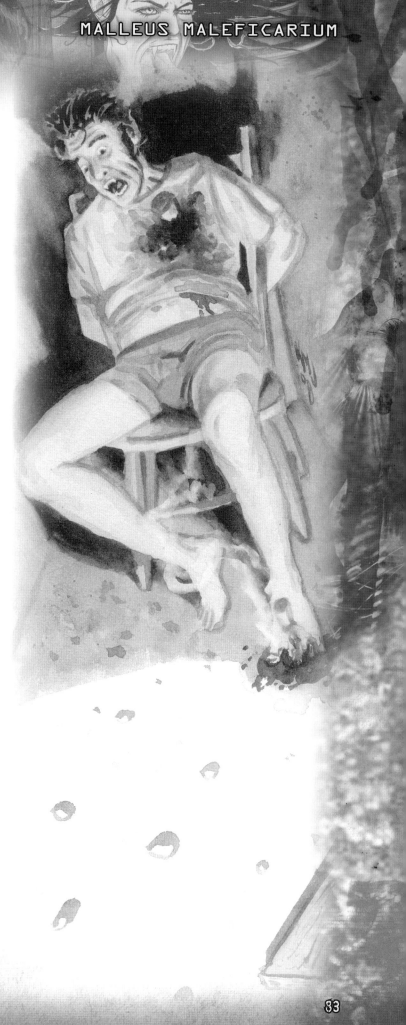

they eschew ties to family or friends (all the more for a vampire to take from them). They don't give themselves over to luxury (same reason). Most of their time is dedicated plainly to the investigation and eradication of the society of the Damned. Heresy must be corrected, and vampires are a pervasive heresy.

The Order of St. Longinus

The foot-soldiers of the Hammer don't like to think about where the world is going. All they care about is taking care of business, and until someone tells them otherwise, that business is vampires. Of course there are plenty of other godless creatures out there to hunt down and destroy, but by far the worst threat to Christendom comes with fangs and an unbeating heart, and as far as these hunters are concerned, that's all they need to know.

Of particular interest to the hunters of St. Longinus are those vampires who claim that their predatory ways have been sanctioned somehow by God. To invent some justification like that—and to further venerate Longinus, their so-called "Dark Father"—is a grotesque blasphemy that cannot stand. Generally, for the hunters of this order, hunting vampires is all business. It's nothing personal. Except, when these heretics are found, it quite often *becomes* personal.

WITHIN THE ORDER: THE SABBATARIANS

It's long been bound to folklore that those hunters born on a Saturday (the Sabbatarians) are more or less *born* as vampire hunters, and possess unique abilities. It's not true, of course. A hunter born on a Saturday is no different than one born on Tuesday.

But that doesn't mean the Hammer of Witches ignores the folklore. Actually, they embrace it. Sabbatarians within the Order of St. Longinus actually *are* better vampire hunters, for the most part, not because of any supernatural ability but because the conspiracy actually trains them more rigorously. They often have access to forbidden Benedictions by dint of their day of birth.

All Sabbatarians within the order are also granted a canine companion—a Labrador retriever (often white or yellow) trained in harrying prey and attacking interlopers.

The Order of St Ambrose

The Ambrosians have so much information they need to sift through, they can barely handle it all. Fortunately, nowadays they have the most wonderful tools at their disposal. The order needs people with information technology skills more than ever, and recruiters frequent the halls of academia looking for bright, promising talent. Of course, not everyone is suitable. A lot of students have never encountered the supernatural, and would very likely lose their minds if they knew the sort of work they were being asked to do. But the few suitable candidates they do encounter are a treasure.

Far as vampires go, the Ambrose hunters provide backup to the hunters of St. Longinus, often building extensive databases of vampires and vampiric interests throughout the city. One might suspect that this keeps them bottled away in some safehouse, and for some, that's true. But investigating vampires often means beating the streets, which means stalking dark alleyways and crime scenes... which means probably coming into contact with the bloodsuckers themselves. The hunters of this order are by no means as combat-capable as those of the other agents within the Hammer of Witches, but they still better know how to use a knife or a stake in a pinch.

The Brotherhood of St Athanasius

Fuck those guys in the Order of St. Longinus when it comes to vampire hunting, that's what the hunters of this order say. Why do they get all the vampire-hunting gigs? Just because they were ordained by Mother Church several hundred years ago doesn't mean they're up to the task in these modern nights.

The hunters of this militant wing want to bring the fight to vampires, want to burn half the city in God's wrath to get to them, screw what the Longinus whelps say. Officially, they're not to get involved. They've got their tasks, and rarely does it involve vampires. But the Brotherhood often does what it wants anyway. Think about it. The Vatican's got its own problems. It can't keep track of what's going on. Communications are imperfect. It's often up to the Hammer cells in a given city to make its own destiny, and so that's what the Brothers of Athana-

sius will do. They've gotten a bit shady in this department, actually—they interrupt lines of communications between the inquisitors of Longinus and the investigators of Ambrose, all in an effort to get a jump on the vampires before their competitors within the conspiracy can.

And let's be clear: these guys are a stone's throw from domestic terrorists. (In fact, more than a few hunters in the order are Belfast bombers with a violent distaste for anything Protestant.) They don't want to take out innocents, of course, but what does "innocent" really mean, anyway? God will sort them out, as is his merciful purview.

Task Force: VALKYRIE

We had him in our sights. Bobby had the temperature gun on him, and he was cold, like-a-corpse cold. The mad bastard smiled. Wouldn't stop smiling, actually. The five of us formed a rough half-circle around him, and the bloodsucker's back was against the wall. Bobby said to the monster, "Nowhere to go, man, nowhere to go." Then the call came in. Radio squelched. The vampire winked. And we got our new orders. We did what we were told. We left him alone. But not before shattering those precious pointed teeth down his dead throat.

Story Hooks

• An armored government truck overturned on the highway. The driver's dead but bears no marks of a struggle. Government records tumble out the back, many in boxes, some caught on the wind. And *some* of those records are VALKYRIE records from as far back as World War II. The characters must retrieve these files immediately; this is a top priority mission. When they get there, they find that a vampire with a cabal of blood-addict thralls are loading file boxes into a black Cadillac Escalade. The cell must give chase. But who are these vampires? How is it that a van carrying extraordinarily sensitive documents simply... overturns on the highway? And how did the vampires know what would be spilling out?

• "Your mission, team, is to destroy this fortified compound outside of Heartwell, Nebraska. The complex is owned by Timothy Sorensen, whom we have in our files as a servant to a haemophagic ENE who lurks somewhere on the premises. Sorensen's become a dangerous religious fanatic, and he's gathered a large cult around him whom he keeps in line by demonstrating ENE abilities of social control which we believe his Master gives him. We need him stopped, but we *don't* want a Ruby Ridge or a Waco. Do you understand? Oh, if you find the Master, do not destroy. Repeat: *do not destroy.*"

The Enemy

To the Men in Black, hunting vampires is a lot more involved than a simple "bag and tag" mission. The Children of the Night are just as capable of playing the spy game as the agents of Task Force: VALKYRIE. Even more so, at times.

Sometimes, senior officers look on the reports of the vampires' schemes and plots, and realize just how much catching up the conspiracy has to do. VALKYRIE certainly has its share of competent spymasters (though it has its share of incompetents, too—this is government, after all), the tortuous cons of the undead seem to hang them every time.

Of course, it doesn't help the agents of Task Force: VALKYRIE when occasionally, the conspiracy seems to be working against itself when it begins investigating the affairs of bloodsuckers. Why are some vampires let go? With minimal or no harm?

Cold War of Terror

This is the reality: America is under attack from all sides. The old girl is beleaguered; rogue nations, tyrant regimes, and terrorists both on and off domestic soil have their guns and evil eyes pointed at the heart of this nation. And that doesn't even count the fact that innumerable monsters seek to do this society harm. Vampires are among such nefarious evil-doers, hiding amongst the people the same way terrorists do—for the most part they look like us and talk like us, only separating themselves from the herd to hunt and spread disease. But, the terrorist analog continues, because they're a broken society that remains hidden. One hand doesn't know what the other is doing, and that's to their benefit; so mired are these creatures in secrecy that capturing and interrogating one does not (or *cannot*) reveal what the others are truly doing. VALKYRIE struggles against this insurgent enemy. They must be domesticated, or they must be destroyed. At least, that's the party line. The reality can be somewhat different.

The trappings and tools might differ—Advanced Armory instead of Benedictions—but at times, it feels as if the Men in Black and the Shadow Congregation are playing the same game against the same enemy. Both conspiracies are fighting a cold war against the same foe, albeit in different ways and with far different tools.

A Tangled Web

VALKYRIE superiors hand out two books as "required reading" for those who may encounter haemophagic ENEs in the field: Sun Tzu's *The Art of War* and Niccoló Machiavelli's *The Prince*. (Some agents and commanders supplement this reading with other texts too, such as anything detailing Greek mythology or Roman history—the vain machinations of the Olympian gods and the Roman emperors are similar enough to those practiced by the vampires.) The vampires may not have read these books, but these books seem to comprise their society's general playbook.

Just as Task Force: VALKYRIE have their Advanced Armory Endowment to draw upon, the vampires have their Dread Powers (see p. 169 and also **Hunter: the Vigil**). Many of these are superlative tools of tradecraft, allowing a vampire to infiltrate facilities, photograph plans, tamper with or steal evidence and sabotage equipment or plant bombs.

However, it's far easier for the vampires to simply plant their mortal servants into those facilities, and let them do all the dirty work for their masters instead. And it's entirely possible that some of those mortal servants are sleepers, some of them in positions of high influence within the conspiracy itself.

The Response

Strictly speaking, the agency lumps the haemophages in with the rest of the monsters: they damage civilization, they work in opposition to democracy, and they must be stopped. End of story, right?

If only. Task Force: VALKYRIE seems unable to mark a universal response when it comes to dealing with vampires. For every bloodsucker that receives a "high priority" sticker on its file (meaning, dust that leech at one's earliest opportunity), there exist two fangs that get a free pass. Larger games are at work at higher levels of this conspiracy, and only those hunters with high Status in the organization (four or five dots' worth) will ever start to see those games exposed.

The Stearne Protocol

When agents confirm the involvement of hae-mophagic ENEs in an ongoing investigation, they must follow a series of complicated procedures known as the Stearne Protocols. The Stearne Protocols are a list of approved and unapproved procedures surrounding the means by which agents may investigate and hunt the suspected haemophagic ENEs.

Supposedly these Protocols are in place to help keep the agents from getting killed. But the Protocols themselves, in practice, are often so ar-cane and confusing that following them to the letter is as likely to get the agents killed as the vampires themselves.

All of this is shepherded by the Stearne Steer-ing Group (SSG), who oversees and maintains the Stearne Protocols. Since the first meeting chaired in 1952, the Stearne Committee meets once every ten years to decide the policy of contact with hae-mophagic ENEs over the whole Task Force. These meetings take place over the course of three days—December 20th, 21st and 22nd—then everybody heads home for Christmas.

To truly "understand" the Protocols and become an authority on deciphering them, one must pass through Stearne certification. Certifi-cation authorizes them to pursue lines of investi-gation independently wherever a vampiric ENE is concerned. But there's the rub: the waiting list to join the cert courses is practically eternal, and even when one finally approaches the front of the line, something always seems to happen to knock most agents out of the running. An agent is assigned a particular task on the day of testing, and is thus bumped to the back of the line. Or the testing facility isn't where it was supposed to be, and the hunter misses his "opportunity" to become certified. Certainly *some* hunters—who seem to fall under intense scrutiny beforehand—actually get to the certification. But they come out and never talk about what goes on inside the testing facility.

Those who are not "Stearne-certified" are *sup-posed* to take orders regarding vampires from only those VALKYRIE superiors who are. If they do not have access to one who is, they must refer the case to another cell, one more capable of deciphering the labyrinthine set of bureaucratic directives. This isn't always put into practice, of course: a govern-ment hierarchy falls down in a lot of places, and

THE DOWN-LOW

What's weird is, it almost seems as if the vampires police *themselves*, doing ADAMSKI's job for them. It doesn't stop ADAMSKI claiming the credit, though, because if the Top Floor found out how inefficient they were, they'd just cut the budget in the next review. But other hunters have noted it, too—yes, vampires are monsters, they're *fiends*, they drink blood, they spread infection, but they don't often make a big show of it. Some hunters have reported tracking down an overt vampiric presence only to discover that he's already greasy ash spread across the sidewalk. Are they destroying their own?

some VALKYRIE cells are left alone so long they start to make up their own "protocols."

Project: ADAMSKI

For some reason, ADAMSKI never really has much to do when it comes to handling vampires, because there's often very little evidence after the fact. Faces blur up on camera, in mirrors and in lineup photos. Vampires who die for good shrivel up to dust. Dead blood addicts just look like regular stiffs. And haemohages' circulatory fluid just congeals to a sticky mass of old human blood in minutes, providing nothing for forensics.

It's really the witnesses that ADAMSKI deals with. Sometimes, witnesses get a whole head of steam about "proving" the existence of vampires. Such individuals represent a destabilizing presence, and generally, the agents of ADAMSKI are happy to issue a dose of Munin serum to keep everybody calm and appropriately fuzzy on matters. (Of course, it should be obvious that such "destabilizing" individuals can be, or end up as, hunters.) One thing that's been sticking in agents' craws lately: why do some witnesses end up dead or missing? Specifically, witnesses successfully issued doses of the serum?

Project: FORT

This team has the least direct or indirect contact with vampires, because their remit is usually elsewhere. However, once in a while an ongoing investigation into what looks like to be some man-

ner of Fortean phenomena turns out to be something completely different. Someone claims "missing time" and an evil presence in their room at night sounds like a case involving extranormal or extra-dimensional incursion, but the reality is, it could be an ENE that drinks the blood or the breath of the slumbering. The agents of FORT hear about some reptilian atavism lurking in the sewers, but it ends up as some bat-faced bloodsucker with leathery flesh.

Strangely enough, because FORT's remit never mentions vampires directly, Stearne certificated agents often overlook them—giving FORT agents much greater freedom to investigate troubling vampire activity than their counterparts in TWILIGHT.

Project: TWILIGHT

The front line agents of VALKYRIE are out there night after night. Many of TWILIGHT's commanding agents are, indeed, Stearne certified. They pursue. They kill. They rack up *lots* of kills, frankly—it's a matter of record, and VALKYRIE never throws any paperwork away.

What intrigues some agents of TWILIGHT, however, is why they only go after some vampires, and not others. There have been times when an investigation into something routine turned up a lead on a known haemophage—only to have some director shut them down and swiftly assign them elsewhere. In other cases, a mission to bring in a leech for questioning suddenly becomes a "burn-and-bottle" directive (burn the vampire, bottle the ashes) on the orders of some Stearne assessor. It's all rather vexing.

Vampires are expert manipulators and string-pullers nestling their way into all walks of life, from the vial-strewn alleyways to the topmost halls of power. Some of the parasites are known to call the highest echelons of society their host. Crackpots claim the creatures run the White House, Parliament, Pentagon, AT&T, Comcast Cable, and NASA. Vampires are certainly pervasive, but it's hard to believe they walk unassailed in the halls of power throughout the world. It's not as if master vampires come into work and punch a clock; monsters looming large, working their fingers into the cracks and crevices of every corporation, government and public service. Right? Yes, but it's not for lack of trying.

BARRETT COMMISSION

THE LEGACY OF POWER

Rumors of conspiracy at the uppermost levels of society will persist so long as there are have-nots enough to start them. (And, really, any combination of old fools making back room deals and casually deciding the fates of the populace qualifies as a conspiracy on some level. Hunters simply have the luxury—if it can be called that—to recognize the world is weirder and more complex than any would want to admit.) We've all heard of the Men in Black, the Masons, the Illuminati: all societies with some nugget of truth to rumors of their machinations. The only questions left are how deep does the rabbit hole go? The Barrett Commission intends to protect the population from vampires and other social monsters that seek to influence the upper tier for their own purposes. Several organizations have been formed and disbanded through the ages among the educated and the affluent: a Shadow Senate in Rome, special tribunals in Istanbul, the American Philosophical Society and Chestnut Street Compact in post-Revolutionary Philadelphia, and of course existing conspiracies like Task Force: VALKYRIE and the Cheiron Group. The Barrett Commission forms not as a new idea, only the most recent expression of an old one. An *essential* one. That assumption? Monsters have entered the halls of power, and only those who walk such halls can rout them.

Who patrols the vaulted halls and ivory towers? The Barrett Commission. They protect the world's assets, trusting their efforts trickle down to the average citizen. The Commission has representatives within government, corporations, hospital boards, the military—they are crumbs hidden in the upper crust. The Barrett Commission was formed specifically to address the supernatural threat lurking around the arterial veins of commerce and government. Effete socialites and spoiled rich kids need not apply; the Commission is composed of men and women who claw, scrape, and work their way to the top and very much plan to stay there. Yes, some are born to privilege, but the fat and happy have a way of wanting to stay blind to the threats around them. Or worse, they try to tame the beasts, cutting deals and inviting parasites into their company. Only the driven—who may lose the sight of the forest for the trees, but know a day's hard work—are invited into the Commission. Everyone else is a security risk.

The Barrett Commission takes its name from one of three founding members, Revolutionary Colonel Shaun Barrett. On behalf of the first President Adams, the Colonel investigated some curious bookkeeping surrounding the office of the Governor of Delaware. Barrett, along with Alfred Bredelmeyer (land owner and banker) and Elizabeth Ducat (Bredelmeyer's niece), performed the investigation over the course of many months. Certainly, corruption was not unknown, but Barrett's trio found the depth of the graft surrounding the Governor remarkable. It seemed that a certain flow of money had been set to actually *bypass* the Governor. They tracked the flow. At its end, they found a human creature, fat like a tick and bloated like a tumor—a blood-hungry thing whose gluttony was only matched by its greed. The monster was apparently associated with several important families within Dover for generations. Unable to abide their discovery, they cut the creature down and burned the rotten estate it had built with the spoils of the people. Sickened and convinced the President needed to be prepared in case this happened elsewhere, Colonel Barrett rode back toward the District of Columbia the following night.

So charged by this shocking news, a special commission was immediately gathered and sworn in to protect the American people from such an obvious threat to their security, right? Wrong. The results of Barrett's investigation never reached Washington; his ride was cut short in Baltimore by an unknown gunman. Similarly, Bredelmeyer was found dead, bled out from a wound in the neck within a fortnight. His radical motions to investigate every major family "from Boston to Savannah" never made it from the pub to a courtroom floor. Thanks due to the natural inclination and ignorance of the time (women were of lesser consequence), Libby Ducat was spared any retribution.

It was her diaries and letters that would survive Colonel Barrett's good name, and her discretion which survives their shared mission into the modern era.

Miss Ducat kept a small list of whom she could trust and how to get word to them. It was not long before this list grew. The hunters of the Commission no longer pursued making their compact official; any attempts seemed to preternaturally fail, as if eyes were watching from behind every painting hanging in the halls of power. This compact still exists today, a secret cabal of the powerful and elite—war hawks and gruff brokers, paranoid land barons and wealthy historians. They operate in modern nights as they have all along: as a group of powerful individuals united in silence to root out the parasites attached to the world's most gainful institutions.

The Enemy

Due to the reach of its individual members, the Barrett Commission appears deceivingly widespread, but their numbers aren't nearly as impressive as their influence suggests. Still, they have grown well beyond a young woman's coded messages to a handful of personnel within the American capital. The story of how and why the compact started is still told to new members and even if some details are forgotten, the moral remains clear: trust no one. Even other members of the compact should be held to agonizing standards of scrutiny.

For all the good the Commission is capable of, it is perhaps the most porous of known compacts when it comes to loyalty. In an organization of powerful people there will always be one or two individuals who believe they can profit from the deal with the devil. Strange bedfellows arise and before long another arm of the organization needs to be amputated for the infection. Personal greed will always be the greatest stumbling block of the Commission and second only to vampires, their greatest enemy remains their peers. While representing themselves by and large as patriots, every commissioner is likely to have a skeleton or two in their closet and many members find themselves particularly vulnerable to blackmail and extortion.

The Commission prefers to do their hunting in board rooms and power lunches than on the streets and open markets. Not that they're utterly untrained in the more pedestrian methods of hunting. Getting a little red out of a white collar is nothing compared to the hundreds of thousands of dollars they stand to lose through inaction. Ultimately, however, the Commission is all about fighting smart. By applying a little bit of pressure all over, it only takes the gentlest push to topple a monster's house of cards that has risen too high. (If that doesn't work, there's a .357 magnum and a wooden stake duct-taped to the underside of that old mahogany desk.)

This compact predominantly hunts vampires, because it's vampires that always seem to hide in plain sight, a tumor that conceals its malignancy and as it does so, develops its own leeching blood flow. Vampires look human, but they're also easy enough to spot: cold body temperatures, no heartbeat, a certain aversion to sunlight. Yes, if the Commission finds other monsters hiding in the shadows of power, they'll commit to action. But as a compact, it's the depredations of the power-hungry dead that consume their greatest efforts and knowledge.

Hunters

You are the very definition of a spin doctor and have cut your teeth saving major corporations from some very significant egg on their face. You can wag the dog all day long, and are known for it in the right circles. Thanks to this reputation, when some Commissioners at Bristol Meyer were discovered unloading "corpses," you were brought in and offered a crash course on what the Barrett Commission is all about.

When you went to work for the mayor you knew you were taking a step up into a whole new world. By the start of your second term you were brought into the back room by a colleague and shown in no uncertain terms what the "Special" part of Special Advisor to the Office of the Mayor meant. This information invigorates and terrifies you, but you see now the city needs you. You just hope they don't see you sweat.

You spent the first half of your life fighting the Man. Young, dumb, and full of yourself, you tried to tear down the establishment just to say you did it. At your mother's behest your Uncle sat you down to have a little "talk." At first you figured you knew where this speech—brought to you by the establishment—was going. By the end of it however, you were bleach white, speechless, and knew just how little you really knew. You start work for him on Monday.

You are the fifth generation in a military legacy. You're proud to serve of course, and would never admit you were railroaded into it by your overbearing father. You delayed field service by going through officer's training, but in wartime, everyone goes. Second guessing yourself all the way, you could only hope you made the right decisions. When you were summoned to Field HQ by the old general who served under your grandfather you swore it was to eat your stripes. Boy were you wrong. Turns out the war isn't about WMDs or oil or any of that shit. And you just got your card pulled.

Divisions

There are three primary Divisions within the Barrett Commission as each member and their affiliates apply their strength where they'll do the most good. These are as much natural cliques as they are imposed divisions of labor.

The **Suits** are the big business arm of the Commission. Their battlefield is the Forbes 500 list. While certainly not altruistic, the Suits *are* saving the world in their own way. Even if it is to make sure there's some world left over for the sake of profit. Historically, the Suits started as the smallest branch of the Barrett Commission but it doesn't take access to their secret history to see how business has held an increasing sway over government and the military interests. That isn't any doing on the part of the Barrett Commission *per se*, but it has boosted the interest and power of the Division.

The **Quorum** is the Division that comes straight from Washington, London, the U.N., etc. Attaches, Lobbyists, Representatives, Clerks, even a Senator or two all comprise the Quorum. The Quorum circles the limelight, but they don't claim it. Far better to be a king-maker in the shadows than to become blinded and exposed on the podium. The few members that have achieved public office are quick to make sure their voice is one of many or their motions are spearheaded by others. Thus are they able to hide in plain sight.

The **Five Stars** are a small but growing segment of military brass among the Commission. Their growth is not a new development as some of the younger members seem to believe, but rather a *renewed* development. Military involvement was key in the formation of the organization and at one time most politicians *were* military men. With the reinvigoration of the Five Stars, the methods the Suits and Quorum have grown accustomed are being challenged by less well-off old soldiers who built their careers on facing problems head on.

This is *my* country, *my* people. If anyone will be using them, it'll be me.

Status

The Barrett Commission gain status by having status. The bigger you are outside the compact, the more influence you bring with you within the compact. They are unique as a group in that someone with enough money and power can buy their way to the upper on their first day of membership. Even still, experience vests quicker than a Roth IRA and the word of a capable cleaner with some dirt under his nails will carry more weight than a fat cat out to protect his ass(ets) when the real decisions are being made.

• You've been brought into the fold but are most likely only aware of your immediate peers. You know the Commission goes beyond your local office but have little idea of the full scope. You gain an additional stipend in order to help the Commission: one additional dot in Resources to a maximum of five. If you already have Resources at the maximum level there is no replacement reward.

••• You've risen above the enlightened chaff. Swimming with the sharks, you've managed to come out of the pool alive. It's time for you to see what lies behind the curtain. You gain a three dot Mentor. If you already have a Mentor at this level, you may gain another Mentor at this level or additional dots in this Merit to a maximum of five.

••••• You have risen to a position of leadership in a compact composed almost entirely of leaders. This is not a position that comes lightly. You have available an almost limitless source of resources, information, and assets as well as a much wider social net. You gain two additional points in Contacts within the fields of Government, Corporations, or Military.

Stereotypes

Aegis Kai Doru: Last week we caught an intruder in one of our museums. Turns out the pajama-wearing little troll was claiming to be on our side, raving about some dangerous gewgaw or another. I told him to come back during business hours wearing proper pants and we'd talk. Then I set the dogs on him. I mean, really.

Ashwood Abbey: Eventually you grow up and realize life is more than where you're sticking your privates next. You want to grow old and die rich? Stay the hell away from these Country Club perverts.

The Cheiron Group: You ask why we never thought about incorporating and advertising in the back of magazines. Why not just paint a giant target on all of our assets and invite the creatures in? Where you see a strong corporate gate I only see the holes in the fence.

Union: Oh, by all means, protect your family and friends. At the end of the night you'll save, what, three lives? Four? Never mind the millions of dollars of GNP falling out of our nation's pockets like a sieve that could save four thousand lives. You want the big picture, work for management.

MaiDen's BlooD SisTerHooD

Pi Alpha Kappa

Some amongst the Maiden's Blood Sisterhood will tell you their spirits have been alive since the beginning of time. Since Lilith refused to lie under Adam, since God cursed Eve to painful childbirth, since Marduk tore Tiamat in twain. They don't all buy into the loftier aspects of the Sisterhood's more mystical principles, but they all agree that the compact offers its women a haven of safety and sanctity, and even more importantly, the opportunity to strike back at those who might dare abuse them.

The Sisterhood was born of the privilege and strength of character found on the campuses of the Ivy League Seven Sisters schools. These all-girl colleges offered tempting morsels to vampires drawn to the academic air and isolation of the student body from their families. The Sisterhood began as one woman protecting her students and grew into a compact shared throughout the Seven Sisters and beyond. A pact of mutual protection, leadership, and community service under the auspice: Pi Alpha Kappa. Outside of academic circles they are known primarily as the growing benefactor of women's shelters, spreading their message off campus and into the world.

In late 1957, Agatha Brewer was a professor of Mythology and Religion at Wellesley University, her *alma mater*. As one of the younger teachers on staff she felt her charge was to change the world. She spearheaded a push to add Women's Studies to the curriculum, and worked very closely with her students trying a more hands-on approach to her professorship. It was from this more personal vantage that she took notice of a disturbing trend among some of her students. More and more of her students would show up so weak and pale they could barely keep their eyes open. Otherwise good students were missing weeks of class on end. She hadn't been out of college so long that she didn't first suspect her girls were up late getting a little too intimate with wine and Harvard boys. It was an assumption her fellow professors seemed content to believe in and be done with.

The faculty assured Agatha it was common enough that some girls were here more to catch an Ivy League husband than procure a diploma. Agatha remembered more than a few such girls from when she attended the school, but as it persisted she felt driven to investigate further. The girls she found were staying up late... but it wasn't boys and booze to which they had fallen prey. Rather, she found the girls in the chapel with some pale woman claiming to be in touch with the great Crone aspect of the triplicate goddess. This woman forced the girls to do things, to serve her on hand and foot and to give her their precious blood. Agatha had seen quite enough.

The next night, Agatha gathered select members of the faculty and student body. Among them was Lena Corwen, the daughter of a powerful donor. Together, they broke up the ceremony. The blood witch fled, and they liberated the students from the hold the succubus had over them. But it was only a year later that the same phenomenon surfaced anew: more anemic girls, all unable to concentrate, some growing ill. This time, Agatha and the other women didn't give the creature the option of returning.

Agatha and the members of that class became the first chapter of the Maiden's Blood Sisterhood. With Agatha's drive and Lena's considerable fortune (well, her *parents'* considerable fortune), the Sisterhood took to the campus year after year, watching for those things that might seek to feed upon the young and naïve. They learned hard lessons time and time again. Some of the girls were gravely wounded, and another died from complications—some questioned if it was worth it. Agatha tolerated no such questioning. She said they must look to better things. Better methods, strategies, codes, equipment, meeting places. By the start of the next school year, Pi Alpha Kappa moved into their house just off campus, and a new era dawned.

From the campus grounds they spread into the city, pitching in for the community as their civic duty during the day, and protecting the townies at night. From Wellesley they branched out, first to the faculty of the other Seven Sisters: Bryn Mawr, Smith, Mount Holyoke, Vassar, Barnard, and Radcliffe and *their* surroundings neighborhoods. Believing them to be a Seven Sisters' version of the "Skull and Bones Society" no one paid much mind to what they attributed to little more than a glorified sorority. Thus the Maiden's Blood Sisterhood spread in plain sight of the uninitiated.

By the 1980s the Sisterhood had spread to dozens of colleges across the United States into Canada, and eventually making inroads through Europe. Their public face became sponsoring women's shelters and soup kitchens more palatably dubbed the "Sister Shelters." This gave the Sisterhood even more to fight—and fight for—among the souls they encountered through their work. What's perhaps fascinating is that the surprising swell in the group's popularity (fueled in part by curiosity over this "publicly-known secret society") necessitated they wear a public face that concealed the true nature of the organization. Girls compete to join the ranks of this "off the radar" sorority without ever realizing what the true criteria for entry really are. They expect that it has to do with good grades or family wealth—when, really, it's about who would be committed to the cause, who would be prepared to stand Vigil with the rest of the Sisters. (But that doesn't mean it's about physical prowess. While that's always a consideration, the Sisters approach the hunt in a myriad of ways, and violence is often last on that last—they prefer an intellectual or social approach to the Vigil.)

The Maiden's Blood Sisterhood achieves a wider reach with each graduating class. Not every Sister continues to directly serve the hunt. Simply put, they've done their tour and they want to go home. Their experiences will always haunt them with a mix of nostalgia and horror, and the compact might haunt them literally with an open clause that once you're a sister, you're always a sister. If two sisters and a dead body show up outside your house, you're expected to pitch in however you can. The concept of compact alumna is largely unique to the Sisterhood and grants them several advantages as their graduates go on to establish the women they intend to be. Slowly the organization vests contacts in major corporations, industries, and positions of influence in every walk of life. The Sisterhood has spread out like a net to bring their two-fold mission (one public, one private) across the world. Unfortunately, the wider this net is spread, the more noticeable the holes in the mesh.

In 1976, Wellesley College fired Agatha Brewer when a student accused her of impropriety. She maintained her innocence but threw herself into the organization full time. She still serves, they say, albeit in a purely executive capacity at her age. Very few girls ever get to meet her anymore and rumors abound: she was turned to a vampire years ago, she's a witch and keeps herself unnaturally young, she remains an active member in disguise, etc. Only members of the Pleiades Council (see below) would know for sure, and they aren't telling

Lena Corwen went missing in the field in 1988. Two of the girls who returned from that hunt swear she was killed, but they won't discuss it, not even now. They'll answer no questions and brook no doubt over their tale.

The Enemy

The Sisterhood "cut their teeth" weeding vampires out of college campuses and they find that to largely be their stock and trade today. Vampires, to the Sisterhood, represent a terrible abuse. And, despite their feminine leanings, it's less about "abuse of women" and more about "the abuse of the young." Students are dumb, really. They don't mean to be. It's just how people in their late teens and early 20s *are*. Vampires are seducers, Faustian monsters, callous manipulators who are happy to use, abuse, then discard the weak and the young. That's why the Sisters stand against the undead.

Every year more vampires—especially young ones—are attracted to school campuses and fraternity rows across the world. Universities are a fountain of fresh-faced souls stepping out into the world for the first time; melodramatic young minds easily misled and in over their heads make easy targets. To the monsters it's like shooting fish (out-of-water) in a barrel. Students are so *needy*. Can't make a college payment? Lost a boyfriend to a rival classmate (or worse, a professor)? Love getting blackout-drunk at the dive bar down the block from the school? Vampires have so much to offer—and, when they get tired of making offers, they can just feed with little fear of repercussion.

No Boys Allowed?

So, the Sisterhood, emphasis on *Sister*. No men allowed, right? Not quite. They don't recruit from the male student body, but the compact allows faculty members, off-campus volunteers, townies—all of whom could be male.

Still, it's a female-oriented compact, and any men that join best be comfortable with that fact. Some cells are very feminist, and men in proximity to such cells may have a harder time gaining Status than females of equal capability.

(It also bears mentioning that other, older vampires find themselves attracted more to the halls of academia than to the student body. The architecture, the pomp and circumstance, the storied campuses and educational methods that have barely changed since the adoption of the Greek model... all of this brings a certain creature comfort to that type of vampire.)

Of course, the Sisterhood has run across all manner of monster from the widely documented to the wholly unique. As membership often includes the future leaders of the world, violence is not their first and only response. Diplomacy, negotiation, and compromise have been effectively used in the past when dealing with the monsters. As one student ironically pointed out, "monsters are people, too." This doesn't serve as an invitation to let one's guard down, only that in approaching any creature, it wants *something*, and if it wants it bad enough, there's always room for negotiation.

The compact has a particularly weird relationship with witches. There is an express mandate within the organization that unless a witch is presenting a clear and immediate threat to the population, the case must be reviewed by the Pleiades Council before action is taken. Reportedly this rule was made when a Chapter killed a student reported to be a witch at Bryn Mawr College and the ensuing investigation almost ended the organization. Despite being a reasonable and clear explanation, it hasn't stopped speculation that one or more members of the Pleiades are themselves witches.

Did you think us shuddering alone and waiting for rescue?

Hunters

You were raised on the front lines. Grandma was a Rosie. Mom burnt her bra in Atlantic City. And then there's *you*. Growing up you felt all the real fights had already been won and third-wave feminism was just pissing into the wind. You were approached your second semester at Barnard—one of your professors handed you an index card with a symbol drawn on it of a triangle with a stylized droplet in the center and a time and place written under it. Boy, are you glad you were curious enough to go.

Daddy was a deadbeat, and Mom blamed you. Rudderless, without model, and striving for attention, you bounced from bad relationship to bad relationship, propping up addicts and slummers who filled both your need to mother and your subconscious desire to be abused. Finally someone stepped in and intervened. They picked you up and pointed you in the right direction.

Rush Week turned your stomach. Watching all these girls clamor for attention with their pep squad cheer and sing-songy chants. You weren't into girl stuff and after your first round of baleful glares it was clear the barrette and braids brigade weren't into you either. That's why you were surprised to find one of the girls from Greek Row waiting for you outside your dorm room one night. She asked if she could come inside and make you a different kind of offer. You suspected she was making fun of you, or maybe hitting on you, but what the hell, it wouldn't hurt to let her talk, right?

You never had much of a choice in anything you did. You grew up in a cult where those decisions were made for you. When to awaken, when to eat, when to work, when to worship, when to sleep, who to sleep with. It never occurred to you to complain, but looking back you can't believe that was your life. Thank the goddess your grandparents found these women to come and rescue you. Now *they* tell you what to do. And you love it.

Those things took your son. They took him and when you saw him again... it wasn't him. Not anymore. He was replaced with something that looked and sounded like him, but he was long gone. That's what the woman who worked at that shelter said. They listened when no one else would. They helped you see your son for what he had become. That's why you don't feel bad what you did to them—all of them—and why other fathers and mothers need to know they don't need to feel bad either.

Chapters

Divisions within the organization and local cells are referred to as chapters, reflecting the sorority and society roots of the organization. Each chapter answers to the national office, still based out of Wellesley, Massachusetts.

The **Pleiades** is the name of the national organizers. They oversee the university society and handle the business end of the compact (i.e. all that "non-hunter" stuff). Other than a few administrative personnel, the Pleiades are known to consist of seven women who make all the managerial decisions within the organization. Their identities are secret to all but a few chapter heads. Largely faceless and aloof, the Pleiades have been known to take an interest in a cell's business from on high.

The **Amazons** are those blessed with strength to stand between a world full of predators and their sisters. For lack of a better term they are the military arm of the Maiden's Blood and refer most often to active hunting cells. A sister doesn't have to be graced with an abundance of physical strength to serve as an Amazon. Strength of will, conviction, or simply having the backbone to stand up and try diplomacy are all shows of strength enough to participate in the Vigil in the most traditional sense. Girls within the Amazons are trained in self defense of course, just in case.

Finally, the **Graces** are the caregivers, sponsors, and recruiters for the organization. They are out on the streets in soup kitchens and shelters, looking for special women to bring into the greater cause. These are women with nothing left to lose and everything to gain, women who want to give something back.

Status

Maiden's Blood members gain Status by helping rescue new members and battling predation in all its forms. Many girls graduate and wish to move on with their lives still serve as alumnae, providing aid, shelter, and a helping hand to their active sisters just as with most fraternal orders. Men are welcome within the Blood but naturally plateau at a Status 3 through no fault of their own.

• You've been sponsored and met your local stewards whether within a university or volunteer work. You are considered a Daughter (or Son) of the Sisterhood and gain Allies (Maiden's Blood Sisterhood) to the second dot. If you already this Merit at this level you gain two additional dots instead to a maximum of five dots in Maiden's Blood Sisterhood Allies.

••• You are fully initiated and have brought at least three sisters (or brothers) to the fold. You are promoted to a Mother (or Father) within the circle. Local and neighboring chapters know your name and you may call upon a broader base of support. You gain two dots in Safehouse to bolster the Size, Security, or Secrecy of an existing Safehouse or one for use by members of the Sisterhood. If you already have dots invested in Safehouse you may gain two additional dots (not to exceed five in any one category).

••••• You are an invaluable resource to your sisters, and an example to all initiates of just how far you can climb. You are among the select few Crones within the organization. You draw your strength from your sisters, yourself, and the spirit that flows between you. You gain the Indomitable Merit (p. 134). If you already have this Merit, you may gain two points in Retainers (Maiden's Blood Initiates) instead. If you already possess dots in this you may gain an additional two dots to a maximum rating of five dots.

STEREOTYPES

Ashwood Abbey: They are just predators preying on predators. The symmetry couldn't be any more disturbing and we are wont to call them monsters just the same.

The Cheiron Group: Lots of our sisters are recruited by powerful foundations and corporations after college. More still have been approached by this organization. European, I think. Funny thing, those that join seldom show up to the reunions. Some aren't heard from ever again.

Lucifuge: Let's face it, we're Ivy League, a lot of us are used to our last names opening doors for us. That spooky girl in lab, though, to hear her tell it there's a lot more to her blood than all of us combined. She gives me the creeps, that's all I know.

Null Mysteriis: I went to a large enough school that the Sisterhood wasn't the only game on campus. This group—real bunch of eggheads—were looking to disprove everything they caught wind of. What a waste. It should come as no surprise most of them were men. No offense.

NIGHT WATCH

THE STREET WARRIORS

Who maintains the Vigil on those streets even cops won't walk after dark? Who brings hope to the neighborhoods to which the world has turned a blind eye? It seems every major metropolis has a street or two they'd sooner forget: every city has those neighborhoods that are so bad, it seems easier to ignore them, let them self-destruct. In such places, crime thrives in the cracks and fractures—but it's not just crime, oh no. The bloodsuckers, they thrive there, too. Lying forgotten and belly up, these broken blocks and bad neighborhoods are just waiting for the creatures of the night to pick them clean without fear of repercussion. It was in such a place that the Night Watch formed out of those who recognized they had no one they could turn to.

The hunters of the Night Watch are the last to leave the clubs at night. They're on the late trains and buses, and they look both ways before crossing each alley. They are the walking, stalking, army of the night. From the humble beginnings of a couple of boys taking back their neighborhood, the Night Watch has marched out into their cities to declare war on the things that go bump in the night (and "marching" is key—it's all about beating feet on the street until dawn). They are the vigilante watchmen of the forgotten streets; they patrol the hunting grounds of the monsters, leaving no man or woman behind for the creatures to take as their prey. The Night Watch try to send a clear and direct message to monsters in their cities: *It's last call. You don't have to go home, but you damn sure can't stay here.*

The Night Watch got started in the Hill District of Pittsburgh, Pennsylvania during the winter of 1970. The story grows a little each time in the retelling, but enough people remember Riley Lewis and Andre Sandoval personally, enough to get the story mostly straight. Crime and decay had the Hill by its throat; the people suffered. And nobody outside the Hill much cared. Attracted by the lack of police presence and the pervasive hopelessness of the citizens, vampires moved into the area bringing a whole host of addictions and societal ills (anything to keep the herd dumb, scared or happy). They brought in drugs and flesh trades. Like a cancer, the vampires' influence grew to overtake the next street and the street after that. Riley and Andre both lost family members to their scourge, and police were content to ignore the problem. After all, what were a few missing ghetto rats?

Sick of the apathy and incensed by the race riots from the previous year, Riley (a Vietnam vet) and Andre (the son of a cop killed on the job) took the matter upon themselves. Along with two friends, Pedro "Pookie" Baez and Leonard Witherspoon, the boys marched down the street one cold morning toward the crooked crack house that a cabal of vampires used as its nest. They gunned down the creatures' servants and burned the place to the ground. No one called the police. No one called the fire department. In fact, within an hour, most of the neighborhood folks were in the streets cheering the four boys.

You picked the wrong street, bloodsuckin' motherfucker!

They announced they weren't done yet and spray painted "Night Watch" at the entrances to the neighborhood, marking their territory. Once the fire burnt out they came back, salted the earth and waited for nightfall. The word spread between neighborhoods like wildfire, the Night Watch had sent their message. Retribution however, was swift.

The other leeches knew they needed a strong response or they could kiss their hold on the area goodbye. The creatures got the name of the boys responsible and the following night Leonard and Pookie disappeared. Their bloodless bodies lay at the opposite ends of the neighborhood to scare the people back in line. Instead, the next morning Riley and Andre woke up to a small mob offering to help finish what they started. Not all of them had the same name for the monsters—hell, some of them didn't even know what they were really facing—but they all knew it was about time they did something. War broke out on the Hill.

The Police feared another set of riots were flaring up and only sought to contain the violence within the neighborhoods, rather than risk fanning the flames. This suited the Night Watch just fine. Local legend tells how a police officer assigned to the Oakland district recalls seeing Riley and Andre walk to the end of a street one night in early spring. Andre was bleeding from a wound in his neck, Riley walked with a limp. They rattled a spray can and tagged the intersection right in front of him. When asked why he didn't arrest them, the cop laughed and reported that his instructions were only to get involved if they did anything *this* side of Baum Boulevard, then he turned a blind eye.

Word spread and rumors of other cities and neighborhoods adopting the Night Watch name and approach got around. Riley and Andre didn't want to waste what they had started once the immediate threat was handled. They formed a patrol schedule and spread out into Oakland, Downtown, Polish Hill and the University area. At first, locals were sure these rough and tumble young men in their street clothes and arm bandanas were coming out to riot and rob them. Imagine their surprise as more testimonials of these young men chasing off muggers and would-be attackers arose. The mayor publicly quashed such stories, and privately decried the Night Watch as vigilantes. The overtaxed police force wasn't exactly in a hurry to *do* anything about it. Some from the neighborhood boast it was Riley and Andre's model that inspired Curtis Sliwa, a night manager at a fast food joint, to form the Guardian Angels less than a decade later in New York City.

Andre and Riley hit the road to help other neighborhoods form Night Watch sets to protect their neighborhoods from creatures of the night—both vampire and human. Through the gang explosion of the mid-1970s, the Night Watch offered membership as a positive alternative to gang banging. However, in many ways they weren't offering a big difference in lifestyle: both shortened one's lifespan considerably, and neither paid much (gangs made some green off of their criminal activities, and the Night Watch made what little it could take from the monsters' pockets). This led to conflicts not just from vampires and supernatural threats, but local gangs not interested in a couple of crazy motherfuckers telling them how to run their turf. Andre in particular had big plans, hoping to see Night Watch spread out of the neighborhoods and ending up as the guardians of every neighborhood in town. Rather than rotting from within and letting the bastards win by no contest, he wanted to invigorate neighborhoods to march out and take back the streets.

Unfortunately, the Night Watch fell short of a civic pride panacea. The Hill District has since fallen prey to urban decay, subsidized housing, gangs and drugs, despite the Night Watch's presence in the old neighborhood. For every kid who buys into it, a lot more don't. Riley Lewis returned to the neighborhood in the early 1990s and successfully negotiated a gang cease fire. This lasted several years, but slowly eroded as attempts to gentrify the neighborhood met with resistance from long time residents. Riley died in the late 90s—some say it was gang retribution, but the hunters of the Night Watch know differently. Twenty years back when the compact was just getting its legs under it, some of the weaker monsters fled the neighborhoods like rats from a ship. One of them came back. The fiend was weak then, but was strong now. And it stole Riley's life, taking both his head and his heart as trophies.

Andre Sandoval's still around, but in Baton Rouge a few years back he took a bullet to the spine after getting in the middle of some fight between a 'banger and the thug's girlfriend. Andre's now bound to a wheelchair and wrestles with bouts of terrible depression. His girlfriend, Gracie Mae Ramirez, has turned her own life around and acts as his proxy in most situations—some say she basically runs the New Orleans Night Watch, and has her hands full after Katrina.

The Enemy

It's war on the streets. The Night Watch knows it's all about turf and who claims it. If it's not the gangs, then it's the goddamn vampires, and in the worst of all perfect storms, it's *both* working in tandem. The enemy moves in. It sets up shop. It gets its greedy, blood-stained fingers into every crack and crevice. Then the beast feeds. Gangs pilfer the neighborhood of its children, putting guns in their hands and shoving them out to do the dirtiest work. Dealers peddle poison. Vampires peddle blood and broken dreams, playing all the angles and working the good people of the streets like... well, what's less than a "pawn" on a chessboard? You get the idea.

The Night Watch won't have any of that. They don't just protect their house or their block like the Union does (and besides, they stand Vigil over some neighborhoods the working-class Union won't touch with someone else's arm). The Street Warriors are *proactive*. They take to the streets. They walk the beat like any cop. They kick down doors. Burn down nests. Unload bullets into whatever stupid fool monster thinks it can glide by in a black Escalade. It's about action before reaction; reaction puts you on the defensive. Action makes you the warrior.

Civic-minded cells in line with Andre Sandoval's vision of the Night Watch are just as active fighting street crime as they are at rooting out vampires. This aspect often gets overlooked as the monsters are fight enough, but that's the theory. When they first started, the Night Watch would wear red bandanas on their arms as a show of solidarity. These days the organization doesn't wear identifiers to avoid being confused with any particular gang and to keep a low profile (their methods don't exactly make them fan favorites with the police). The hunters of the Night Watch are supposed to stick together, two at a time *minimum*.

Life in the Night Watch is a dangerous and too often short one. The fervent methods and lack of organizational support claim a lot of young lives. When many of these kids feel their alternatives are selling rock on the corner or joining a set and banging, the Night Watch offers a chance to scratch out something positive in inches. To burn brightly for a greater good, even if briefly. To kill those who would kill you and your family. The ironic shame of the life remains, the deaths of their members are often reported as the tragic byproduct of the very life these kids—these *soldiers*—turned away from in order to do something greater.

The Hard-Knock Life All Over

The Night Watch is likely a bit different in every city. They have no overarching membership, though some cells communicate from city to city, and some even get together in the "spaces in-between" to talk tactics. As such, the face of the Night Watch in Detroit might very well be totally different than what one finds in, say, Boston or Miami.

In Philadelphia, for instance, where violence (and the murder rate in particular) has skyrocketed, the Night Watch is alarmingly aggressive. Some have suggested that they're just as bad as the gangs that pervade the city's worst neighborhoods—they shake down residents for cash to fund the hunt, they run tons of illegal guns, they brutalize any monster they find regardless of its effect on their "people."

In Los Angeles, however, you'll find a wholly different approach to the Vigil—the Night Watch there still takes the fight to the monsters, but it does so humbly, protecting the locals to an almost obsessive degree. The head of L.A.'s Night Watch, Oscar Martinez, is actually a new student of Buddhism, and has infused the compact's activities with some of the philosophies. They also make heavy use of the homeless among their ranks in the City of Angels, as those who live on the streets are ripe for the picking when it comes to a vampire desperate for a throat full of warm blood.

Hunters

Hell, you used to run this street. All the H, crank, dope, and snow used to come through you as far as anyone in this hood knew. Supply and demand. Way you saw it everybody won, especially you. Till one night you showed up a little early for a meeting with your contact and saw where this stuff was really coming from. Now you can't sleep at night.

Some part of you blames yourself. You know it's ridiculous but the neighborhood wasn't this bad when you joined the service six years ago. Now that you're back it makes your skin crawl to see broken vials and syringes where you used to play as a kid. You just want to clean up your hometown; if the Night Watch can offer a way to do that, then you're in.

You brother was going to be somebody. Get out of the hood, get educated, get a real job and be somebody. But he insisted on running with the Night Watch, wanted you to be safe when he'd gone. Those blood-sucking motherfuckers took him away from you instead. You can never be your brother; he was the smart one who knew how to win people over. But you can take up where he left when it comes to cracking fangs.

You don't have a claim of growing up on the streets or graduating from the school of hard knocks. Truth is you grew up a middle class kid in the suburbs, but one night while leaving a club the Night Watch saved your life. You saw too much that night to just go back to your life. You want to help too.

Sets

In gang terminology, a "set" is kind of a unit—a subdivision—of the larger gang. Here, different streets call for different tactics and no one M.O. is going to win the war. Distinct regional differences are the strength of the Night Watch and develop into different Sets.

The **Street Angels** are the most public face of the Night Watch and take their name directly from a woman saved by Andre Sandoval himself. The quote from her police report made the local news stating "this man came out of nowhere, like some sort of street angel." It's unclear as to whether this name influenced the Guardian Angels or the other way around. Regardless, this is the common name for Night Watch members who patrol the streets, subways, and alleyways outside their immediate neighborhoods.

The **Archangels** is a title earned by elite thugs in an area with no less than three confirmed kills under their belt. They are recognizable by the wing tattoos on either side of their neck, symbolizing how the bloodsuckers can't get to them thanks to the angels on their shoulders.

The **Chain Gang** are old heads in the game (though in this group, the oldest are in their thirties and forties). Usually these members have retired from running the streets and serve in a more organizational or "executive" capacity. The more socially-capable members take up the public face and deal with authorities, organize neighborhood defense and host seminars.

Status

The Night Watch awards status by cracking fangs, protecting turf, and taking back streets. There's room enough for a few folks with silver tongues and public faces, but when it comes down to it, success in this war is more easily measured in broken teeth.

• You've been a part of the organization long enough to have your own kit, and a regular patrol. You are recognizable within your own neighborhood as running with the Watch. The needs of the beat have learned you a thing or two while looking for bloodsuckers to smack down. You gain a free Specialty in Streetwise (Who's Who), Larceny (Fences), or Stealth (Stalking).

••• You've had an impact at the local level whether it's from flushing out vampires or keeping people safe from more mundane threats. Your name is circulated at the national level as someone the guy to talk to when they come to your neighborhood, and within your Set you're able to call some of the shots. You gain two dots in Retainers (Night Watch).

••••• You're officially an old head, regardless of age. You have done some enormous service to your neighborhood, city, or the Night Watch organization that makes you a celebrity within the compact and almost certainly around your neighborhood. You gain a dot in the Fame (Local) Merit to a maximum level of five.

Stereotypes

Ascending Ones: Those cocksuckers have been dealing dope on this block for half a decade. What, I'm supposed to mind my manners 'cause they claim to be fighting the same fight? Obviously not, motherfucker. Obviously not.

Task Force: VALKYRIE: Man, I would not come to my hood with all that kit on. People are gonna think those dudes are ATF or SWAT and run out the back. They got an interest on these streets they can come see me. I'll show them where the problem is.

The Long Night: I believe in God just fine, son. But my God don't sound like the same dude those guys are talking about. They hunt for their reasons and I hunt for mine. They can help if they want. Just don't come preaching up in here.

Union: Yeah, we got a few things in common. No doubt, no doubt. But we aren't the same, hell no. They think they come out of the bad neighborhoods. They think they got it hard. Fuck that noise, man. They need to come up in this block, see what happens when they ignore the problem or when they only try to protect their own houses, you know?

THE CAINITE HERESY

THE UNBELIEVABLE TRUTH

A monster stalks a nightclub dance floor. He sees his prey and moves; a party-goer barges past him, shoulder against shoulder. The monster whirls around; the figure has vanished into the crowd. He can feel something in his pocket. A fruit knife, around which is wrapped a note. It reads: *Who is Cain?* Suddenly, he realizes that the people on the dance floor aren't standing anywhere near him. All eyes are on him, and he has nowhere to turn.

A pale corpse arrives in his lair: his possessions lie scattered across the room. Someone has smashed the glass cabinet that contained his books. Only a few torn pages remain, lying on the floor, from his precious collection of antiquarian literature. Spray painted on the wall in red: an unfamiliar hieroglyph. Beneath it, these words: *Who is Cain?*

A young killer, new but enthusiastic at the blood-sucking game, finds himself pursued through the streets by humans with blades, stakes and oil-soaked rags. He panics. Every figure he passes in the alleys, on the corners, in shadowed doorways, whispers: *Who is Cain?*

The ancient murderer finally manages to corner the mortal who has caused him so much trouble, who has destroyed his minions and driven him away from his domain. He grasps the throat of the haggard, gaunt shaven-headed woman and begins to squeeze. She spits out three words along with the blood in her mouth, and she smiles. He leans forward and says: *What?* She repeats it once more as her windpipe collapses: *Who is Cain?* Her body goes limp, and the live grenade in her hand clatters to the floor...

Who is Cain? The question's meaning is more important than the answer. If those three words don't inspire what passes for terror in the withered hearts of the walking dead, it's a testimony not to their inefficacy, but to the determination of the people who use them.

A vampire hears the words, and he's already ash. They have him. He's doomed. Who cares what the answer is? Asking the question is what matters. Asking the question is the act of vengeance.

Once, long ago, the Cainite Heresy began as a doctrinal heresy within Christianity. Now it exists as a heresy in a broader sense. Independent of affiliations in religions and political parties, the Cainites are representatives of a broader kind of heresy. Now they're heretics in the sense of people whose worldview defies the orthodoxies of the societies in which they live. In this World of Darkness, people ignore the supernatural. They pretend there's no such thing, look beyond it, demand normality, enforcing it through social conditioning and sometimes through medicine and even the law. Hunters don't pretend. They refuse to. But the Cainites' heresy is that their refusal to pretend is made manifest. They keep their own organization desperately secret, but their crusade is to throw the world of the undead wide open. The monsters hide among us: so they have to be cruelly exposed. They have to be seen. They must not escape the notice of the world.

The truth *will* come out. Many Cainites believe vampires are no more or less than the descendants of Adam's murderous son—and they must be dragged into the light of day.

Every Cainite has suffered somehow at the hands of vampires. Here's a recruit who the heretics rescued from slavery—he was cattle, a regular food source with no will of his own. His companion was a vampire's agent, kept in thrall through the addictive power of damned blood and a vile mixture of twisted love and icy fear. The Cainites found her, killed the vampire, and brainwashed her into blank fanaticism. Both of

"I ask again: Who is Cain?"

them take orders from a man who tracked down and crucified the beast who drank his wife dry, and found it didn't feel any better. When the Cainite Heresy found him and offered him a place in life, he jumped at the chance.

But the more he hunts, the more vampires he kills, the more he thinks that perhaps there's something else going on. Where do the Cainites get their information from? How come they always seem to know where the vampires are? Who taught them magic?

They're victims taking revenge. They're wild-eyed lunatics, desperate to make the world know about the dead. They're a crazy suicide-cult. They're the only ones brave enough to stand against the lies the world tells them. The vampires exist. The world *will* see. And then the monsters *will* all die. One by one, if necessary.

History

The members of the Cainite Heresy don't bother to explain where they came from. Their business is survival and revenge. They keep the most detailed records they can of the vampires, their society and their nightly doings, but the Cainites don't care about the past, beyond word-of-mouth stories of Cainite heroes and undead monsters of the past. Cainites die, too, often unexpectedly, often before they can pass on their links to the past. They pass on the magics they know, and they pass on the fact that the vampires made them suffer. And that's all. The rest is insignificant beyond living to fight on and destroying the vampires.

And as far as they know, no one else knows about them. Actually, while they're a pretty well-kept secret, compacts and conspiracies exist that know more about the Cainite Heresy than the Cainites do themselves.

If the scholars of the Lucifuge, the Loyalists of Thule and the Shadow Congregation actually talked to each other, they might manage to work out that the Cainite Heresy of the early medieval period was originally a heretical sect in thrall to a vampire who peddled a story about the Mark of Cain and the position of the human race as cattle for the undead (read: "bearers of the Mark of Cain").

In the Malleus' Maleficarum's archive exists a manuscript of letters by St. Jerome, fourth-century translator of the Latin Bible and prolific theological writer. This particular edition is unique in that it contains one letter not copied in any other known edition of Jerome's writings. The letter is addressed to Jerome's friend and soon-to-be enemy Rufinus. It reads:

I entered into a brief verbal controversy with one George, whom you may know is the apparent leader of the schism they call the Cainites. They are unique in that they were apparently once a heresy; they claim that they had been deceived by a demon in the form of a dead man but that they had seen the truth and did away with the fiend.

Even though George and his followers have accepted the True Catholic Faith, they are nonetheless unorthodox in their thinking, and dangerously so.

They believe that some among the dead bear the Mark of Cain, as God gave to the Murderer of Abel and which Cain transferred to blood through damned descendants. Moreover, they claim that the vile bearers of Cain's mark feed from the innocent of Rome every night, and that these creatures, neither truly man nor corpse nor devil, must be destroyed lest they become masters of those still within the Light of Truth. They greet each other with the words "Who is Cain?" without ever really seeming to know what the answer to their question is beyond the obvious, that he was the first murderer and the son of Adam. Perhaps the question should be "Who was Cain?" but I half-suspect that the Cainites think that Adam's cursed son yet walks the earth.

I do not really know what they are. Demons abound in these nights, and witches are common. George speaks with such fervor that I cannot but think that there is some grain of truth in his rantings...

Jerome goes on to talk about witches and some prodigies—a two-headed lamb, a child born with a second face on the back of his head. That sort of thing.

But it's enough. The Shadow Congregation, themselves concerned mostly with vampires, have kept an eye on vampire-hunting organizations since the moment Ambrogio Baudolino got them a papal sanction.

The Library of the Lucifuge in Milan has the only—fragmentary—copy of the *Euagetaematicon*, a book attributed to one Vitericus Minor. This 14th century hand-written codex, copied from something much, much earlier, tells of how the mark of Cain is really the blessing of God on the dead. It says that the mark of Cain is the "burning of the sun and the thirst for blood above all." Cain, the book says, is God's true agent on Earth. Jesus Christ is only the agent of Cain, who still walks the Earth, a dupe empowered with dark miracles to ready the living for their role as cattle. Hints as to the missing section of the book suggest that Cain empowered a vampire in a similar role to Jesus, a messiah for the dead who prepared the predators to feed upon those whom Jesus had prepared to be prey, the lion to the lamb. It's not by any means the most heretical book ever written. But a marginal gloss towards the end of the manuscript, written in Italian by one of the Lucifuge's agents, reads: *They have cast off their shackles; they yet survive. This I rescued from the flames, that we might remember.*

The Malleus Maleficarum also holds a chronicle describing an event supposed to have occurred in the Carolingian era. One page, halfway through, describes a group of "paladins" who pursue a cabal of witches or revenants, only to be ambushed by a group of wild-eyed peasants. The peasants easily beat them to death with sticks. Why? They wanted to get to the monsters first and destroy them themselves.

In the Munich library owned by the Loyalists of Thule, an octavo printed by the same press that printed the first edition of Calvin's *Institutes* lists thirty groups who are an offense to God and good governance, and who must be suppressed. The seventeenth group listed is the Cainite Heresy, who receives only a few lines in the book. The book says that they "*provoke fears in the populace of the invisible world and of the dead, that anarchy may result.*" It describes them as "*witches, whose obsession with destroying the works of Satan has led them into error. They employ the tools of Satan against Satan, not heeding the admonition of Our Lord that a house divided against itself cannot stand.*"

Witchcraft is of course a preoccupation with the Aegis Kai Doru. A cache of Latin documents in St. Andrews, Scotland, includes one originally written in the sixth century, supposedly from the time of the semi-mythical prince Ambrosius. It was found along with a hand-written Jacobean translation, a vial of still-fresh blood contemporary with the original manuscript, and four human knuckle bones. The text describes a contemporary description of an occasion on which the Guardians captured a supposed witch and tortured him. The prisoner apparently took a quite considerable amount of breaking. But he did break, and when he did, he said that he was using, in the translator's words, "*magics denied the hungry dead, the better to deny them their provender.*"

He had been a vampire's slave; his friends had set him free, body and soul, and he did their bidding now. The Guardians, perhaps sensing competition, tortured the man further. He had nothing more to say. By the time they were done, he was barely recognizable as a living human being. The translation ends with:

"*We do not regret our mistake, for through it we know that these men are men like us, who may have aided us in our work. Keep watch over his treasure, and should his brothers return to claim them, offer them to those who would use them wisely, along with his mortal remains, that they may know it as a sign.*"

Evidently, the owners of the text never saw the Cainites again, or never heeded the instruction of the writer. A Cainite might still know what to do with the blood, but the significance of the bones would likely be lost on her.

The Lucifuge has access to copious journals attributed to the ubiquitous and quite possibly fictional Chevalier Thélème. In the volume of the Chevalier's journals marked as being from 1812-1843, he describes an occasion in the first half of the 19th century when a mismatched group of Russian commoners destroyed a vampire the Chevalier was pursuing with magic, before turning on him. The peasants went too far. In a rage, he dispatched all but one of them. Before he killed the last man, they had a conversation of sorts, conducted at saber-point. The man believed that the Chevalier was a vampire; like all of his companions, the man had suffered at the vampires' talons and fangs and could not be reasoned with. His desire to pay back the dead for un-described slights and sufferings had blinded him.

Project TWILIGHT's records include a 1967 report marked EYES ONLY detailing an operation in which TWILIGHT agents tried to find links between anti-Vietnam war protests and vampiric influence. They didn't, at least not directly. But an agent who infiltrated one of the peace groups found himself in the midst of a bunch of hippies who seemed to think that the government (and its war lobby) was the real victims of undead influence. The walls of their commune, the reporting agent tells, had "the usual mix of subversive and anti-American graffiti daubed on its walls; however, among the various slogans I saw the phrase: *Who Is Cain?* When asked what this meant, the members of the commune would not reply. From this point on, they treated me with suspicion."

A 2005 report from an Operation ADAMSKI operative stationed with the US Army in Baghdad tells of a group of "suspected insurgents" who thwarted attempts to cover up a PS/ENE incident. They had, so the report says, "*taken extreme measures to neutralize a PS/ENE enclave, but had at the same time taken steps to ensure that US authorities would find their remains. Why they should behave in this way remains unclear. The suspected insurgents did not harass or harm the ADAMSKI team directly. However, thanks to their efforts, the operation must be deemed a failure. The whereabouts of the culprits are unknown.*"

The Cheiron Group issued a directive in 2006 suggesting that "any groups naming Biblical figures as part of a pretext for their attempts to preempt or deny potential resources should be avoided."

THE VAMPIRES DON'T KNOW?

Actually, a few vampires know about the Cainites. But the fact is that just as vampire hunters don't know as much about vampires as they think they do, the vampires don't really know much about their hunters.

Sometimes, it seems to an undead monster that all the living ever seem to do when it dawns on them that there are vampires is to start whittling chair legs into stakes. It's a pain in the neck, and not in a good way.

A more sensible vampire might know that the Catholic Church and the US Government are on to the undead, but even then, he's inclined to arrogance when "mortals" are concerned. He simply doesn't think that the living can hurt him. They're cattle. The night society of the vampires has existed for two thousand years plus, and the humans haven't destroyed it yet.

Now compare that to a group of people who—apparently—don't even seem to have a papal sanction, a rag-tag bunch of wild-eyed nutters who want revenge for something (join the queue) and who babble something about Cain. Of course, then they're bringing on the blood magic (which they shouldn't know how to do). A vampire who survives that knows he has a problem, but then his next problem is convincing his vampire pals that this bunch of misfits is a problem...

On Survival

Heresies don't survive 1600 years. That's not how human society works. Whole civilizations have risen and fallen in less time than that. Sure, an outsider group can ensure its survival by becoming powerful enough to take on the establishment—it worked for Christianity and Islam, both of which began as heresies in their own way—but they don't stay the same.

They will hunt on 7th and Gordon tonight.

Five of them, two dead men, three dead women.

Bring fire. Ask the Question.

That's how things work in the real world, anyway. The Cainite Heresy has survived for 1600 years, without ever once becoming a social establishment. The Cainites of the fourth century would be hardpressed to recognize the men and women who make up the Cainite Heresy now, and the modern breed of heretics have little regard for history beyond their collections of vampire lore and word-of-mouth stories about the exploits of former generations. But they're still Cainites. And the simple reason is that through all the centuries, the thing that *has* remained constant is that the Cainite Heresy has existed in the context of another society: the society of the dead.

The Cainites don't really know the ins and outs of vampire society. They have a better idea than the other conspiracies—even the Malleus Maleficarum, in fact—but in the end, they barely scratch the surface of what the vampires are doing. It doesn't really matter. As long as there are vampires, people will suffer. They will always bleed the innocent dry, and abuse the vulnerable. They warp minds. They violate corpses. They blaspheme against religions and rape the laws of science. They are parasites on human society. They can do nothing else. A vampire may think herself humane. She may even feed off rats rather than people. But time brings temptation, and it becomes easy to feed from the living. The vampire cannot help it. It's in what one might inaccurately call her nature to prey on the living.

And as long as the living dead prey on the living, people will exist who survive and know what it is that made them suffer. Just a few, granted, out of the vast mass of humanity who choose not to see the hidden world, but enough. And a very few of those get found by the Cainites, who give them a chance to get even.

And here's the other reason they survived: magic. The very fact that the Cainites have a very limited kind of magic stolen ("denied") from the vampires has kept them from complete destruction. When you have a precious thing to guard, a power to exert and a secret to keep, you find yourself wanting to protect it. And protecting it means passing it on to the next generation. If the Cainites hadn't somehow managed to steal the secrets of blood magic from their undead nemeses, they would probably have died out completely sometime in the middle ages. As it happened, the Cainites' centuries-long conflict with vampires who wanted their secrets back kept them going. They had something to fight against. The undead failed to stop them at the beginning and they spread too far.

The Cainites are small proof of a massive and (to the vampires) terrifying truth: if the human race knew about the vampires and people organized themselves en masse to destroy them, the vampires would lose. Sixteen hundred years, and the undead have lost track of the Cainites. Sure, sometimes the undead suspect organized resistance, and fight them, and maybe even wipe out Cainite cells spreading across entire regions, but the fact is, they keep coming back.

They survive, and they survive because vampires do. Vampires cause pain. Pain breeds grief and resentment. Resentment fosters the desire to revenge. The vampires survive because people in general don't want to believe in them. And so the Cainites and vampires have become locked, unknowing, in a struggle that's going to last until the very end of the world. The vampire doesn't really know about the Cainites, and couldn't stop the depredations that continue to create them and people like them even if it occurred to him for the merest split-second that doing so might help. The Cainite didn't ask to be dragged into the shadows—but revenge is quite possibly all he has left.

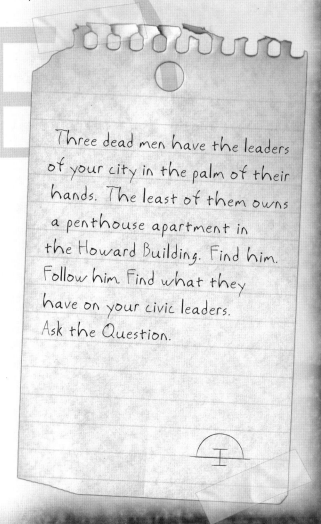

Three dead men have the leaders of your city in the palm of their hands. The least of them owns a penthouse apartment in the Howard Building. Find him. Follow him. Find what they have on your civic leaders. Ask the Question.

The Hand of God, Or Something Comparable

Even taking into account the Cainites' blood magic and the parallel survival of scattered, secretive minority cultures (in Jewish and Romany communities, for example) over centuries and even millennia, *even* taking into account that vampires exist, the question still springs to mind: how come they're still around?

It's impossible. They're too scattered, too isolated, too separate. There's no way in Hell, Heaven or any other place that they could really function as a working vampire-hunting conspiracy. But they *are* alive and well and turning vampires to dust. How come? For that matter, how is it that a cult of brainwashed slaves gathered up the strength of will *en masse* to turn on their master? And how on earth did they manage to learn magics otherwise only ever used by vampires?

The answer is simple. Someone or something kept them alive all this time, presumably for some purpose that hasn't been revealed.

The highest-ranking Cainites can't tell anyone this—if they do, it's curtains—but when they reach a certain point in terms of respect and experience, they begin to receive messages. Information on vampires. Leads as to the best places to find them. Tip-offs as to reprisals. A vagrant walks up to a top-ranking Cainite and presses a grubby hand-written note into his hand. A heretic receives an e-mail with no sender address telling him the name and location of the closest Queen of the Damned. A cell leader receives a letter every Sunday, postage paid but no postmark, no visible postman. Who sends these missives? Who receives the secret reports that Cainite leaders place in the postboxes of deserted houses or to e-mail addresses that don't exist?

• **It's another conspiracy.** A smaller, older conspiracy than the Cainites themselves took the opportunity to manipulate the original followers of the heresy into destroying their master. It influenced them, preserved them and sometimes aids them.
The Nine Daughters of Nibiru (see **Hunter: The Vigil p. 18** and **Witchfinder p. 18**) still exist, or at least the severed heads of three of them exist, kept eternally alive by a terrible ancient enchantment. The three remaining heads of these ancient immortal women sing constantly of things that have been and will be. A hereditary line of guardians and scholars guards the Daughters' heads and transcribes and translates their pronouncements; they keep track of Cainite cells. The heads know the names of the Cainites' leaders, recruits and enemies without being told (no one really *talks* to them, as such). They give the orders; their guardians pass them on via a network

of agents, hardly any of whom are in the know. In ancient Mesopotamia, the Nine Daughters of Nibiru counted the vampires as their enemies. Back then, the vampires were half-gods, the evil truth behind myths of immortal *Daevas*. The agents of the Nine Daughters fought the vampires through seven great empires until, realizing that the world was changing and they could not endure for long, they manipulated a Christian sect duped by a vampire into gaining freedom and stealing the secrets of blood magic.

None of that is in fact true. This is the truth: back in the fourth century, the last remaining members of the Birds of Minerva (see **Hunter: The Vigil p. 18**; they're also mentioned in **Slasher**, if you have that book) discovered the terrible truth of the Roman Empire: the vampires not only existed in vast numbers, but in fact were the secret masters of the human world, possessed of a terrible plan to make the human race their cattle. After dozens of desperate assaults on the vampires' underworld, the Birds of Minerva took another tack and suborned the Cainite Heresy. The Birds of Minerva disappeared into the shadows, never again directly facing their enemies, and using the Cainites to do their bidding.

This is also a complete lie. In fact, the Cainites are tools of the Inner Church, a secretive order who command several other conspiracies for their own almost unknowable ends. The Inner Church is the Ultimate Conspiracy. It seeks absolute control over the world, and the night-society of the vampires is, in the thinking of the Inner Church's illuminated leaders, the greatest threat to this. Either way, the Cenobites of the Inner Church may not even be human. Any ordinary house can be a cloister of the Inner Church; any human can, for a brief moment, become "overshadowed" by one of the Inner Church's Monks and Nuns, their will and memory used to transmit messages to their Cainite dupes. The Cainites shed the chains of one controlling force, only to become slaves to another.

None of this is true, either. The fact is…

- **It's God.** The LORD Himself exists and has placed the Cainites under His Almighty hand. This isn't the God of the Bible, or at least not of the parts that sane people want to believe in. He doesn't need the Cainites' devotion, He needs their service, and for this purpose He sends his Angels, his Dominions, in a multitude of different forms, to command the Cainites. Their purpose is to destroy the vampires, because they are His only mistake, the fall-out left by the original Mark of Cain. Actually, the truth is far, for worse.

- **A cult of vampires are behind the Cainites.** That's right. All but the most obtuse vampire hunters know that vampires have factions, and sometimes fight. One faction, which hardly any vampire hunter knows about is dedicated to destroying other vampires. All of them. Which is why hardly any vampire hunter knows about it: because it's a bigger threat to the other vampires than it is to the human race. Also, they are of a slightly different order of monster. They're harder to spot. Hence, this particular sect doesn't come under the radar of the vast majority of hunters. Anyway, this vampire sect, whose reasons for destroying the other undead are wholly unclear, has been active since at least the time when the Cainites overthrew their vampiric master. The vampire-killing vampires weren't behind that—those original Cainites really were exceptionally lucky and strong-willed, and their vampire leader was simply nuts, a slightly pathetic but nonetheless dangerous individual who had no idea how he was leading the Cainites into the world of the undead.

The other vampires have their means of destroying their enemies, and what better way of destroying the other vampires than finding a way to make them public?

It's crazy, of course. If the Cainites ever found out that their Sources are the very monsters they've been bent on destroying for centuries, they'd go nuts. But really, how likely is that? The vampires have been pretty good at hiding their tracks, and by the time a Cainite gets the message he's been sent, the vampire moves on. Even if a Cainite were to discover that his Source were a vampire, what could he do about it? These are the people who taught the Cainites how to hide and survive. And what truly fanatical Cainite—they brainwash many of their members—is going to *believe* that the ultimate mind behind 1600 years of vampire hunting is another vampire? He finds it out, and maybe he comes to the conclusion that the vampire killed and took the place of his "real" Source. Or perhaps he thinks it's all a lie.

And even if *he* finds out the truth, how is he going to convince every other Cainite on Earth of it? They kill traitors. Finding out the truth is a good way to die at the hands of your friends.

But the thing with the vampires isn't true, either.

- **The Cainites are the unwitting agents of Cain.** Who is Cain? He's the ancient progenitor of the vampires, he's truly alive, and he regrets his mistake.

This is the least believable explanation of them all. Perhaps one of these other explanations is true. Perhaps none of them are.

From: <undisclosed>
To: Celia Carroll
Subject: Who is Cain?

___

We know who you are. We know when you died. We know where you're hiding.
Look behind you.

Organization

Long ago, the Cainites were nomadic. They sometimes took the roles of wandering entertainers, lepers, gypsies, or wandering monks. In this age of cities where it's easy for a person to vanish, it's more common for Cainite groups to stay in one place for years or decades at a time. A Cainite cell in New York exists as an invitation-only encounter group for "blood disorders," meeting every Tuesday and Thursday night. A cell in Cardiff exists around a policy think-tank based in the Welsh Assembly. In Kolkata, nearly a hundred Cainites survive across the Hindu, Muslim and Sikh communities, working under the cover of a union of small businessmen in the many markets and bazaars scattered around that vast, labyrinthine city. A Buenos Aires police detective with a penchant for obscurantism manages a small network of Cainites, some of whom have never even heard of each other—which is how it should be. It's for their protection. The detective is getting old, however, and he's losing his edge. He knows he's going to have to bring others into the group. But who can he trust? And in Philly, they inhabit a basement of a church with all the intensity of the religious cult they once were.

Cainite cells don't have any one common degree of organization. Some cells have autocratic leaders. Some operate on a democratic basis. Some have committees who choose members when they need to. Secrecy is paramount. Cainite leaders have access to the magics stolen so long ago, and for those things they don't know, they have the "Sources," their mysterious suppliers of lore, who provide in various media—notes, e-mails, letters, text messages, whispered messages from passersby—the means to learn more, if the Cainites ask.

Safehouses

The Cainites' safehouses are often mobile. A group in the South-East of England uses a reconditioned London Routemaster bus, which also houses a theater company. A privately-owned cargo carriage on a train that runs across the east coast of the USA contains sleeping quarters for a half-dozen Cainites. Its inhabitants change regularly; the key to the carriage is in the hands of a dozen Cainite leaders, connected years ago by the Sources. A traveling fairground uses several brightly painted trailers to carry its attractions and rides. One of the trailers never unloads a ride. Most of the carnies are Cainites, and that's where they keep their arsenal, and a few rooms for Cainites on the run. Even static safehouses have a good degree of access to transport. Bus stations and train stations are common choices. One of the vast, well-kept stations in LA's subway system has a door, behind which waits a small collection of books, a firewalled internet connection and two bunk beds. Transience as a concept can take the place of actual movement. A third-floor room in one of the hotels in the intensely-busy Paharganj area of New Delhi is reserved for Cainites who pass through, hiding among the tourists.

Information

In the Middle Ages, the Cainites operated a kind of courier system, a network that enabled them to share information on the enemy in secrecy. They shared signs and passwords. Cainites knew each other. During the Reformation, Cainite leaders took the opportunity to print—always anonymously—some of these things. Printing was a risky business. Printing presses were easy enough to locate, and the very act of printing a thing put one in great danger.

Even so, a very few copies of these untitled miscellanea still turn up. The Loyalists of Thule have one. The Aegis Kai Doru has one which has at some point gained magical powers of its own. The only identifying mark is the Cainite Sign on the cover, the symbol the Cainites have used since the vampire brought them together.

The Sign

The Cainite Sign—a design supposed to represent, in abstract terms, the First Murderer, appears across the world. Few people know what it means, least of all the vampires who—according to some of the Cainite's lore—are too concerned with deciphering their own tags and symbols.

Is that true? It probably isn't. Its meaning, at least, is apparent. It adorns the walls of burnt-out vampire lairs, of the places where the monsters used to hunt. It marks places where, in two nights' time, every Cainite in fifty miles will congregate and face the dead.

What it doesn't mark is a Cainite safehouse, or lair. It's not a sign of safety. It's a sign of war. See it, and know that the Cainites have been here, or will be here soon, and that they will bring fire.

The Question

The Question is, of course, "Who is Cain?" and the act of asking it is, for the Cainites, the closest thing they have to a war-cry, the message to an uncomprehending vampire that he isn't going to walk away. Actually, some vampires do walk away, and some dispatch their opponents before they ever have the chance to utter the fateful words.

The question does bear thinking about, since, in a movement that disregards so much of its his-tory the way the Cainites do, it's an anomaly. Who is Cain? At least one source of Cainite scholarship—a password-locked web resource—tells the story of Cain and Abel.

Cain and Abel sacrifice to God. Cain is a crop farmer. Abel is a herdsmen. Both bring the best of their produce. God accepts Abel's offering of blood and flesh, and rejects Cain's wheat. Cain takes offense. He kills Abel. A midrash on the scripture tells how Abel mocked Cain. Cain, in his anger killed his brother. God found Cain, and asked him where his brother was. Cain replied: "Am I my brother's keeper?" God curses Cain for his anger, his murder and his impudence. The mark God places upon him changes him. And God says that those who harm Cain will be cursed to the seventh generation.

But few of the stories really say what the Mark of Cain was. The Cainite version of the story says that he was a vampire, the first vampire, and that he defied God in discovering that he could pass on his curse to the dead.

The one true living vampire, Cain, still exists. He is somewhere out there, walking the Earth. He guides his children. Maybe he's sorry about what he did.

Maybe he isn't.

The Enemy

The Cainites' obsession with vampires causes them sometimes to ignore other monsters, but even so, the nature of the Vigil is such that a hunter looking for one kind of monster finds another. A witch, a werewolf, a slasher or another monster might display, in his *modus operandi*, some of the signs of a vampire attack. A desecrated corpse. Stories of shape-shifting. Signs of Satanic magic. Blood, in copious quantities. Yes, monsters and villains with absolutely nothing vampiric about them might well show some of these telling signs, but the fact is, how do you tell if that blood was shed by a vampire or a witch unless you pursue the monster? By the time you figure out that it's not the monster he's looking for, it's too late and you're fighting for your life. But that's how the hunt works.

What follows is what the Cainites think they know about vampires. They are surprisingly knowledgeable. But not everything they think they know is true.

The Vampire Families

Cainites recognize several kinds of vampire, but over the centuries they have come into contact with one kind of vampire more than any other. The Cainites' blanket term for these intensely social, near-human creatures is "The Families." Cainite lore differs as to whether the Families divide themselves into three, five, twelve or dozens of factions and groups. Just as a Cainite scholar thinks that he's compiled enough reports to pin down exactly how the vampires divide themselves, here comes something unexpected. Is the vampire who commands swarms of bees a sign of another sub-division of the Families, or is she an isolated freak? Do the vampires who seem to be devoted to some Christian heresy count as a Family, or are they a faction?

Most Cainites recognize three definite Vampire Families: Creeps, Beasts and Masters. Creeps are the vampires who have the power to hide themselves from view. Sometimes, they have clairvoyant powers. Many of them know magic spells. Beasts are often hideous. Some have the power to change shape. Some openly worship Satan. Masters are perhaps the most dangerous. They have the power to control the minds of people and animals. Sometimes the control is direct; sometimes it's subtle, working on the emotions. Either way, it's near-inescapable for a hunter without recourse to magic of his own, and Masters have nearly brought ruin to the Cainites on many occasions.

As different as they are to each other, the three (or five, or twelve, or dozens of) kinds of "Family" vampires have certain abilities and weaknesses in common. They all exhibit supernatural physical abilities, although how they are exhibited varies from individual to individual. They don't get older, although they do appear less human as time advances, adopting paler skin, a predatory aspect and a reduced ability to deal with humans without scaring them. Old vampires don't pretend to breathe, don't blink, and look much paler than their human counterparts. While Cainites have observed how vampires can make themselves warm and mimic life, vampires can't apparently do it for very long.

Vampire blood is addictive. Drink the blood of the same vampire three times, and you're that vampire's slave.

If you drink a vampire's blood after having been bitten, you become a vampire. If the vampire killed you when he bit you, you become a Family vampire of the same kind as the one that created you, or a Minion. If you were still alive after being bitten and then drink that vampire's blood, you become a Half-Vampire.

Half-Vampires can be cured. Full vampires and Minions can't.

The Families have a variety of supernatural powers, ranging from mind control, clairvoyance and shape changing through to bizarre abilities like mimicking the Stigmata, turning into shadows or causing storms to rise without warning.

All of them share weaknesses for sunlight and fire, and behave with dread when threatened with either. A stake through the heart doesn't kill a vampire of the Families, but it does immobilize the vampire, allowing you to burn the vampire to ashes, which is the only real way to destroy the monster forever. Bullets don't work against vampires.

Most of them don't show up properly in mirrors or film—they appear blurry. But this isn't true of all of them. The Cainites have no idea why this might be the case, though individuals are given over to myriad theories.

The Cainites know from bitter experience that most of the folklore weaknesses of vampires aren't effective. Nothing stops a vampire from entering a house uninvited. Crosses don't hold vampires back, and things like garlic and running water don't work either. Very rarely, however, one of these vampires recoils at such things, and the Cainites know rituals which force a vampire to obey the old injunctions.

The Cainites counsel caution. These vampires vary wildly in power and almost always do something unexpected. Cainites never face them alone, and never without a plan, after having observed them for a very long time in groups of three or four (or, at any rate, in the company of other hunters). When they finally do go in, they try to take the vampire by surprise, asking the Question at the very last minute. The very oldest and most dangerous vampires often merit—in the Cainites' eyes—suicide missions: a "victim" with heavily-drugged blood or an agent entering the monsters' sanctum with incendiary devices strapped to her chest.

Most of all, a lot of Cainites have found the things they know severely lacking. Some think it's all bullshit. Some think it's all gospel. And some have added or changed things. Cainite knowledge isn't monolithic, and it's rarely even close to complete.

Minions

The Cainites recognize that the more powerful vampires appear to be able to create minions, vampires who are neither as powerful nor as smart as their creators. Mostly, they seem mindless, either appearing to be like zombies or like ravening blood-stained beasts.

Unlike the more social vampires, you can't reason with a Minion before staking it. You have to skip the cunning and just kill the beast.

Minions are dangerous for their sheer physical power. The Cainites hunt them down as they would a rabid man-eating tiger: with caution, and quite a lot of manpower. They try to keep their distance, on the whole, preferring to lure such a monster into a deserted area and destroy it from out of the range of its claws and fangs, with crossbow bolts and Molotov cocktails.

Half-Vampires

In folklore, it is said that the child of a human woman and a vampire is a *Dhampyr*, a creature half-man, half-vampire. It's not true at all. In fact, the Cainites know from experience that vampires create Half-Vampires from living humans, just as they create full vampires and minions from newly-exsanguinated corpses. The Cainites know for certain that no such thing as a born Half-Vampire exists.

Half-Vampires aren't quite the same as Minions, although they serve the same purpose—they serve and guard the Family vampires. A half-vampire is still living, but through the application of a vampire bite and vampire blood, has some vampire powers. A Half-Vampire doesn't have fangs, but he or she does need blood to survive, and at least some of it should be vampire blood, which is their main weakness—Half-Vampires are made and controlled by the vampires who feed them.

As long as they keep feeding from blood, Half-Vampires don't age. They sometimes have the same supernatural powers as their masters, but never quite to the same level. They don't have any especial weakness to sunlight or fire, and still show signs of humanity—breathing, blinking, warmth of the skin—even if they are centuries old.

The important thing to know is that Half-Vampires can be cured. A Half-Vampire deprived of vampire blood goes through a withdrawal process. This doesn't mean they're worth saving. Most Half-Vampires are still the slaves of the vampires who made them, even if they cease to be Half-Vampires. And all Half-Vampires age quickly to the

age they *should* be when their source of blood goes away, meaning that an old Half-Vampire might die of old age after going through Cold Turkey. True, some Half-Vampires go rogue, and a very few, after having been cured and "repurposed," have even joined the Cainites. But even so, the best Half-Vampire is more often than not a dead one. The Cainites have ways of spotting a Half-Vampire and a Cainite who somehow became a Half-Vampire or a Half-Vampire who tries to join the Cainites is asking to be tortured, "cured" and killed, and not necessarily in that strict order.

Cainites tend to be more confident around Half-Vampires. Most wouldn't dream of kidnapping and interrogating a full vampire of the Families for fear of falling prey to its mind-bending powers. Half-Vampires *do* feel pain, however, and do respond to torture, even one with little will of her own. The most effective torture is the simple threat of withdrawal of the blood. An old Half-Vampire almost always talks if you take her blood away and promise to give it back. The addiction is too much. Of course, the Cainites can never permit such a creature to exist without being "cured," but she doesn't have to know that until after they've found out where her Master sleeps and what his assets are.

Thieves

Since the very beginning, the Cainites have been aware of creatures that inhabit corpses and make them vampires. They're a different order of monster. The creature appears to be an owl a bat, a cat or a rat in its normal form. It's insubstantial, however, and can fly into an intact corpse and take it over.

They have many of the powers of the Families. Sunlight doesn't harm them. But the corpse a Thief inhabits continues to decompose.

In the end, the main difference between these creatures and other vampires, as far as the Cainites are concerned, lies in their behavior. They're alien. Completely alien. Their actions are bizarre, even by the standards of the undead. Cainites who encounter them often mistake them for Family vampires, at least until it becomes apparent that a Thief works alone. Cainites tell stories of a Thief's lair with a "wardrobe" of fresh corpses and a basement full of silent, imprisoned victims, their minds enslaved by the monster's infernal powers, patiently waiting to be killed and inhabited when the monster's current bodies grew a little ripe.

Thieves are really hard to kill. Destroying the bodies only drives out the monster. Driving the creature into sunlight without a body to inhabit kills it, but that's easier said than done. Magics exist to destroy such things, but the creatures are so rare that the Sources rarely teach them. One Cainite found that her only chance of destroying the thing was to get a coven of witches to stumble upon the thing and face it themselves. They destroyed it, but the unfortunate Cainite didn't get out alive. In fact, she was its last host body before the witches destroyed it.

Other Blood-Drinkers

The Cainites know full well that other vampires exist. Most of them, unlike Minions, Half-Vampires, Thieves and the Families, whose spread is worldwide, are regionally bound. In the Far East, some vampires feed on human breath or eat livers. In Indonesia, the heads of cursed corpses detach from their bodies and fly through the night in search of blood, trailing entrails and gore. A kind of living vampire native to the Philippines appears as a normal woman by day and as a razor-mawed monster by night. In the Middle East, taloned *Ghûls* feed on the corpses of the dead. Insubstantial revenants who straddle the line between vampire and ghost arise without warning in China and Japan. And across the world, a dead woman or a suicide re-enters her body and becomes hungry for revenge and blood.

All of these monsters require different tactics to bring down. The lore is there, but, unlike the lore on the main kinds of vampire, it is fragmentary and split between different Cainite cells. The Sources don't know as much about these monsters, either.

In the end, Cainites facing monsters like this are on their own.

Six Signs That You've Bought into the Cainite Heresy

The Cainites are extremists. You can't have it any other way. They sometimes work—secretly—alongside other hunters, but even when compared with no-compromise types like the Long Night, they're in a league apart. The Perfected affect many of the behaviors common to revolutionaries, sects and fundamentalists across the world, both sacred and secular.

None of these things are official tenets of belief. Rather, they're signs of the mindset that the Cainites promote, support and perpetuate among their members.

1. There is No Salvation Apart From Us

Either you're with us or against us. If you don't see the worth of the Cainite Heresy, you're out. Damned. One of the vampires' slaves. Whether you actually even know vampires exist or not is beside the point. Likewise, it doesn't matter if you've actually been given a chance to apprehend the tenets of the Cainite Heresy or not. You're either in or out.

It creates in them a strong desire for orthodoxy and a certain degree of paranoia. Most fundamentalist groups and extremist political groups (revolutionary Marxists, for example) believe the world is against them, no matter how powerful they are, and are quick to label members who diverge from the accepted orthodoxy as traitors, purging them through violence or social exclusion. The Cainites are different in that they have evidence that the world *really is* against them. It doesn't matter if that's a distorted view of the way things are. Monsters exist. They would kill you if they knew who you were. Or worse.

It doesn't matter that they don't know that the Cainites exist. The vampires are *there*. The Cainites have seen them and have suffered at their corpse-cold hands. No better means of ensuring the orthodoxy of the Cainite Heresy's adherents exists than a simple reminder that the monster had you once... and they can have you again. The Cainite Heresy is the only way out. It's the only solution.

2. The Outside World Is Worthless

If everyone who's Not With Us is damned, it means that nothing good can come out of the outside world. The Cainites live *in* the world, but they've seen the true masters of the world. Hence, they make a point of not being *of* the world. In a sense, they retreat into a kind of ghetto where they view the outside world's news media and events through the lens of their "secret knowledge." A government minister gets indicted for corruption and has to stand down? Vampires are behind it. The War on Terror? A vampiric plot.

No development is worthwhile, no news is good. Compromise is pointless. The only good is to be gained from destroying the thirsty dead, all of them. A group of TF:V field agents bring down a vampire overlord and call in a retrieval unit to truss him up. The vampires are in chaos, but their master, says the Cainite zealot, is still at large (the vampires control the government anyway, remember). A circle of dedicated hunters free dozens of innocents from some factory farm where they were bled to death for the sake of some lazy and greedy vampires. So what? The vampires are still out there. It doesn't matter if hunters stop a pack of werewolves from eating people: the vampires are still out there. It doesn't matter if the Malleus Maleficarum ends an alliance between a cabal of witches and a vampire court: the vampires are still there. It doesn't matter if a vampire appears to side with humanity, helps a hunter pact to depose his master and promises that he won't ever feed from the innocent. He's a vampire. He's still walking. They must be destroyed. All of them. No compromise, no mercy. It's all or nothing. There is no middle ground, no hope in small victories...

3. Compromise Is a Really Bad Thing

...which brings us to this.

The worst thing a Cainite can ever do is "compromise." It's the ultimate sin, the thin end of the little wooden wedge that props open the door to Hell. The Cainites don't work with organizations that are in cahoots with the System. Which, in their mind, is nearly everyone.

Except that they do. Cainites do stand alongside other hunters. They just don't consider themselves as part of the group. Even if they are. It's a kind of doublethink. It permits them to maintain good relationship with other hunters whom they privately consider deluded or ineffectual.

4. The Whole World Works Like We Say It Does (Even the Parts That Don't)

Like religious and political extremists of every stripe, it's the way of a Cainite to shoe-horn pretty much everything they encounter into the same narrow worldview.

The vampires control everything. Uncaring bureaucracies? Vampires. Terrorism? Vampires? Childhood obesity? Vampires. Sexism, racism and all those other -isms? Vampires. Every single time.

5. We're Working Towards Our Own Version Of The Apocalypse

In the end, the only victory the Cainites will accept as a victory is the destruction of every vampire that ever existed. Nothing less. The vampires have to cease to be. People who serve the vampires will probably die, and the witches and werewolves will have to go, but until then, the Cainite Heresy must strive for the day when the people are ready to rise up and destroy their oppressors.

After the Final Battle, it'll all be perfect. Apart from all the people who have to die.

6. If You Leave or We Kick You Out, You Never Come Back

Sometimes, a Cainite might come to the conclusion that the stalk-and-destroy-them-all ethics of the Heresy might not be the whole story, that there are other ways to pursue the eternal Vigil. A hunter who starts thinking things like that and asking questions gets kicked out. A higher-ranking Cainite tells her that she's out, no appeal, no explanation. He warns her that if she tells anyone at all, she's dead. And then the Heresy cuts her off. Any friendships she had among the Heretics are over. No one returns her calls. And at the same time, they're watching her.

And the moment they're satisfied she's betrayed them, she's marked, along with anyone she knows.

Cainites and Others

None of this precludes Cainites from working with other monster hunters, or even having them as friends. But she may not trust them, and she certainly will pause for a long time before saying who she is or revealing the magic she knows.

A Cainite in a mixed cell in London aids her friends when facing any other monster, but when it comes to vampires, she only works with them as long as they agree that the vampires have to go. She goes right over the head of colleagues who have a problem with the idea of the vampires' existence being made public. She isn't afraid to look a fool. The world has to know the truth. And her friends—who don't know who she really is—have to accept that. To be fair, they do, because she's a demon in a fight.

Another Cainite in New York works alongside a group of people who don't belong to any of the other compacts or conspiracies. They let him call the shots, and in return, he looks out for them. Some of them are potential recruits, in his eyes, but none of them are cannon fodder. He's too decent for that.

And there's the thing. For all their sometimes suicidal fanaticism, it's vital to remember that the Cainites are fighting to save the human race. If they start to lose the fact that human lives are more important than the lives of the vampires, and the reason why they're fighting in the first place, they cease to be worthwhile in the hunt.

The Cainites are well-intentioned. They're difficult to reason with, and almost as difficult to work with, but their vengeance has the added quality of a concern for humanity. Their certainty is that the vampires must be destroyed because the human race deserves more than to be prey for a monster.

Hunters

You were persecuted in your own country for your sexuality, or your religious beliefs, or your race. You came here to the West to find a better life. But the traffickers who brought you here chained you up and sold you to a factory farm, where they bled you and a hundred other people slowly to death, so they could sell the blood to the dead. One day, you found your chains loose. You escaped, and when the Cainites found the place, they found you just about to beat the owner of the place to death. They said, "Go ahead," and then they took you home.

Maybe you weren't the parent you wanted to be, but you tried. God help you, you tired. And what happened? Your son (or daughter) ran away. They left you. Went on the streets. When you finally tracked him down, he smiled with cold white fangs. He laughed at you. You showed him tough love. You weren't the only one looking for him, it turns out. They found you and told you that you could stop it happening to anybody else's children.

Your parents died. You never forgave them for that, for the childhood you had, stuck in care, shunted from one foster home to another. Except that one night, you saw your mother waiting by your kitchen window. Wearing sunglasses and a face like some vicious-looking statue. Definitely your mother. She ran away before you could bring yourself to speak or to follow. But the second time, you caught up with her, and you spoke, and you realized what she had become. She had left you to become *this*. You thrust a kitchen knife through her eye before she even knew what was happening, and beat her into dust with a frying pan when she tried to get up. Something snapped; you went looking for the monsters that made her what she was. They proved a little harder to kill, but by chance the Cainites came, and when they left, they took you with them.

The telephone rang twice: you tranced out. You read the keyword in the text message: you followed complex post-hypnotic commands. The Mistress spoke: you shivered in ecstasy. You remember the taste of her blood, the feeling of gaseous fingers groping inside your forebrain, wiping parts of your mind, re-arranging others, making you hers. They killed her. Something snapped. You became confused, lost. They took you away, locked you in a room. Flashing lights. Loud music. Shouting. Drugs. You couldn't have the blood. You must have aged ten years in a month. But the Cainites made you right in the head again. They saved you. They gave you a new name and a new master. The telephone rings twice: you trance out.

The big man vanished one night. You and the boys were going to fight it out to see who was going to get his job, when he came back... different. Pasty-skinned. Even more vicious than before. He always had extreme tastes. Now the girls who visited his crib didn't always come out alive. And if they did, they weren't looking so well. You started getting sick of being on corpse disposal duty. That wasn't part of the deal. You started having words with your homes—not all of them, the ones he hadn't forced to take a drink from him. And one night, you took him to pieces with crowbars, and went out looking for his bloodsucking buddies. You nearly got in a fight with another gang on the way. Then you realized they were out for the same kind of blood. And they had moves you were really interested in knowing.

You were the golden boy down the precinct—until you started to ask too many questions about a spate of disappearances, following a trail that led right to the door of City Hall. You can't fight City Hall, at least not when the people running the show aren't really people at all. You got stymied at every turn, but you wouldn't let it lie. In the end, they took your badge. But when you were looking for evidence, you found other people interested in fixing the inhabitants of the Council Chambers. You still can't fight City Hall. Turns out you can burn it down pretty easily, though. You're not sure about these people, but you're the subject of a statewide manhunt now, and you've got nowhere else to go.

You watched you lover disintegrate. He died, but still kept coming back. First, it was all right. Promises of staying together forever. Promises of power and love. But he was cold. And it wasn't long before he went mad, started leaving corpses around the house. You weren't a loved one, anymore. You were a victim. A grave-digger. You took the law into your own hands one day. And then you waited for the rest of them to come and get you. They didn't. Someone else did.

The other kids at the club thought the vampire thing was cool, and you did for a while, but after a while you realized that they weren't playing, and you saw them happily give themselves to… that… monster. You couldn't fight it. You would have been dead if the crazy people hadn't weighed in. Of course, now you're stuck with the crazies. And they've taught you things and showed you things that make you wish you *were* dead.

Ideologies

Cainites don't really divide up into factions as such, given how varied they are in practice. But certain ideologies appear again and again. The Cainites don't always use these labels themselves as such, even though the stereotypes hold true.

Extremists want to see the vampires destroyed *now*. The only hope for the human race's survival is a solution to humanity's vampire problem. They counsel mass destruction, hoping to make the vampires public, so that they might get the world's governments on their side. They imagine the day when the authorities will know and understand, and dream up plans for means and facilities to imprison and exterminate the undead in vast numbers.

On the other hand, **Revolutionists** take the view that the authorities and the large media outlets are hopelessly compromised, and so the mass destruction of the vampires must happen at the hands of the people. They're the ones who try to get information into mass media, out on the internet and in pamphlets handed out on street corners. Unlike the Extremists, who try to appear sensible and reasonable, Revolutionists sometimes come across as wild-eyed, fervent… and a little crazy.

Fatalists comprise the biggest number among the Cainites. They simply believe that although trying to alert authorities and people is all well and good, the only people who really have the tools at hand to defeat the monsters are the Cainites. The danger is that they sometimes have a tendency to take non-Cainite lives a little lightly. And that's a slippery slope to go down.

Status

Cainites earn Status through killing vampires, pure and simple, although a lot of that depends on the *way* a Cainite kills vampires. A Cainite who through cautious and patient planning ends a whole nest of the monsters gains more respect than a berserk fighter who gets the goods but risks his companions in the process.

• The character has been initiated into the Cainites. You can spend Merit dots on the Cainite Endowment: Rites of Denial.

••• With enough experience in the field and enough exposure to the Cainites' particular kind of magic, the character develops an almost uncanny ability to know when the monsters are near. The character develops a version of the Danger Sense Merit, which affords a +1 dice pool bonus to the usual Wits + Composure roll when vampires are directly involved, or +2 if the character already has the Merit.

••••• The character begins to receive communiqués from the Sources, and has a telephone number or mail drop in which she can drop questions. This is equivalent to a three-dot Mentor.

STEREOTYPES

Network 0: I know a man who's willing to get any visual evidence you have out on the internet. But he never does anything with my footage. That's the problem when you're facing something that doesn't show up on film. He asks too many damn questions.

The Loyalists of Thule: A friend of mine spent some time hunting with this librarian. He said the guy was really committed… but not in the right way. As if he had something to prove. Useful, but not trustworthy.

Task Force: VALKYRIE: The vampires run the government. The men in the black cars might be bringing the monsters in, but answer this: if they're so concerned about protecting the nation, why do they spend so much time covering up? Don't give me that crap about "protecting the public." They're up to something. If they really cared, they'd have made the monsters the enemy in the War on Terror.

Malleus Maleficarum: The vampires run the Catholic Church. We've known that since the beginning. The only question is: which ones? Sure, you see the Catholic witchfinders bringing down the vampires, but they seem to be strangely blind about which ones they bring in. We know the dead have factions. One of them is using the Catholics. Mark my words.

Frank Crowe understands why, in cases of abuse or difficult domestic situations, Social Service may be called in, but that doesn't mean he has to like it. It was only because he had a certain amount of clout within his department — and a talent for bullying desk-monkeys with epaulets — that they never investigated his own family life, although sometimes it got close.

Frank had, until Simon May, never met a social worker he really respected. But even May never really earned his trust. He certainly wouldn't have ever told him about how, after the Thing We Never Talk About happened, he took to the bottle. Or about how, when Bianca was eleven or twelve, how he used to hit her.

He stopped. They brushed it under the faded carpet of the Sandfields terrace. And then Pauline died, and his daughter's anger exploded. She lost the capacity for forgiveness, and he had made it so she could do nothing else.

She was her father's daughter.

⊱─━─⊰

"Do you know a Miss Bianca Crowe? In a business capacity." Frank shifts a little in the chair. "No relation," he adds.

"I'm sorry. I am simply not permitted to give out details of those with whom we deal." Mrs. McIntyre is apologetic. "It's for the protection of the children. To let you see the records... or to go through them for you is wholly out of the question."

Frank doesn't like children's homes. He doesn't like the idea of children without parents; he doesn't like to think about what happened to them before they came here. The thought of the girl he rescued three nights ago comes unbidden to his mind; he feels pangs of guilt and regret. He wonders if the Frenchman is making good on his promise to shut those places down.

This place, the children's home, was the second pointer he had been told by the voice on the phone. No indication as to why. Just the exhortation: *Go there. See what she did.*

"Well," says Frank, "Do you mind if I take a look around?"

Mrs. McIntyre, who looks more suited to the stock market floor than the management of a children's home, bites her bottom lip and seems hesitant. Frank is convinced she will say no. The intercom on her desk buzzes three times. Mrs. McIntyre stiffens. She pauses before pressing the button and saying, in an almost theatrically positive voice, "Yes, Miss Polak?"

The oddly-accented voice at the end of the line says, "I can show him around. Get someone to bring him to my office."

"Yes," says Mrs. McIntyre. Frank thinks that maybe she shudders a little, but then, in his experience, it's hardly unusual for someone in management to be scared of their subordinates. He's seen it over the years all over the place: desk officers terrified of drill sergeants, hospital registrars cowed by ward sisters, and of course — he smiles whenever he thinks of this truth — police superintendents at the mercy of detective inspectors. A certain kind of middle-manager exists who has the real balance of power in an institution. Why should this Miss Polak be any different?

But of course Frank, although blessed with a certain acuity, is often blind to the truly strange, and it is only after a nurse has come to fetch him and take him to the Night Manager's office that he thinks, *hang on — how did she know I was in here?*

⊱─━─⊰

Roxy Mitchell is about 25 and blonde and fairly pretty. Frank, in more buoyant mood, would be leering over her at this point, but he is not in a buoyant mood. And he is wondering about the Night Manager.

"Where's she from?" He says as they walk through quiet, dark corridors, passing dormitory after dormitory full of sleeping children. This particular home is an anachronism; homes like this don't really exist anymore. They like them to be smaller these days.

"Somewhere in Eastern Europe, I think. I remember she maybe said something about being from somewhere like Malkavia. Or maybe Malkovia. Something like that."

"Never heard of it."

"Me neither. But there's so many of those countries over there, right? They've probably got a Eurovision entry this year."

"Heh. Yeah. She all right?"

Mitchell goes silent, seems about to say something, and holds her tongue. "She's all right. Look, here we are."

The door to the Night Manager's office is closed; a blind covers the inside of the door's window. Mitchell knocks on the door. A heavily accented voice says, "One moment!"

"Right. This is where I leave you. Nice to meet you, Inspector." She offers a hand for him to shake.

He accepts the hand and knocks on the door. "You too, love."

And she's gone. He waits alone outside for a moment; the voice says, "Come in."

Behind the desk sits the palest, and possibly the ugliest woman Frank has ever seen. She resembles nothing more than an eel, with the forward-facing mouth full of small white teeth, the widely-spaced round watery eyes, the lank graying hair combed back over an eczematous, glistening forehead. She wears a half-unraveling grubby cardigan over a nurse's uniform that looks like it has never actually been washed. She smells of sweat and the special kind of grease that masses in unwashed hair.

"I understand you want me to show you around," she says.

"Yeah, love. I'd appreciate it."

"I am not your 'love,' Inspector."

Frank is not accustomed to apologies. He shrugs. "All right." He looks around the office, blows air through pursed lips. "So. You going to show me around, then?"

Inasmuch as Frank is able to tell from what passes for expression on that face, she is irked. Which is the idea, really.

<hr />

She is brusque with him, shows him the dormitories, into which he is not allowed to go, the playroom with the toys, the TV room, the library, the infirmary. The walls are all painted with storybook characters, with Big Bad Wolves and giants and clowns, but somehow, the place makes Frank uneasy. Frank is by no means possessed of much in the way of empathy, but even so, this place seems to him to be a sad place. It depresses him.

He says little. She shows him the infirmary.

"Wait, haven't we been here before?"

"No."

They go around the caretaker's office, and the staff room, and Nurse Mitchell waves happily at Frank, before seeing Miss Polak and lowering her hand. Then they go to the library, and the infirmary.

Frank becomes unsure that he isn't just having a case of *deja vu*. He's tired.

Eventually, Miss Polak says, "Perhaps you should come down into the basement rooms."

She shows him more rooms. Here, the murals on the walls are frightening and in places very strange. A room described to him as "the infirmary" appears to him to have the same beds, but chains and manacles attached to the walls. And yet, she is showing him these things casually, without making reference to them. She is so matter-of-fact. He would say something, if he was himself, but he's really not himself, and this very fact is apparent to him. Maybe all this is getting to him. Maybe he's going mental.

After the third room full of beds and chains, the Night Manager shows him adult rooms, well-furnished, containing personal effects, but with the kinds of doors that would suit a high-security prison. Only they bolt on the inside. Again, she makes no reference to the doors, which is wrong, and he says nothing, which is wrong... they pass a third room, and suddenly Frank stops.

On the bedside table is a photo of a little girl and a smaller boy. Frank, ignoring the Night Manager, who continues talking, walks into the room, and picks up the frame and looks at it, and suddenly something snaps, and he is himself again.

The picture is of Bianca, aged five or six, and of Gary, aged three, just before... Gary, who they never talked about after... whose (*say it*!) death made Frank something of the man he is.

The Night Manager comes into the room after Frank. "Inspector Crowe, this is a private room."

He turns on her. "You are running a prison here."

Those round fishlike eyes widen slightly. "No," she says, speaking directly for the first time. "We are running a safe refuge."

"Not for the kids. What are you doing to the kids?"

"Nothing yet." The door to the room closes of its own accord. Did she just slam it?

She advances on him. "Then what is all this? And why do you have a picture of my daughter and my... son?"

"Your daughter. Yes. I understand now."

"You know her."

"I think maybe I do. But you do not."

"What?"

"I don't think you should leave here," says Miss Polak. She is almost a head shorter than him, but suddenly she fills the room. She swats at him with a flick of the wrist and he flies over the bed with the impact. He tries to crawl away out of the room, but she kicks him in the side, just gently, and yet hard enough to make him crumple.

"I was hungry," she says.

Frank fumbles in his pockets for his gun, but he cannot find it. She leans over and picks him up by the lapels with one hand. Her teeth look very sharp. He is still fumbling in his pockets, and his right hand closes around something hard and plastic. He pulls the stun gun out and pushes it under what passes for her chin and squeezes. She jerks back. He zaps her again, and again. She begins to convulse. And another squeeze. And then Frank turns and runs, and gets almost as far as the door to the stairs before the Night Manager's hand is on his collar.

"You are nicked," she says, with venom in her voice. She lifts him off his feet and throws him across the corridor and into what seems to be a kitchen. Frank tries to get to his feet and get to the cutlery drawer, but can't; she picks him up by the shoulders and holds his face onto the hob of the cooker. Frank finds his gun, fumbles with it. Then she turns on one of the gas rings. Then she turns on the second one down. Frank cocks the gun with his thumb somehow — he's never managed to do that before — and tries to push it backwards. The next knob down turns on the one under Frank's face, the flame jets directed right in his eye. She reaches for the knob, and Frank pulls the trigger. The bullet goes through her kneecap. She yells and lets go.

He is up and out of the kitchen. She stands up. She shouldn't be able to do that. He shoots her, full in the stomach, at point blank range. She jerks backwards. But then she straightens, and starts to laugh. She is still laughing when the third bullet hits her arm; the fourth, and the last one he has, hits her so hard, she falls back over the hob.

She straightens again, but this time, Frank backs up and stares. Her cardigan is on fire, and then her uniform. She registers that she is burning, and she begins to shriek, to flail around, to smash things in a wild panic. Frank dives out of the way as she rushes out of the door and down the corridor. The flames

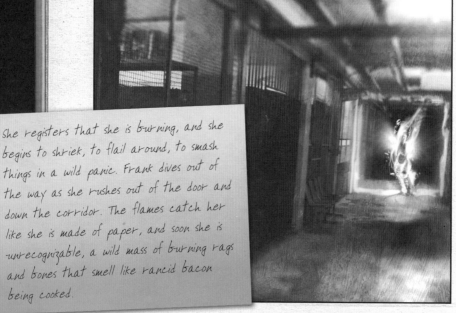

She registers that she is burning, and she begins to shriek, to flail around, to smash things in a wild panic. Frank dives out of the way as she rushes out of the door and down the corridor. The flames catch her like she is made of paper, and soon she is unrecognizable, a wild mass of burning rags and bones that smell like rancid bacon being cooked.

catch her like she is made of paper, and soon she is unrecognizable, a wild mass of burning rags and bones that smell like rancid bacon being cooked. She collapses. And the flames begin to catch the carpets.

The fire alarms go off. No sprinklers.

Frank suddenly has a thought. He rushes into one of the guest rooms and grabs a duvet. And he takes it into the kitchen and lights it. Then he puts it back on the bed. And then, before the fire in the corridor overcomes him, he is out through the stairwell door and into the upstairs corridor.

Frank runs nearly headlong into Nurse Mitchell, one of several nurses who are gathering up sleepy boys and girls and getting them to leave in an orderly fashion. "Where's Miss Polak?" she says.

"She saw the kitchen on fire. Someone had left the hob on. She went to get a fire extinguisher."

She sees the state of Frank's face and does a double take. "What happened to you?"

She doesn't get an answer. Another nurse says, "Where's Mrs. Mcintyre?"

"In her office," says another nurse.

"You get the kids out. I'll go and find her," says Frank.

He finds Mrs. Mcintyre in her office. She looks up. She has a blank, dazed expression on her face. She has her thumb pressed down on the intercom button. It's giving off a squealing noise. "She didn't stop screaming," she says.

"They're evacuating the place," says Frank. "You have to go. You have to get out of here."

"She is still screaming. Can't you hear her?"

"Love, this whole place is going to burn down."

She stares at him.

He shrugs and pulls her swivel chair out from behind the desk. She looks at him as if to say, *what are you doing?*... but she does not resist when he leans over, picks her up, and hoists her over his shoulder.

Outside, Frank stands with the nurses for a time. The building is old, and its fire precautions were inadequate.

A fireman tells one of the nurses that it likely cannot be saved.

Social Services will, inevitably, be called in and the children will gain new placements in smaller homes.

Frank wonders how many of the staff knew about what Miss Polak had in the basement. Mrs. McIntyre is staring into the middle distance, saying nothing, talking to no one. Frank wonders what sort of hold the Night Manager had on her. And he looks at the children, and sees how few of them seem upset that the home is burning down, and thinks that maybe it's for the best.

He reaches inside his pocket and pulls out the picture Bianca drew for him when she was a little girl. And he wonders what kind of princess she is now.

Frank waits for his contact in one of the cleaner and better-managed gents' public toilets, just outside Bethnal Green tube station.

Frank is fine with this: he has met people in worse places. Although now he looks at the state of his trench coat and the time of night, and looks at the CCTV camera, and thinks he's in serious danger of being pulled in for "cottaging".

He leans against the row of basins, reading the notice on the wall:

The Exclusion of Mirrors

Tower Hamlets Borough Council regrets that for reasons of public decency, the decision has been taken not to place mirrors in these public facilities. We apologize for any inconvenience this may cause.

A man in a suit comes in. Frank says, "Evening," and the man stares at him. The man eschews the urinals and goes in one of the cubicles to pee. He leaves without bothering to wash his hands, never fully taking his eyes off Frank.

"Filthy sod," says Frank.

No one else comes in. Frank gains an uncomfortable impression that the CCTV is trained directly on him.

He stands, feeling vulnerable and cold.

A woman's voice, softly spoken, correct in its accents, says, "Excuse me. Are you Frank?"

She is standing beside him.

"Jesus Christ on a pushbike!" Frank is slightly put out. "Where did you come from?"

She is a small dark-haired woman in her early thirties, dressed in a strange cross between formal and eccentric. She has an old-fashioned suit on, with a pencil skirt, but is wearing a CND badge on her lapel, and another that says "Camera Obscura." Her blouse, with the frilly collar and sleeves, doesn't match with the suit. Her skin is smooth and her green-brown eyes shine like polished buttons. Like she's a doll.

"Love, what in bloody hell are you doing in here?"

"I picked the venue. I mean, it's not really very savory, yes, but it has its advantages."

"Look. You're on film, darling. They're going to come and arrest you." He motions at the camera.

She looks up, and runs a hand over her slightly messy black hair. "Oh, that doesn't worry me too much." She looks at him, smiles, and cocks her head to one side, offers him a hand to shake. "I'm Frances. Like your name, only with an 'e' instead of an 'i.'"

"I know how to spell 'Frances,' love."

"Can I call you Francis?" She seems genuinely pleased.

"Only my mother ever called me that. And only when I was a kid."

She tosses her hair by way of a shrug. "Oh, that's understandable."

"You're Simon May's contact, then."

"Am I?" She touches her lips with the back of her hand, almost as if to check that they're still there. "I have no idea who he is."

"He said you were a friend of a friend."

"She's not strictly a friend, as such. I just owed her a favor."

"All right." Frank isn't comfortable around her.

"So what do you want to know?"

"There are people stockpiling blood. They are bleeding these poor sods to death in these factories and keeping the blood. And the same people may or may not be involved in long-term... abuse... at this home for kids. I want to know what my daughter has to do with it."

"And your daughter is..."

"Bianca Crowe."

"Blonde. Likes gold hoop ear-rings, about so high—" Frances puts her hand up at a height about four inches taller than herself. "Piercing in her top lip. Or did have, until recently. Wears a suit."

"Apart from the last thing, yeah."

Frances becomes solemn. "You know what I think?"

"What?"

"I think you should leave London. I think you should get out of here and go back to wherever it is you came from."

"Is that a threat?"

"No. Honestly, I meant it as advice."

"Are you saying my Bianca is involved in something?"

"Um, I'm not sure I can say, really."

"Fat lot of good you are."

"Look. Some of... us... think that something bad is going to happen. And some are trying to find ways to sit it out."

"I don't understand."

"No. I didn't think you would."

"Are you patronizing me, love?" Frank is beginning to get annoyed.

"No. No, I'm not. Look. I'm sorry. This really isn't working out the way it's supposed to."

"Yeah. I got that." Frank turns to leave.

"Listen. How much do you want to find your daughter?"

"Don't be ridiculous. It's the whole reason I'm here."

"I know where she... is staying."

"You got an address?"

"Yes. But you have to promise."

"Promise what?"

"Don't mention me. If she found out I told you where she was, I'd be in deep trouble."

"I don't see what she could do to you."

"It'd be pretty permanent, I think."

He scoffs, but he says he won't tell. She gives him an ad-dress in East Ham. She tells him it's actually Wayne Thomas' house, but that Bianca stays there all the time these days. She has a pen and notebook handy and writes it down for him. She hands it to him, and looks down, and looks up, and she has vanished.

<hr>

When Frank gets back to the guest house, he finds Mr. Thélème sitting on his bed.

"I call that a fucking liberty," says Frank, throwing his coat onto the bed next to the old man.

Mr. Thélème has seen better days. He has a black eye; three fingers of his left hand are in bandages. A long cut runs down the side of his face and down his neck.

"You cut yourself shaving or something?"

"I had a little bit of trouble. How about you?"

"I've had a better couple of days. Or nights, maybe. I think I barely seen any daylight since last week."

"That is something of an occupational hazard, I think."

"In what sort of occupation? Police work?"

"If you want to call it that."

"So what you doing here, Pierre?"

"I wondered if you might be interested in my findings."

"Might be. What you got?"

"You are skeptical of the existence of vampires, *hein?*"

"You could say that."

"And yet you've faced at least one already."

"How do you work that out?" Frank takes his shirt off and throws it on the floor. He looks at the bruises he sustained."

"In the orphanage, last night."

"How do you know I was in the orphanage?"

"I have my own contacts. Hmm, it looks like you have had some difficulties yourself."

"Nothing I couldn't beat the shit out of. No vampires, though. I think I would have noticed."

"So. What *did* you see there?"

"It amounted to the same thing as the farm. They were getting ready to chain up kids and do things. I don't know, torture them. It was fucking evil. I'm glad I burnt the place down."

"Would you say it was a hideout of some kind?"

"Yeah. I think that's what the mad bint in the home said. Something like that."

"So. We have a place to hide, and we have a source of a stockpile. And we have evidence that there is a force of which our vampires are frightened."

"It don't make any sense."

"It only makes sense if you accept that they are vampires."

"For the last time, there is no such fucking thing as a vampire. There's got to be a sane explanation."

"They are a cult of cannibals or blood-drinking socio-paths, perhaps, who, with the inevitable self-importance of the sect, fear that the police will swoop upon them, and so have arranged to hide themselves away, with children to eat and torture and refrigerated blood to drink."

Frank undoes his belt and takes off his trousers. He stands in front of Mr. Thélème in his boxers. "I'm having a shower," he says. "I want you gone when I get back, sunshine."

"I will. But before you go," says Mr. Thélème, "can I ask you one thing?"

"You can ask."

"Did the accounts you took from the farm — or any of your other investigations — lead you to any names? Do you have any leads?"

"No. Now fuck off."

Mr. Thélème is good for his word. When Frank comes out of the shower, he's gone, leaving no trace that he was ever there.

The vampire hunter has many tools: stakes, hammers, rope, a can of gasoline. The hunters of the conspiracies have their own unique implements in this war: entreaties to dead saints, demonic prayers, strange grafts, and so forth. But the vampire is not without tricks and toys—she can twist minds, heal the worst wounds in moments, even turn to a carpet of mist that slides under a hunter's door whilst he sleeps. Both sides are armed, but the vampires' weapons are alien and eternal.

New Tactics

Hunters at any level can learn and design Tactics to improve their effectiveness in the Vigil. Vampires have several unique advantages and weaknesses and wise hunters have deduced a number of ways to avoid and exploit this uniqueness, respectively. Below are just a few examples of the tricks hunters employ to turn the long battle for the night to their favor.

Arson

Prerequisites: *All:* Larceny 2, Science 1, Survival 1, and Composure 2.

Requires: 2 to 5 (-1 for every person above 5)

Dice Pool: *Primary:* Wits + Larceny; *Secondary:* Intelligence + Larceny

Action: Instant

Description: Fire can seem alive. It breathes, feeds, moves, grows, reproduces; possessing many of the signs of life. Like any wild and dangerous animal, if it can be properly tamed it can be used. One of the most vulgar expressions of fire's vast utility is, of course, arson. A cell can find a hundred ways to exploit this Tactic for use in the Vigil. Destruction of evidence, distracting authorities, smoking out the enemy, insurance fraud, etc. Considering vampires have a downright supernatural fear of the stuff, its relevance against their kind is a no-brainer.

True arson is far more than starting a fire and letting it burn—any "professional" arsonist knows that. Arson cares for the fire; feeds it, leads it and encourages it along its way all while covering the arsonist's tracks. The cell as secondary actors take care of the path, spreading tinder and accelerant as needed. Subtlety and plausibility are the watchwords of a good burn job, and the cell should focus on arranging the existing environment more than spreading some wood chips, upending a gas can and running off into the night. Tipping a bookcase over the couch, to lead to the drapes in the kitchen near where some stray grease from the oven awaits, etc., helps paint a better scene when and if curious investigators come through.

Caleb, those people back there, they wasn't normal. Normal folks, they don't spit out bullets when you shoot 'em. No sir.
—Loy Colton, Near Dark

The primary actor's job is to find the best place to start the blaze, making a nest for the fire to be born while waiting for his cellmates to clear the area. He gives the flame its first spark of life and gets the hell out of there before the whole place goes up. Multiple primary actors (from multiple cells) could amplify the effects by starting multiple fires if the fire is meant to spread through a lot of stories in not a lot of time. The cell's efforts will necessarily draw attention unless they've greased a few palms or targeted a remote enough location that no one is likely to report the burning in time.

Depending on the cell's desired effect, the authorities might finish the job for them. The resultant water damage can be just as destructive to materials, structures or evidence; and the concurrent investigation might require a vampire tenant to abandon the site for fear of discovery regardless of the damage done to the publicly accessible portions to their den.

More advanced cells might add a postscript to this Tactic that involves setting fire to a suspected vampire den under a noonday sun, leaving the monster no respite. This method is imperfect however, as the cell runs a much greater risk of immediate response from the local fire department during daylight hours (unless the cell was counting on the speedy response per the above). Another variation popular among military types turns the night back to their advantage and involves setting up snipers outside the burning nest, shooting anything that comes out screaming. The bullets might not kill them, but might severely hamper the desperate monsters' attempts to escape their fiery doom.

Organizations: The Union often have the tools, access and know-how to get rid of unwanted neighbors or potential nests that are in need of some urban renewal. Task Force: VALKYRIE agents are no strangers to cover-ups.

Potential Modifiers: Accelerants (+1 to +3), Old building (+2), Wooden frame (+1), Masonry structure (-2), Stone structure (-3).

Roll Results

Dramatic Failure: Some simple miscalculation causes a misfire: the fire-starter burns herself in the process taking 2 lethal damage. The fire flares out before it can start.

Failure: The materials are spread too thin or the kindling suffers an early break. If the fire starts at all, it extinguishes itself almost immediately.

Success: The fire is set and the area is sure to be destroyed as desired while leaving no traceable evidence back to the cell. The fire begins as the Size (1) and Heat (+1) of a Torch. Every five turns, the fire goes up anoth-er level of both Size and Heat, to a maximum of Inferno (3) and Bunsen Burner (+2). If it reaches that point, the fire becomes very difficult to stop: assume that it burns despite the best efforts to put it out. Firefighters will need at least one hour to put out the conflagration.

Exceptional Success: The Arson is swift and unmerciful. The fire grows to the Heat of a Chemical fire (+3) and will take two hours to extinguish—though it will likely burn one or several buildings to the ground before that occurs (and the fire naturally burns itself out).

To Purchase: 16 Practical Experience; 13 for the Union; 11 for Task Force VALKYRIE.

Battle Hardening

Prerequisites: *All*: Athletics 2, Stamina 2; *Partial (1)*: Stamina 3, Expression 2 (secondary actor)

Requires: 2 or more

Dice Pool: *Primary*: Stamina + Athletics; *Secondary*: Stamina + Expression.

Action: Instant (roll made at end of five-day regimen)

Description: The Vigil is a physically exhausting commitment that exacts a demanding price and gives nothing in return. A body in motion tends to stay in motion and a healthy body tends to stay healthy. Hunters as a rule should try to stay in shape, but working out and Battle Hardening are as dissimilar as running is to jumping. An individual can be bulging with muscle but still get winded from a 100-yard sprint or tear a muscle and put themselves in traction for weeks due to lack of proper preparation.

Battle Hardening is about strengthening a cell's constitution in order to reduce fatigue and decrease valuable recovery time away from the hunt. With a steady and daily routine of stretching, intense cardiovascular exercise and pushing the body beyond what each individual believe themselves capable of, the cell becomes limber and ready to face the intense physical demands the Vigil can place on a body. Especially when facing off with the preternatural physicality of vampires and myriad other monsters they face.

This Tactic behaves slightly differently than normal and involves one secondary actor working as instructor, pushing the cell to commit to the daily regimen. There's usually only one or two secondary actors—the rest are all primary actors, and gain bonus dice in the normal way. The more effective the instructor (secondary), the more those working the regimen (primary) get from the Tactic. The instructor performs the regiment with the rest of the cell—this is important if she wants to gain some benefit from the exercise.

This Tactic is only complete when the cell commits to one hour's worth of training for five days in a row. The rolls to work this Tactic are made at the *end* of the five day period; those hunters unable to commit to this regimen for that long fail to gain any benefit from this Tactic.

Some examples of appropriate exercise include wind sprints, "Hit Its," bicycle sit-ups, lunges, and other exercises where the rigors of the activity apply directly to one's Stamina—the goal is the loosening of muscle groups rather than tightening them through feats of Strength.

Organizations: The hunters of the Ashwood Abbey may come off as spoiled hedonists, but they are perhaps the most physical of the compacts and desire to maintain their physique and edge over their prey as much as—if not more than—anyone. The Ascending Ones need to maintain exceptional mental and physical acumen to keep their bodies pure (the body is a temple, after all) and able to transmute the toxic substances they consume.

Potential Modifiers: No stretching (-2); distractions (-2); participant is wounded (-1); performed stretching beforehand (+1).

Roll Results

Dramatic Failure: The participant pushes himself too hard and strains a muscle. The hunter suffers a -1 penalty on all Physical actions for the following 24 hours.

Failure: The participant never gets into a rhythm, or might "cheat" her way through the exercises. She gains no benefit from the Tactic.

Success: Successfully maintaining the Battle Hardening over the five day period grants the following results for the five-day period *after* the initial five-day Battle Hardening technique is complete:

• The primary actors gain bonus dice on any Stamina rolls or calculations involving deprivation, disease, fatigue, or temperature extremes. The bonus is equal to successes rolled in the Tactic. The secondary actor only gains +1 to these rolls regardless of how successful she was at this Tactic.

• The primary actors gain +3 to their Stamina scores in regards to calculating how long the hunters can hold their breath (see "Holding Breath," p. 49 of **World of Darkness Rulebook**). The secondary actor only gains +1 to this calculation.

• Primary actors gain +1 to Initiative.

• Primary actors all heal bashing damage more swiftly: one point per 10 minutes of time.

Exceptional Success: Successful primary actors gain +5 to the calculations for holding breath and +2 to Initiative.

To Purchase: 14 Practical Experience; 11 for the Ashwood Abbey; 9 for the Ascending Ones.

Cauterize

Prerequisites: *All:* Brawl 2, Dexterity 2, Medicine 1. *Partial (1):* Weaponry 2, Crafts 1, Wits 3 (primary actor).

Requires: 3 to 6 (-1 to the primary actor's dice pool per member over 6)

Dice Pool: *Primary:* Intelligence + Weaponry. *Secondary:* Strength + Brawl (grapple)

Action: Instant

Description: Vampires can heal the most grievously crippling wounds in minutes, sometimes *seconds*. Open a bloodsucker up and a hunter can watch the beast mend itself right back to good-as-godforsaken-new. They're a hard enough breed to hurt in the first place and watching one stitch itself up with a smile is demoralizing to even the best hunters who take up the Vigil. So it should come as no surprise this Tactic spikes in popularity every couple of years. It's not uncommon to hear some vets swear by a hot iron or acetylene torch among their checklists of absolutely required field gear when facing down a nest of fangs or other similarly regenerative monsters.

The goal is to leave the critter with a memento of the hunters' efforts: a wound that acts as an ugly reminder of the fight for nights on after (maybe even weeks if it's a particularly good one). If the cell is prepared and practiced with the Cauterize Tactic they must be ready to go at any time. This proves necessary for success since the window in which the need for Cauterize opens and closes can be minimal. Everyone must be prepared to play any part if needed at a moment's notice. The starter gun, so to speak, is whenever any member of the cell manages to cut a good chunk out of—or off of—the monster.

The primary actor needs to already be prepared or waste precious seconds—even minutes— getting ready, by which time it might be too late. If done properly, it should take no more than a turn to initiate the Cauterize Tactic. The primary actor opts to go last in initiative order if he isn't already or he'll end up going next turn (and a lot can happen between now and then). As many secondary actors as are available attempt to grapple the creature and hold it still while the primary actor sears, brands, or otherwise aggravates the wound. If using open flame, the primary actor would be wise to avoid letting the creature see it or it might lose control in blind panic (see "Frenzy," p. 163).

How to perform the cauterizing is another matter but where there is a will there's a way, and hunters have devised all sorts of interesting methods of getting flesh to quickly sear. Road flare, battery powered curling iron, clothes iron, heated fireplace poker, acetylene torch, lye (and select other flameless chemicals), electric brand, rewired electric bread knife, heating coil stripped from an area heater... all are methods reportedly used to great effect by cells over the years. Rumors persist that holy water, salt, or garlic might work depending on local tradition. Few hunters want to be the first one to try such an unproven method however, and there are no documented successes on record using such materials.

Organizations: An undetermined number of Long Night cells have started reportedly branding monsters' wounds with holy symbols and words, slowing the healing process with God's wrath. No more will they spring back from injury with the help of Satan and the spoils of the innocent. Equally and oppositely, many among the Lucifuge have the ability to summon Balefire and thus always have a form of brand at the ready.

Potential Modifiers: Turns passed since initial wound was caused (-1 per turn); the wound is a severed limb (+2).

Roll Results

Dramatic Failure: The hunter gets overconfident and falls right into the monster's hands. (And hey, now the creature probably has a hostage!) The Tactic ends.

Failure: Either the device isn't hot enough yet, the participants can't keep a good enough hold, or the hunter simply misses the target. No wounds are taken and the creature has another round to heal itself.

Success: The cell causes the creature a single point of aggravated damage; the creature may not heal any *other* levels of Health lost (or regrow a lost limb) until that point of aggravated damage heals. Additionally, the searing pain causes the vampire a -1 penalty to all her actions until that point of aggravated damage is healed.

Exceptional Success: The hunter is able to lean in, burning deeper into the flesh and meat of the wound, adding another aggravated damage. The creature must now heal both before healing other damage or discarding the -1 penalty.

To Purchase: 15 Practical Experience; 12 for the Long Night; 10 for the Lucifuge.

Eviscerate

Prerequisites: *All:* Brawl 2, Dexterity 2, Wits 2. *Partial (1):* Weaponry 2, Survival 1 (primary actor).

Requires: 3 to 6 (-1 to the primary actor's dice pool per member over 6)

Dice Pool: *Primary:* Dexterity + Weaponry. *Secondary:* Dexterity + Subterfuge

Action: Instant

Description: Vampires need blood to animate their bodies, fuel their powers, and heal their wounds. The Eviscerate Tactic hopes to cost them in that regard by spilling more blood than the creature stands to lose. The cell rushes the monster from all directions, feinting and trying to goad the creature into overextending itself and leave its belly exposed. Once it does so, the primary actor exploits the gap and opens up the creature's breadbasket. The damage tends to be less severe but the enemy's spoiled resources more than make up for it.

The primary actor opts to go last in Initiative order if he isn't already or he'll end up going next turn where the situation might be different. The secondary actors use their Initiative to make runs at the vampire from all sides, one by one. Their make their rolls exactly as if making a normal attack roll, including subtracting the creature's Defense normally; however, no damage will be dealt as no actual attack is made. The trick for the secondary actors is to get close enough to provoke the creature to defend against her or reach out for her in counterattack but pull back at the last second. Once the vampire has been run out from all directions, it will be left overextended and turned away from the primary actor, exposing the flank or midriff. Now the primary actor steps in and opens the creature up like a bag of soup, ideally spilling its precious lifeblood out over the floor beyond its means.

Organization: Loyalists of Thule are not the type to directly confront their foes, but when they do, they like to make sure to strike where it counts. The Cheiron Group needs harvestable parts, and for that they need whole, fresh bodies. With the Eviscerate Tactic the Field Agent hopes to send the critter back to the lab coats in one piece.

Potential Modifiers: Vampire has low Wits of one or two dots (+2); Vampire in frenzy (-3)

Roll Results

Dramatic Failure: The hunter trips over her own feet and into the waiting arms of the monster. The Tactic is over immediately until the hunters can rescue their cellmate and regroup.

Failure: The participant follows too closely to the previous hunter's path, failing to confuse or overextend the vampire at all. The hunter contributes a -1 penalty to the primary actor's net pool.

Success: The hunter manages to cleave into the monster's belly or side, opening it up and causing massive blood loss. Successes are halved (rounded up) and applied to the opponent as lethal damage

and Willpower loss. Any significant reduction in Willpower (especially reducing the creature to none at all) may cause the creature to check for frenzy (see "Frenzy," p. 163). If the creature has a Health track full of lethal damage and is reduced to Willpower 0, the vampire likely enters the deathless sleep of torpor (see "Torpor," p. 164).

Exceptional Success: Beyond the extra successes and attendant damage, if the creature's Willpower is reduced to 0 it immediately falls into torpor regardless of how much lethal damage the beast has suffered.

To Purchase: 16 Practical Experience; 13 for the Loyalists of Thule; 11 for the Ascending Ones.

Helter Skelter

Prerequisites: *All:* Resolve or Composure 2, Stealth 1, Intimidation 1. *Partial (1):* Brawl or Weaponry 2 (primary actor).

Requires: 3 to 8 (-1 to the primary actor's dice pool per member over 8)

Dice Pool: *Primary:* Strength + Brawl or Weaponry. *Secondary:* Dexterity + Expression

Action: Instant

Description: Vampires are predatory creatures with every possible advantage on their side. Supernaturally strong, fast, and enduring, vampires don't tire, bleed, or even bruise, and they have little reason to hold back for fear of long-term injury or death. To enter into the arena with one or challenge it to fair fight would be dangerous at best and probably suicidal. This is why smart cells who want to stay in the Vigil longer than their first night throw all sense of fairness out the window. (Some hunters like to be honorable and "play fair." Those hunters usually get dead. After all, is it fair that vampires drink blood, turn into mist, and command swarms of rats? Didn't think so.) Luckily, vampires have several natural aversions that can be exploited to try and balance the scales—even if only a little.

This Tactic when performed correctly involves the primary actor squaring off *mano e mano* with a vampire while the rest of the cell clamors and creates as much distraction as possible. Waving flashlights, torches, strobes, flashbulbs or even glow sticks; while clanging on pipes, screaming, singing hymns, chanting, and cat-calling. All in a prolonged effort designed to keep the creature from being able to focus on its foe. Vampires are creatures of the night and shrink instinctually from fire. Drawing from this instinct, strobing lights and other bright sources of illumination tend to make them just as twitchy. Beyond the base distraction of the noises created by the cell, vampires often seem possessed of supernaturally-enhanced senses and this Tactic could be agitating or even painful.

A major caveat in using this Tactic is that vampires are quite prone to going into a state of mindless rage (see "Frenzy," p.163) when hungry, agitated, or actively afraid. That has its advantages but presents an extraordinary risk. To be successful with this Tactic the secondary actors are looking to distract the opponent while the primary actor fights it, not enrage it. The cell has to keep their presence a nuisance while remaining non-threatening. Wagging a torch nearby is enough to keep the creature's attention. To approach or try and do too much and suddenly you're going to need a whole other Tactic to get away from the rampaging beast.

To achieve the best results, the cell would want to choose the place and time, leading the creature into an ambush. However, if the cell is minimally prepared with a couple lighters, halogen flashlights, and a shrill rape whistle, they could perform this Tactic anywhere, anytime.

Organizations: The Long Night liken this Tactic to the story of David and Goliath and chose a champion among them to confront the beast, and the congregation circle around it singing hymns, praying loudly, and passing candles and torches around. The Ascending Ones call this Tactic the Rising Sun (in reference to an attack coming from the east at dawn to blind an opposing army).

Potential Modifiers: Target has the Meditative Mind Merit (-3); creature has some other method of heightened sense (smell/ESP) (-2); cell forced to improvise (-1); using real fire (+1); target has the Enhanced Senses Dread Power (+2), hunters have surprise (+2); near dawn (+3); hunters possess fire of 2 Size or +2 Heat (+3)

Roll Results

Dramatic Failure: The hunter gets too anxious and too close. The monster immediately frenzies and a secondary actor becomes the first target.

Failure: The vampire could care less about the hunter's effort. He is nothing more than a buzzing insect in the ear of a giant.

Success: The secondary actors' successes are pooled, and the players determine how to distribute those successes. Successes can go toward the following:

• Toward the primary actor's attack roll as dice (per normal Teamwork action).

• Toward the primary actor's Defense score.

• Toward reducing the vampire's Defense, Initiative or Speed.

Example: Gwendolyn, Eamon and Angus are the secondary actors and roll a total of four successes between them. They give Kamaria (the primary actor) one bonus die. They add one to her Defense. They subtract one from the vampire's Defense score, and one from the vampire's Initiative score; thus, they 'spent' all four of their successes. (They could have just as easily reduced the vampire's Initiative by four or given the primary actor four dice to his attack roll.)

These bonuses count in the same turn (or if the vampire has already gone this turn, during the vampire's next action). The cell can continue to use this Tactic turn after turn, but doing so necessitates re-rolling the Tactic's action (and redistributing successes where desired).

Exceptional Success: The creature is temporarily blinded and teeters on the verge of panic. Any failure in the following round of combat on the part of the opponent counts as a Dramatic Failure.

To Purchase: 14 Practical Experience; 11 for the Long Night; 9 for the Ascending Ones.

Invisible Fence

Prerequisites: *All:* Investigation 2, Wits 2, Composure 2. *Partial (1):* Weaponry 2 or Firearms 3 (primary actor).

Requires: 5 (-1 per hunter under 5)

Dice Pool: *Primary:* Wits + Composure (or other as described below) *Secondary:* Wits + Investigation

Action: Contested (Wits + Stealth)

Description: A classic image in folklore involves vampires disappearing before the eyes of their pursuers. This ability has been confirmed in vampires and other supernatural critters by hunters all over the world. Knowing it can happen and seeing it for the first time are two completely different things, however. With regular drilling and practice any hunter, even the newly uninitiated can be taught the best way to respond through the Invisible Fence Tactic.

When and if a vampire disappears from the hunters' view, the cell immediately circles the area in which the creature disappeared. The cell establishes a perimeter with the primary actor in the circle, presumably with the vampire if the response time was quick enough. Circling is the easy part; the primary actor still has to find the creature and rob it of its advantage as quickly as possible. In the past, secondary actors would tighten the circle with the hopes of herding the creature toward their teammate, a method which got a lot of good people killed. Learning from experience, anymore secondary actors contribute by keeping their distance, kicking up dust, shining flashlights—or even better, laser pointers—through the circumference of their circle looking for broken beams and other anomalous refractions. Pinpointed or pigeon-holed, the primary actor's job is to attempt to pinpoint the creature so it can be handled in some fashion. Some highly trained personnel might trust their aim with a firearm to do the job but that is something the cell will want to be comfortable with beforehand. Any option is a controlled risk.

It should be noted, the ball is firmly in the primary actor's court and it's up to him what to do with the vampire once he thinks he's pinpointed it (and provided it stands pat). Once revealed, for instance, the cell can easily segue into another Tactic such as Helter Skelter or Tar and Feather. If the cell intended the vampire no harm in the first place, they might try and talk it back into the light now that they've evidenced they're not a couple of rubes or fang-chasers. Any number of solutions make themselves available and creative cells should be able to find ways to turn the situation to their advantage.

Organizations: The intellectuals of Null Mysteriis know that there is no such thing as true invisibility—it's a trick of the light or perhaps some form of advanced hypnotism. Whatever it turns out to be, the creature is still very much in the room. VALKYRIE squads drill for these situations enough to break swiftly into formation once a creature goes "dark."

Potential Modifiers: Small room, less than 20 square feet (+3), medium room, less than 100 square feet (+1); large room more than 100 square feet (-1); dusty (+1); brightly lit (-2); wide open area (-3)

Roll Results

Dramatic Failure: While trying to establish the perimeter, the hunter trips over her own cellmate, leaving an open opportunity for the creature to make a clean break.

Failure: The hunter doesn't properly cover her area and contributes -1 to the overall result.

Success: The primary actor thinks he knows where the creature is—perhaps he spots the dust patterns changing in such a way or sees the laser pointers refracting. He immediately alerts his cellmates. Any attempts by the creature to escape the hunters' "invisible fence" suffer a -3 dice penalty.

Exceptional Success: The primary actor gains +1 to any attacks made against the creature, even while it remains "unseen," provided it's successfully corralled with Invisible Fence.

To Purchase: 16 Practical Experience; 13 for Null Mysteriis; 11 for Task Force: VALKYRIE

Lobby

Prerequisites: *All:* Manipulation 2, Politics 1, Socialize 2, Expression 1; *Partial (1):* Politics 2 (primary actor); *Partial (2):* Persuasion 2 (secondary actors)

Requires: 4 or more (-1 to all pools per member under 4)

Dice Pool: *Primary:* Manipulation + Politics; *Secondary:* Charisma + Persuasion

Action: *Primary:* Instant; *Secondary:* Extended (no target successes necessary, the secondary actors may continue to accumulate success to add to the primary actor's roll; each secondary actor roll is equivalent to one week's worth of work).

Description: Some vampires nestle within the dark and terrible heart of politics. Such creatures are without a doubt the most populous monster at this stratum in society (short of the politicians themselves). Feeding, gaining influence, and pulling strings in the highest halls of government all are part of the vampire's wheelhouse. Behind the scenes they sit, fat and bloated, spending their eternal nights greasing palms, twisting minds, and redirecting funds. The names might never appear in the newspaper, but true to parasitic form they lurk just under the skin. The common man can feel powerless enough against Big Government without the added treachery of the forces of darkness. Hunters face the latter as a matter of course, but earnest cells find a way to bring the Vigil to those leeches suckling at the marrow of government, business and high society.

Lobbying is a concerted effort to influence public policy or authorities in a way that stirs them to act against the interests of a vampire (or the creature's whole accursed society). The scope of this Tactic affects local level (townships, boroughs, and city) politics only as the theater for most games. The Lobby Tactic is slightly more mutable than the muscle memory response or a Tactic like Hamstring or Staking, and as a result may take myriad shapes. Directly contacting local representatives, public demonstrations, "donations" (i.e. bribery), grassroots campaigns and petitions to rally the voting citizenry are all valid methods.

Secondary actors get out among the constituency and try to get their issue into public opinion and get people talking about it. Going from door to door, getting signatures on petitions, calling neighborhood meetings, organizing letter writing campaigns or simply bringing it up in conversation as often as they can. With the word out in the street the primary actor makes the effort to bring the issue directly to their local representative or office, hopefully with the weight of the community behind her.

Organizations: The Union hunters are often subtle masters of the grassroots campaign. With their feet planted firmly in the community their voices carries farther and clearer than that of some fat cat politician. The Malleus Maleficarum are no stranger to the halls of power and red tape (the Catholic Church is arguably one of the oldest and most tangled bureaucracies, after all); with one of the largest social networks in the world they're rarely at a loss for signatures, too.

Potential Modifiers: Bribery (+1 to +3 per point of Resources invested); vampire is heavily entrenched in the community (-1 to -5 depending on how severe—and how *many* vampires are so embedded)

Roll Results

Dramatic Failure: The supernatural forces are made aware of the cell's attempt to rally the people and effect policy against them. The cell draws some unwanted attention and makes a permanent enemy if they hadn't already. They also suffer -1 to all Social rolls made to affect community members for the next month.

Failure: The cell was outbid, a few signatures short or in all ways too late. The money is spent and the time is invested, but the effort fails to have any effect on policy.

Success: The cell finds sympathetic ears within the community and inspires them to action. The collective efforts pay off and influence local business, culture and government in a way that directly benefits the cell and their community or goes against a vampire's wishes. The following results occur:

- The hunters gain +1 to all Social rolls made within the community for one week.

- The vampire loses a dot of Allies, Contacts or Status. (Note that hunters may continue to apply this Tactic week after week, damaging the vampire's Status.) The vampire has lost face within his society, and his power lessens.

- As a result of diminished influence, the vampire also suffers -1 to all Social rolls made regarding human members of the local community.

- The Storyteller should be encouraged to come up with other, perhaps more abstract benefits—is there now a new streetlight hanging over the vampire's once-dark feeding grounds? Does the local homeless shelter now have a couple security guards? Is the defunct park and playground (where all the vampire's addicts gather, waiting for a taste) now revived and once more made friendly to the citizens? The vampire's interests can be damaged in a way that affects the story and creates conflict, but doesn't only need to rely on mechanical effects.

Exceptional Success: The bill or motion sails through with overwhelming public support. The primary actor gains a dot in Status (Local Politics).

To Purchase: 16 Practical Experience, 13 for the Union, 11 for the Malleus Maleficarum.

Stalking Horse

Prerequisites: *All:* Socialize 2, Streetwise 1, Persuasion 1; *Partial (1):* Subterfuge 2, Expression 1 (primary actor); *Partial (2):* Stealth 1, Investigation 2 (secondary actors).

Requires: 2 or more (-1 for every member below 4)

Dice Pool: *Primary:* Dexterity + Subterfuge *Secondary:* Presence + Socialize

Action: Instant

Description: Vampires are social parasites. No other monster *needs* people nearly as much as they do. Sometimes, the best place to encounter them is out in the public where there exists the potential for a lot of eyes watching or innocents near. However to be truly proactive in the Vigil, one has to hunt them on their own feeding grounds.

Once, bird hunters noticed that their prey, while easily spooked by the presence of man, seemed otherwise indifferent to the presence of other non-predatory animals. By using their riding horses for cover, hunters found themselves able to get much closer to their prey, none the wiser for their presence.

Like any predator, most vampires look for the easiest prey, not one who's going to put up much of a struggle. This scratches battle-ready hunters right off the list. However, like with the titular Stalking Horse, the hunters might themselves able to get in better position with the right cover. The method to this madness relies on the primary actor's ability to put on all appearance of being alone, available, and acting from a position of weakness (drunk, lusty, ostracized, sickly, or some other vulnerable state). Meanwhile, the secondary actors engage any other targets likely to draw predatory attention, or move to intercept anyone else attracted to the lone figure that is their cellmate. In this way, the group herds the vampire unwittingly to the target of their choice.

The secondary actors make their rolls and add any successes to the primary actor's attempt to call attention to herself. Once the vampire is successfully on the hook, he will either lead the presumed "victim" to a more private place or the hunter can separate herself from the herd, hoping that the fang will follow. Either way, the rest of the cell excuse themselves and follow along to close the trap.

Success on this Tactic successfully isolates the creature (whether in an alley, a closed-off restroom, or wherever it is that the hunter leads the vampire). They've also cornered a very dangerous predator away from any likely witnesses. The results of this isolation are up to the individual cell. While the Ashwood Ab-

bey might delight in abducting the creature or abusing it right there in an alleyway, the Null Mysteriis might enjoy the chance to interview the creature in exchange for some of the blood it claims to need. In either situation, the group should keep itself girded for trouble or at least aware of how quickly they can get back into the public eye.

Organizations: It is said the Ashwood Abbey has refined and perfected this Tactic while hunting within their vast social networks. The widespread members of the Lucifuge often find themselves in a position to hunt the hunters in their own territories (although they call this Tactic "Judas Goat").

Potential Modifiers: Hunters know the vampire's feeding preferences and attempt to mimic those preferences (+3); the primary actor is bleeding (+2); hunters are improperly dressed (-2); hunters know nothing about the vampire in question (-3)

Roll Results

Dramatic Failure: Somehow, the primary actor exposes his intentions (or has them exposed by the secondary actors). The vampire now knows a game is going on, and can either escape... or play the game and maneuver the hunters the way *she* wants.

Failure: The primary actor doesn't put off the right vibe of desperation and isolation and fails to draw any attention to herself.

Success: The hunter throws off just the right amount of isolation and weakness to attract their social predator and may lead him or wait to be led depending on what the cell has in mind. In a combat situation, the vampire has no inclination what is coming and may not roll to detect surprise.

Exceptional Success: The tables are so effectively turned, the vampire loses her Defense for the first two turns of combat.

To Purchase: 14 Practical Experience; 11 for the Ashwood Abbey; 9 for the Lucifuge

Stakeout

Prerequisites: *All*: Composure or Resolve 2, Wits 1, Investigation 1, Stealth 1, Streetwise 1; *Partial (1)*: Larceny 1 (primary actor); *Partial (1)*: Investigation 2 (secondary actor)

Requires: 3 or more (for every hunter above 5, the cell suffers a cumulative -1 penalty to any Stealth rolls requires to remain inconspicuous)

Dice Pool: *Primary*: Wits + Intelligence; *Secondary*: Wits + Investigation

Action: *Primary*: Instant; *Secondary*: Extended (players can continue to roll and accumulate successes as long as they choose, though extended stakeouts run a higher risk of detection; each roll is equivalent to one 24-hour period)

Description: A vampire den, a museum filled with forgotten Relics, a ship-yard expecting a mysterious shipment, an airbase in the middle of the desert that isn't nearly as abandoned as reported. The World of Darkness is full of places that a hunter cell would want to get in without an invitation. Stake Out is the smartest way toward getting it done. This Tactic, strictly translated involves positioning multiple hunters around the location in rotating shifts to observe the location at all times of the day. Once a requisite amount of observation has been catalogued, the cell uses this pooled information to create a map not only of the location, but of the various schedules, foot traffic, and average daily activity of the locale.

The secondary actors station themselves around the target and surrounding area and take notes about what they see and when. If possible, at least one member of the Tactic will want to get as far inside the location as she can, whether it's a public place with operating hours, a tour, or a quick scam that lets a hunter in to "check the pipes."

Once successfully stationed and inconspicuous (a Storyteller may necessitate Stealth rolls to remain concealed; if the hunters are discovered, the Tactic ends), the secondary actors begin taking their notes. By taking shifts and different vantages, the cell will be able to conjure a working model of the local security force and what to expect once inside. These observations are looking for more than when a store closes, how many windows are on the second floor or how many employees man the front desk. The cell wants to take note of patterns in foot and vehicle traffic around the location, guard rotations, idiosyncrasy in building designs, and a dozen other inconspicuous items that might come in handy.

Note that all secondary actors do not need to be present for every hour of every day—but the cell needs to rotate and keep at least one secondary actor "on duty" at a time. Many cells may take up to a week or so to properly "stakeout" a location, but the Storyteller should note that every night beyond the first that the cell stakes out a location they suffer a -1 to any Stealth rolls made to remain inconspicuous (that van that sits there for several days is going to start drawing some attention).

The primary actor takes the accumulated information and puts it to practical use. The hunter might draw up a map or refer to blueprints. He might take notes and construct some kind of plan out of what the secondary actors have witnessed. And then he'll take that plan and likely put it into action—whether the objective is to steal an artifact, set a fire, or let the rest of the cell inside, the hunter hopes to have the necessary advantage to stay one step ahead.

If at any point the stakeout is interrupted, successes gained by the secondary actors are not lost, but they can gain no more by continuing the Tactic. The primary actor must make do with whatever information the secondary actors gleaned by that point.

Organizations: By dint of its general expertise, Network 0 brings a lot of technological improvements to an old game. By setting cameras instead of milling around outside, hacking security payroll instead of counting heads and other modern conveniences, they can cut a lot of guesswork out of the operation. The hunters of Aegis Kai Doru are adept at getting into places they weren't invited, taking what they want, and leaving without a trace of their passing. They make it look easy, but a lot of legwork goes into that appearance.

Potential Modifiers: Hunters are well-concealed (+2); hunters using cameras (+2); hunters live nearby (+1); high walls or other obstructions (-2); heavily guarded (-3)

Roll Results

Dramatic Failure: The infiltrator forgets a crucial piece of information or translates an action into its direct opposite (*Was it the right window with the loose mooring or the left?*) almost certainly raising the notice of security or a neighbor's suspicion. Any attempts to interact with the environment are at risk: the first failure in such a situation becomes a dramatic failure, instead.

Failure: The hunters fail to glean any pertinent information from the stakeout.

Success: Success gives the cell the following benefits, which apply only when the cell aims to interact with the location (likely *within* the location):

- The cell gains a bonus to Initiative scores equal to the primary actor's successes gained. (This bonus only applies in regards to the location: if the hunters were trying to break into the location or battle a vampire within a staked-out haven, the bonus applies. If they were ambushed getting out of the van, the bonus does not.)

- The cell gains +2 to any Stealth or Larceny rolls made regarding the location (i.e. breaking in, stealing an item, hiding from a patrolling thrall, and so forth).

- The cell gains +1 to any roll meant to detect surprise while within the location.

Exceptional Success: The cell also gains +1 Speed while operating within the location.

To Purchase: 16 Practical Experience; 13 for Network 0; 11 for the Aegis Kai Doru.

Tar and Feather

Prerequisites: *All:* Composure 2, Dexterity 2; *Partial (1):* Computer 1, Crafts or Expression 2 with a specialty in Film (primary actor); *Partial (2):* Athletics 1 (secondary actors).

Requires: 2 to 5 (-1 penalty for every hunter over 5)

Dice Pool: *Primary:* Dexterity + Crafts, *Secondary:* Dexterity + Athletics.

Action: Instant

Description: One of the problems in collecting valuable data from vampire encounters comes from a strange supernatural "side effect" that doesn't allow them to be filmed or photographed. Folklore claims this is the same phenomenon that prevents some vampires from reflecting in mirrors. Photographs and mirrors reflect the soul, and as vampires do not have souls (or so the story goes), they appear as dark smudges, blurs or obscured in shadow even when there should be none.

Modern ingenuity has found a way around this problem even if it is a crude one. The name of this Tactic isn't entirely accurate but conjures the right image. The idea being that some of the secondary actors attempt to douse the creature with some kind of adherent material, tar, glue, grease, syrup—anything sticky. The rest of the secondary actors coat the target in particulate matter, like sawdust, pebbles, sand, grass clippings—something they *can* film. All while the primary actor secrets himself a safe distance away and lets the cameras roll—a sort of "poor man's motion capture."

This Tactic usually involves ambushing a vampire on the street, relying on the safety of being out in public to save them from retaliation. For more thorough investigations, a secure location might be required, that is, if the cell is feeling ballsy. In a pinch smaller cells might simply drench the creature in paint or dye in an attempt to save themselves a step. They have to be careful not to obscure the target as to be just as unrecognizable as a dark blur would have been, or stuck with ridiculous footage that just looks like some poor bastard they doused in paint.

Ultimately, the hope is that the creature is provoked to do something supernatural or otherwise damning while on film. Once successful, the cell may attempt any number of follow up efforts while the creature is caught on tape, however most non-combatants use the most common, "run and gun" method. For every relative success there are dozens of completely unusable failures. Still, the Vigil is won in inches and this relatively new Tactic might still be refined into even more useful forms with advances in technology, and good old-fashioned trial and error.

Organizations: In their ongoing pursuit for irrefutable proof of the supernatural, Network 0 perhaps has the most vested interest in this particular Tactic and often stage reckless fly-bys on suspected vampires. The Cheiron Group is responsible for the most successful version of this Tactic to date, by setting up a controlled suite and using photoreceptive particles and blood dosed with a magnetic dye to map a vampire's body. It is unfortunate that the subject escaped before completion. Efforts are in place to replicate this level of "recordability" in the field.

Potential Modifiers: Windy area (-2); Poor lighting (-1); Paint or dye only (-1); Well lit (+1); Digital Equipment (+2).

Roll Results

Dramatic Failure: Whether hurling the grease or dust, a sharp blowback or slip of a finger sends the material into the hunter's own eyes or that of one of his cellmates. The afflicted individual suffers a -2 penalty until they can successfully wipe away or flush the material from their eyes.

Failure: Through any combination of settings, technique or equipment failure, the recording simply fails to catch any valuable footage whatsoever.

Success: In the course of the Tactic the creature performs some unearthly feat or otherwise reveals its monstrous nature. It might not be irrefutable, but it's nevertheless a success. Hunters trying to track the creature using video technology gain a +3 to any rolls made to do so. In addition, even ground-level tracking of the creature is improved (it leaves behind a trail of feathers, chalk, photoreceptive silica, whatever was used in the tactic), and ground-level tracking efforts (whether using Investigation or Survival) gain +2 dice.

Exceptional Success: The coating is so thorough it even pierces a creature's potential invisibility—if, after being "Tar and Feathered" the creature drops out of sight using a supernatural ability, hunters still gain +1 to try to spot it on camera or with one's bare eye.

To Purchase: 12 Practical Experience, 9 for Network Zero, 7 for The Cheiron Group.

New Traits

In dealing with vampires there are many advantages, weaknesses and other tools in a hunter's arsenal to be brought to bear in the ongoing Vigil against the night.

New Merits

Hunters sometimes are naturally possessed with or develop advantages outside of their compact or conspiracy that have particular utility in the long Vigil versus the tireless undead.

Language: ConLang (•)

Effect: Used commonly in SWAT, Military or SCUBA where silent communication is a necessity, a small catalog of gestures can communicate limited concepts such as "stop," "listen," "proceed," or "surface." More complex expressions are seen in professional sports where entire playbooks are drilled down to a series of gestures and cadences allowing a team to make adjustments without tipping off their opponents. No matter how deep in the Vigil a cell is, if it wants to survive they should endeavor to come up with ConLang ("constructed language"), a series of code words or hand signs allowing them to communicate in plain sight or hearing range without tipping their hand. This can come in especially handy versus seemingly omniscient vampire masters that can hear pins drop and seem able to smell lies.

A series of quick hand signals, similar to the aforementioned SWAT or SCUBA applications need not be very extensive to be incredibly useful to hunters in the field. While this conjures images of black helicopter-deployed soldiers of Task Force: VALKYRIE, a cell of the Long Night or Loyalists of Thule has every reason to develop personal systems of communication (sometimes to keep secrets from other hunters). A closed fist means "stop," fingers pointing to the eyes means "watch/be aware," two fingers pointed down in front of the face means "vampire," two fingers up means "demon," and so on and so forth.

This Merit grants a +1 to Tactic rolls for each member of the group possessing the same Merit. Obviously, more than one hunter must possess this Merit for it to provide its bonus to them. If any of the hunter's cell does not possess this Merit, they suffer a -1 penalty on same as they find themselves out of the loop. That is to say that if a hunter is the only one in the cell who doesn't know the code, he's at a clear disadvantage.

Indomitable (• to •••••)

Prerequisites: Resolve •••, Composure •••

Effect: Whether due to resolve, strength of will, or sheer bloody mindedness, some people just won't bend.

The hunter with this Merit is altogether less prone to suggestion of any sort, be it mundane or supernatural and gains a bonus to resist outside forces imposing their will on her. Be it by Intimidation, Persuasion, or Dread Powers, the hunter gains a bonus equal to the dots in this Merit on all Composure or Resolve rolls to resist attempts bending her will to someone else's wishes.

Unbondable (••)

Prerequisites: Stamina ••, Resolve •••

Effect: The hunter is highly resistant to the intoxicating effects of vampire blood. Vampires require twice the necessary dosages (six instead of three) when attempting to bind this hunter to its will or improve her disposition toward it through blood. *Available at character creation only.*

New Endowments

Vampires are like roaches: where you find one, you find many. They dwell in damn near every city and town, though only rarely can the creatures of the night survive out in the wilderness. Why? Because in true parasitic fashion, vampires cannot subsist without humanity—or at least, without the blood inside them. The hunter conspiracies would never have survived to these modern nights if they couldn't get over the seemingly ubiquitous threat posed by the creatures that stalk the night. Some even claim to "specialize" in dealing with their kind. Each conspiracy may have a different tack on how best to interact with the parasites roaming the cities of the world but none ignore them. Whether used to eliminate, subdue, or bargain, below you'll find an assortment of tools derived for—and in some case, *from*—the so-called Children of the Night.

Advanced Armory

The field agents of Task Force: VALKYRIE are no greenhorns when it comes to dealing with the haemophagic ENEs colloquially known as "vampires." Early in the young organization's tenure the VALKYRIE hunters cut their teeth, so to speak, developing an arsenal to deal with the vampire menace. Strangely, R&D has tapered off over the years and hit stagnation. The official story has the conspiracy's limited funding being routed for more immediately "worthwhile" endeavors.

Hod Rounds (•; Renewable)

When wooden bullets were found on Axis soldiers in WWII, they begat a number of military urban myths: poisonous splinters, shredding limbs, all sorts of nasty intel without visual confirmation. Facts are, wooden bullets were used most often as tracers for grenade launchers or as training bullets fired in desperation. Horror stories left over from WWII have created bugbear-like gremlins and foo-fighters out of a largely ineffectual ballistic. VALKYRIE, however, knows that gremlins and foo-fighters are all too real, and they've fought too many bugbears.

The development of wooden rounds to deal with vampires was a no-brainer and versions have been field-tested and improved upon since the early 1900's—well before WWII. The bullets are made of compressed fibers formed around a soft center of fresh mistletoe. The soft center heats up upon firing and builds up pressure within the hollow of the bullet, shredding on impact.

Technically, the bullets are cheap to manufacture, but VALKYRIE doesn't use them with any frequency (and they're so alarmingly low-tech that some claim use of Hod Rounds to be "embarrassing"). As such, it's impossible to get more than what one dot allows, which is two full clips. A special request form can be filed if an agent

DON'T ASK QUESTIONS

VALKYRIE agents often frown on low-tech, decidedly unadvanced Advanced Armory solutions like Hod Rounds. Having a handful of tarnished wooden bullets dropped into your palm doesn't have the same potent resonance as being handed a rifle that fires uranium flechettes, right? Yes, Hod Rounds serve some utility and smart agents can see that. But that doesn't stop agents from asking, why the mistletoe, exactly? Can't you just make a Hod Round out of any type of wood?

The real answer is no, you can't. Mistletoe felled Balder. In Virgil, you find mistletoe associated with death, the underworld and supernatural might. It's also been bound up with supposed miracle cures. Wood from other trees doesn't' seem to work. Mythological significance goes the extra mile, here.

Of course, VALKYRIE requisition agents won't tell you that. Any agent asking such loaded questions will meet with the fairly standard response: "Don't ask questions."

feels he might need more than that for a raid or similarly large scale strike, but many hunters question where such requisition forms even go. A Task Force: VALKYRIE RFID chip is not needed to fire Hod Rounds.

Function: Use of Hod Rounds in a weapon reduces its efficiency in most cases—any Dexterity + Firearms rolls made to use a weapon loaded with these wooden bullets suffers a -2 penalty. However, when used against vampires, Hod Rounds have two notable bonuses. The first is that due to the bullet shredding into splinters on impact, half of the damage done (round down) to a vampire can be converted to lethal upon impact. Also, if a hunter wishes to make an aimed shot to "stake" a vampire with Hod Rounds he suffers no penalty for the aimed shot as the bullet shreds (outside the -2 penalty noted above), improving the hunter's chances of a splinter finding the heart. For more on staking rules see **World of Darkness Rulebook** pp. 165-166.

Huginn Visor (•• or •••)

Vampires seem to have no end of abilities to sway the minds and will of mankind at their disposal. There is one drawback, however, and that is a seeming need for eye contact—the window of the soul, so to speak—on the part of the vampire. That's where the Huginn Visor comes in, made of a dark, reflective glass that makes such contact nearly impossible. Civilian issue sunglasses prove ineffective against the powers of the enemy, so much so that an agent would not trust his cell's integrity to simply wearing dark sunglasses. Doubly so considering the kinds of sensitive information Task Force: VALKYRIE agents are privy to. The solution lies in just the right combination of polarization and treatment with strange "chemicals." Field agents used to joke the stuff comes from the wings Top Brass pulled off of faeries. They aren't far off.

The primary style of Huginn visor is innocuous enough to be worn in the field, and lends weight to the image of the prototypical Man in Black. Little do civilians know just how important those dark glasses can be.

The two-dot version is the sunglasses. A three-dot version actually represents a contact lens variant. This variant is stealthier, not to mention with a swift swipe a vampire can knock a pair of glasses off a hunter's head. However, the lenses are slightly less efficient (see below).

Function: If a monster's mind-altering Dread Powers (such as Fury, or Sleep) necessitate eye contact, the creature suffers a -3 penalty when used against an agent equipped with the two-dot sunglasses variant, and -2 dice if the agent is equipped with the three-dot contact lens variant. Note that both versions of the Huginn Visor can damage an agent's ability to see in poorly-lit areas—in such places, the wearer suffers -2 to all sight-based Perception rolls.

Odin Reticle (•••)

Prerequisite: Huginn Visor (••)

The Huginn Visor (two-dot sunglasses variant only) can be outfitted with a small LCD attachment called an Odin Reticle. This little display overlays one eye and its purpose is to pierce the supernatural stealth possessed by vampiric and other ENEs. Intel suggests vampires are not capable of achieving true invisibility; rather they cloud the minds of pedestrians to overlook them. Just in case, R&D didn't take any chances. Applying the Odin Reticle over one eye, an agent becomes capable of piercing any ENEs' attempts to evade detection through a variety of techniques. The ENE will appear apparent in the eyepiece by way of a process called Resonant Afterimage Processing (RAP).

Despite early successes, only a limited amount of Odin Reticle prototypes were made. Agents interested in field testing equipment should contact their superior officers for more information.

Function: The Odin Reticle snaps in place and remains largely concealed by the Huginn Visor. A thin cord runs back to the power source and processor that rests in the ear, no larger than a standard issue earpiece. Hunters equipped with an Odin Reticle gain a bonus of +3 on any dice roll attempting to detect vampiric and other ENEs using stealth- and evasion-based Dread Powers (such as Lurker in Darkness).

Logehamarr Personal Flamethrower (•••••)

Fire is a great equalizer. It burns structures. It sears flesh. And some creatures, like nocturnal haemophages, are particularly susceptible to the element, possessed of an aversion that is both physical and supernatural. Said plainly, it burns them something unmerciful. All of this goes into making the Logehamarr Personal Flamethrower the ultimate offensive expression of Task Force: VALKYRIE.

Flamethrowers are not a modern creation. The 5th century Byzantine army would pump "Greek fire" through brass tubes at enemy forces. Modern-day flamethrowers are more advanced but still function the same way. They have three components: the fuel reserve, the gun housing and the ignition system. The fuel reserve contains a fuel mixture that produces almost the same effects attributed to the "Greek fire" used centuries ago. The fuel reserve also holds a pressure tank that pushes the fuel through the system. The gun housing controls the rate at which the fuel flows. The ignition system is at the end of the spray nozzle and ignites the fuel as it leaves the weapon. By strictest definition, flamethrowers do not shoot fire;

they shoot liquid set aflame. This liquid can even be bounced off walls, so it can reach unseen areas. The Logehamarr Personal Flamethrower would appear to operate on the same principal as a traditional flamethrower, but the result is far different—especially when you consider the strange, green-hued flame that jets from the weapon's tip.

Function: Traditionally, flamethrowers are used to attack fortifications and bunkers. The Logehamarr Personal Flamethrower has been modified with the design of being more effective as an antipersonnel weapon. The Logehamarr Personal Flamethrower attack is resolved via a Dexterity + Firearms attack as a long burst of autofire with base Damage 0: the user gains a +3 bonus to his attack roll, and may attack multiple targets if he's willing to suffer the required penalties (see the **World of Darkness Rulebook**, p. 160). Characters without a Heavy Weapons Specialty in Firearms take a –2 penalty to this roll. The burst of fuel emitted by a flamethrower is the size of a bonfire for the purposes of damage (Damage 2), and burns with the intensity of a gasoline fire when against mortal and other supernatural targets (+2 Damage bonus). Any character struck by a flamethrower attack is automatically set alight, and on the following and subsequent turns, he'll continue to take as much damage as he took from the initial attack per turn until extinguished (see p. 180, **World of Darkness Rulebook**). The flame affects vampires a bit differently—it does aggravated damage to vampires, as does any exposure to fire, but even the *sight* of the strange green flame is enough to launch a vampire into an immediate fear frenzy. If the vampire can see the fire, then the vampire automatically enters a fear frenzy, and desperately tries to escape the scene. (See "Frenzy," p. 163.)

Benediction

At one time the Shadow Congregation was the first and last name in hunting the Damned, and Mother Church has a long memory. While other conspiracies were still groping around blindly for purchase, the Hammer of Witches was excising the undead cancer from the heart of Europe. Not surprisingly, they have a number of Benedictions specific to smiting the unholy dead in the name of the Father, Son and Holy Ghost.

Type	Ranges	Capacity	Strength	Size
Logehamarr	10/20/40	5	3	4

Fiacre's Staff/ Benediction of the Rose

Saint Fiacre could reportedly turn fallow earth with the end of his staff and have it come to life as if tilled and gardened by a skilled hand. Other eyewitness accounts say he commanded boulders to move out of his way and off the grounds of his garden. This gift has since been refined into a weapon. The folklore of a wooden shaft through the heart forcing the damned to slumber or fall to dust finds root because vampires are a rejection of the natural order and God's will. The touch of life is so accursed to them that contact with same is a terrible burden. The Staff of Saint Fiacre as a Benediction takes this aversion further to a degree that the abomination is rejected by all of God's unspoiled creation.

Historically, Saint Fiacre banned women from his parish. Accordingly, access to this Benediction has long been forbidden among female members of the Malleus Maleficarum. While some within the Church still resist the more enlightened times of the modern world, women are no longer forbidden from achieving Status within this conspiracy. In an effort of compromise, there exists a version of this rite refined by the Brides of Christ and other female parishioners aligned with the Shadow Congregation. This version is known as the Benediction of the Rose after Saint Rose of Lima, whose dedication to Christ (as well as her love of tilled earth) was reportedly profound and unrivaled. The effects are the same and any and all changes are cosmetic at most.

Any object or material blessed with this Benediction may be used to cause harm to vampires and specifically can be used to pierce the heart with the same rules and effects as a wooden stake. Objects that work best include unforged iron, unalloyed metals, unprocessed wood, plant life and un-quarried stone. Those items are not quite as common as they were in the old days, and modern practitioners find cut stone and mildly refined materials to still be effective, if less so. An old fashioned fire poker, a marble urn, or pewter cane might suffer a penalty to the blessing but still effective. (Items made to serve as weapons to begun with cannot be blessed by this Benediction.). The item must still be sharp and sturdy enough to perform the act of staking or being used as a weapon. Blessing the object necessitates praying over it while using it to disturb any form of earth, even if the dirt is found in a window box or sandbag. It is, of course, altogether preferable to stay as true to the image of Father Fiacre or Sister Rose overturning God's own soil.

Cost: 1 Willpower

Action: Instant

Dice Pool: Stamina + Benediction

Roll Results

Dramatic Failure: The Benediction backfires and the user find herself rejected by the very objects she intended on using. She takes one point of lethal damage as the item creates an intense heat the user cannot bear to handle.

Failure: The invocation falls upon deaf ears and the selected object gains no benefits.

Success: Items blessed by this Benediction ignore penalties for being used as improvised weapons and, in addition, gain a bonus on attacks against vampires or other forms of undead. The bonus is equal to successes gained on the Benediction roll (maximum of +5). This lasts for the remainder of the scene.

Exceptional Success: As above; as a rather strange addition, lethal wounds caused by the blessed item often sprout flowers—roses, most commonly—only a few turns after the damage has been done.

Suggested Modifiers

+5	Fiacre's Staff is performed on August 30 (Feast Day of Saint Fiacre)
+5	Benediction of the Rose is performed on August 23 (Feast Day of Saint Rose of Lima)
-2	Item is made of processed material

La Langue Des Saints

Vampires are quite familiar with the art of lies. Their every interaction with the living world is one grand deceit, a profound masquerade where behind every mask waits another mask. However, no lie escapes God's sight and behind every lie is the dark seed of guilt. By invoking Saint Francis de Sales, hunters of the Malleus Maleficarum have found a way to ensure that seed grows into a tangle of catharsis among the lowly and the wretched.

A great peacemaker, converter and diplomat, Saint Francis has become a patron of confessors. By calling upon his name, the hunter can command the truth of vampires or similar abominations. Saint Francis himself guides the tongue of the foul target and all who are near can be sure the next answer it provides will be without deceit.

By spending a turn in prayer, the practitioner points and commands his target to speak true before God. The vampire must answer the hunter as truthfully as possible. Questioners should be careful to word their queries wisely. The undead are as accomplished at lying as the Devil himself.

Cost: 1 Willpower

Action: Instant and contested

Dice Pool: Composure + Benediction versus target's Resolve + Subterfuge

Roll Results

Dramatic Failure: The Benediction backfires. Saint Francis has found deceit in the heart of the practitioner and taken offense to her demand for truth. She can tell no lies for 24 hours.

Failure: No effect; the vile creature may continue to twist the truth as it pleases. The practitioner may try again at an increased cost of 2 Willpower.

Success: The vampire is compelled to answer a number of questions equal to the number of successes the hunter gained over the target. Only the hunter may speak the questions, for only the hunter is possessed of Saint Francis' Benediction. Also, note that "truth" is a bit flexible—if the vampire believes that he did not kill his last victim (even though reality says otherwise), then the vampire will answer according to what he genuinely believes. Truth is relative to the speaker.

Exceptional Success: As above, but now the creature also gains a mild derangement as if it has just lost a point of its Morality. Overwhelming guilt assails the monster. Storytellers should note that this could provide an inroad toward rehabilitation of the creature, should the hunter decide to attempt it. The creature may endeavor to reclaim some of its lost Morality if urged to do so.

Suggested Modifiers

+5	Benediction performed on January 24 (Feast Day of Saint Francis of Sales)
+2	Target is Catholic
+1	Practitioner is canonized
-1	Target is not a vampire
-2	Target's Morality is 7 or above

Song of Daniel

Lambs lying among lions—that is the promise of God's Paradise and the power behind this Benediction. History is full of accounts and images of the Saints walking among wild beasts unharmed. Perhaps the most well known is that of Daniel in the lion's den where playing a simple song caused the beasts to lie down, refusing to harm him. Blaise, Vitus, and many others have used some form of this hymn throughout history and it survives into these modern nights. Vampires and other creatures are sometimes said to have the soul of a beast lurking inside them, and this Benediction aims to soothe that savage spirit.

It is highly doubtful this Benediction is the same song Daniel used; this hymn is no less effective, however. Hunt-ers of the Malleus Maleficarum over the centuries have used it not only to calm animals in their presence but have also discovered that it can quite literally soothe the savage beast within vampires, werewolves and other raging beasts.

When sung, the Song of Daniel spreads an air of calm over the wildlife surrounding the practitioner. This may be used to approach a specific creature, or let her move through nature without disturbing the local fauna and draw unwanted attention to herself. Beyond that, this Benediction may be used against vampires or other creatures suffering frenzy or similar states (see p. 163) to bring clarity back to their mind and a small peace to their soul.

Cost: 1 Willpower against animals; 2 Willpower against creatures

Action: Instant

Dice Pool: Charisma + Benediction – the highest Resolve score of potentially-affected creatures

Roll Results

Dramatic Failure: The target is enraged instead. Area animals view the invoker as a threat and respond with an immediate fight response. Smaller creatures, like rodents, are likely to break off and flee in short order, but larger creatures and predators will need to be repelled. Vampires or other similarly enraged creatures targeted with this Benediction are not calmed and the hunter becomes the sole focus of their supernatural rage.

Failure: The Benediction has no effect and animals will behave and respond normally to the hunter's presence. Monsters remain in frenzy and will need to be turned away through other methods.

Success: The hymn takes hold of the heart of the beasts. Animals in the area are calmed and will let the hunter pass without thought of fight or flight. Vampires or other out-of-control creatures will find themselves subdued by a supernatural peace overcoming them (see "Frenzy," p. 163). In addition, the hunter gains bonus dice (equal to successes) on any Animal Ken rolls (for animals) or Social rolls (involving cowed monsters). This Benediction's area of effect is equal to twice the hunter's Benediction score in yards. It lasts for one full scene.

Exceptional Success: For the remainder of the scene, any animals or creatures must expend one point of Willpower per turn of attack *unless* they are defending themselves.

Suggested Modifiers

+5	Song of Daniel performed on February 3 (Feast Day of Blaise)
+1	Vampire in frenzy of fear
-1	The animal is a predator/target is a werewolf
-3	Vampire in fight frenzy

Loyola's Fire

This Benediction—allowing one to never be far from God's light—is named and credited to the Saint best known for bringing the light of the Church to dark places. Ignatius of Loyola, founder of the Society of Jesus (better known in modern nights as Jesuits), was a knight before coming to the cloth and often found himself in dark places in need of shelter, warmth, and light.

By invoking the name of Saint Ignatius, the hunter may imbue an object with his blessing and cast a holy light through the darkness. This light illuminates all as if through a crack in Heaven. Its glory is such that the undead cannot suffer to be in its presence.

This prayer is uttered over a cross or similar holy object. It is possible to perform the Benediction with the power of the practitioner's faith alone, but at a penalty. The primary purpose of this Benediction brings a very real illumination to the surrounding area that the unnatural dead cannot abide. Despite the obvious utility of this "secondary" feature of the Benediction, it remains technically a side effect. Practitioners calling on Ignatius without need of his light will find it significantly more difficult than those followers truly wandering in the dark.

Cost: 1 Willpower
Action: Instant
Dice Pool: Resolve + Benediction
Roll Results

Dramatic Failure: No light radiates outward, but the one performing the Benediction becomes apparent to any and all supernatural fiends within yards equal to three times the practitioner's Benediction score. It's as if the hunter is standing in the open on a clear day; this carries through walls or other obstructions.

Failure: Loyola's light is not made manifest.

Success: A light is cast from the object (or the performer's hand if no object was available) in a radius equal to three times successes gained in yards. Vampires must succeed upon a Resolve + Composure roll or suffer from a frenzy of fear (p. 163). Ghosts, zombies, and other undead react similarly to the light even if they otherwise do not suffer from frenzy. Any creature thus affected will do whatever it can to escape the light—often fleeing until it tires. For every turn spent in the light, the creature loses one point of Willpower (for vampires, this may appear as the blood drying within their bodies—flesh grows tight, even desiccated).

Exceptional Success: As above. In addition, those caught within the light suffer a point of lethal damage.

Suggested Modifiers

+5	July 31 (Feast Day of Saint Ignatius of Loyola)
+2	Blessed object (i.e. sacred reliquary)

+1	Religious or other appropriate object (i.e. normal Bible)
+1	Pitch black
-1	No object
-2	The area is lit
-3	Profane object (i.e. pornographic magazine)

Mantle of Orleans

This Benediction is associated with Jeanne D'Arc, the young French woman famously besieged by visions of Heaven. Unable to ignore the Lord's call to arms, she waged a military campaign that helped save France near the end of the One Hundred Year War. Wrongly condemned for heresy by the politicians of the time, Saint Jeanne has posthumously been cleared of all charges, and beatified and canonized in short order. She serves as an inspiration to women in the church and all who bear arms in the name of God. It is no surprise that the Malleus Maleficarum have come to hold her in such high regard when it comes time to raise the standard of war. Specifically, this Benediction invokes her glorious success under Heaven in lifting the siege of Orleans in only nine days. This prayer blesses the practitioner's brothers in arms as they battle unholy forces. The companions of the practitioner receive a blessing that guides their blows and turns aside their enemies' attacks in turn. In the course of the prayer, the hunter invokes Margaret of Antioch, Catherine of Alexandria and Michael the Archangel to aid in battle as they once graced Saint Jeanne.

She must remain in prayer for every turn she wishes to continue issuing the blessing. For every turn the practitioner remains in prayer, members of her cell gain bonuses to all combat rolls and attributes (i.e. Defense, Initiative). This doesn't necessitate rolling or expending Willpower every turn, only the act of prayer itself. If interrupted (she is otherwise stopped from speaking or is attacked, for instance), the Benediction ends. She may not attempt to use this Benediction again until 24 hours have passed.

Cost: 2 Willpower
Action: Instant
Dice Pool: Manipulation + Benediction
Roll Results
Dramatic Failure: The practitioner *and* her cell are besieged by visions of the Archangel Michael standing in Holy Judgment. The cell suffers a -1 penalty to all combat related rolls and -3 to their Initiative for the remainder of the scene. The Benediction is over and the

They Are Dead, Yet They Walk

It's up to you: are vampires the same thing as the shambling dead, the rough-hewn Reanimated (i.e. Prometheans), ghosts, and anything else that makes use of a defunct corpse or a restless spirit? Technically, no, they're not the same. But in terms of *game mechanics*, you might rule that any Endowment that fucks specifically with vampires can be used to affect those other types of "walking dead," too. Some of the Endowments here make specific mention of this, but others don't. It's your call, as Storyteller, as to how large a tent these Endowments represent. Can all such unliving abominations crowd beneath it?

practitioner may not continue the prayer or try again for one full turn of the moon (28 days).

Failure: The invoker's prayer fails to be heard and the cell gains no benefit or blessing.

Success: The Benediction is successful and other members of the cell gain the following benefits: +1 to Defense, +1 to all combat-related rolls, +3 to Initiative, and +3 to Speed. These bonuses last for as long as the hunter prays (maximum one full scene). Note that the hunter using this Benediction does not gain these benefits, and may do nothing except pray if she hopes to keep up the blessing. Those in the cell gaining these benefits must be within 50 yards of the praying hunter.

Exceptional Success: As above, but the cell now gains +2 to combat-related rolls.

Suggested Modifiers

+5	May 30 (Feast Day of Saint Jeanne D'Arc)
+2	Holding a blessed item (a sacred banner, a sanctified sword)
-2	Distractions (loud noise, trembling ground, the combat is going on inches from the hunter's face)

Castigation

"Vampires own the night." It's a sentiment shared by most hunters, to be sure. However, the Children of the Seventh Generation know that vampires only lease the night from its true ruler. Whether met with resistance or welcomed with open arms, the legacy of the Lucifuge is one of very old power—powers that they draw from the same ultimate source as their foes. The members of the Lucifuge find an eerie lot in common with the Castigations they wield and the abilities of the kin they hunt. Whether that is a boon or bane, only time and the crackling of Hellfire know for sure.

Prima Dictum

Blood is the animating force behind the vampire's impossible life. Some suggest it's blood that keeps vampires somewhat human—as a human element, the blood perhaps keeps them from turning into the mindless dead, shambling toward an open patch of sunlight. It could be said that blood is also the power of the Lucifuge. Through the veins of every member in their twisted family tree flows the distilled power of the Prince of Darkness. Such infernal genetics—at times—come with a certain amount of privilege. Some family members have discovered the ability to deny vampires access to that which they rely on most—the very fuel that keeps them going in their cold mockery of life-blood. Generally, hunters who know the dark syllables of Prima Dictum do not like to linger long on the how's and why's of what it does, for fear that its origins contain madness for the castigator.

By drawing his own blood, the hunter utters a curse that burbles up from the depth of Hell. She brings the supernatural authority of her bloodline to bear, denying the vampire access to their precious animating fluids. It's unlikely that full rigor mortis steps in, but the creature's

limbs start to tighten—the mystical transubstantiation of blood into will begins to fail on a fundamental level.

Dice Pool: Resolve + Occult + Castigation versus target's Resolve + Potency

Cost: 2 Willpower and 1 point of lethal damage (this damage must draw blood, and the blood *must* splash the vampire; this may necessitate success on a touch attack, first)

Action: Instant and contested

Roll Results

Dramatic Failure: In drawing the blood and uttering the attendant guttural curse, the hunter evokes quite a different response, sending the vampire into frenzy (p. 163) with herself as the primary focus of said frenzy.

Failure: The Willpower is spent and the damage is taken, but curse doesn't come and the vampire is unaffected.

Success: The hunter wins the contest. The vampire's body stiffens; it becomes difficult for the creature to move. The vampire suffers a penalty to all Physical rolls—the modifier is equal to successes gained over the creature. In addition, any rolls made on behalf of the vampire to use Dread Powers are penalized by -1 die. This penalty lasts for the remainder of the scene.

Exceptional Success: As above, except now the vampire may not utilize any Dread Powers that necessitate an expenditure of Willpower (i.e. the creature's own blood).

Abaddon's Call

Hunters the world over tell tales of encountering undead creatures that aren't vampires: lurching zombies, hungry ghosts, vengeful revenants, etc. Many who take up the Vigil are forced to wonder from whence such creatures come. What wills an otherwise unexceptional corpse to get up and start shambling around? Sometimes it's the work of witches, sometimes possessing spirits, and sometimes it's the power of the Lucifuge. This Castigation allows the hunter to command a corpse to rise and come to the aid of its new master for a short duration—though rumors abound of ways to make the effects permanent.

The use of this power is incredibly vulgar and not publicly tolerated by the Lucifuge, but this is largely a conspiracy of iconoclasts and outcasts, so rules don't always apply.

The force that animates the corpse is not necessarily that of the previous tenant. Popular wisdom would suggest a demon inhabits the body but it could possibly be a compelled spirit or simply the user's own unconscious that dictates the actions of the body.

GIVING THE DEVIL HIS DUE

Players of Lucifuge hunters may purchase versions of this power that hinder the movements of other creatures, but he must purchase this ritual once per type of creature. So if the hunter wanted to hold sway over vampires and ghosts, the player would purchase Prima Dictum (vampires) and Prima Dictum (ghosts).

The power works the same, but it's not necessarily the blood that "rebels" within the creature's body. A ghost finds it Corpus turns turgid, inconsistent. A werewolf discover that her bestial musculature spasms and defies her will. A demon's body reacts to the world as if it does not belong here (think of the possessed girl's herky-jerky movements in *The Exorcist*). And so forth.

Cost: 1 Willpower, X points of bashing damage (see below)

Action: Extended (number of successes required equals two times the number of days the corpse has been dead, to a maximum of 20 days; each roll is equal to fifteen minutes, and during each roll the hunter suffers two points of bashing damage as he is wracked with aches and seizures).

Dice Pool: Resolve + Medicine

Roll Results

Dramatic Failure: The body animates as if by a normal success in all ways, except it will focus its attention solely on ending the one who called it to life, attacking ceaselessly until it is felled.

Failure: The hunter takes the wounds, but nothing occurs: the Castigation doesn't elicit even a twitch from the body.

Success: The use of this Endowment wracks the user's body with pain as she exerts her will over death itself. The raised body is in all ways a shambling simpleton and is only good for following simple instructions ("Go get me that book from the second floor," is fine, but "Drive my car northbound on Route 22" will be met with gaping confusion). If called to fight it will do so in the most brutish and straightforward manner possible. Every attack will be an "all-out attack" (see the **World of Darkness Rulebook**, p. 157); it cannot use weapons or tools; it does not roll for Initiative (automatically going last); and

it will pursue its target with no regard for its own safety or that of the practitioner and her cellmates. If the creature sustains more damage of any type than it has Health levels it returns to its inanimate state (a lot worse for wear, but hey, it was already dead) and cannot be used for this infernal purpose again. It only rises for one hour of time per the hunter's dots in Castigation, but with the cost of one permanent Willpower *dot*, the creature will remain shambling about for as long as it is able. As above, it doesn't heal damage and retains any wounds (even those from, say, accidentally tumbling down a set of steps) for the remainder of its potentially-short unlife.

Exceptional Success: As above, but the creature doubles its Defense and Speed scores (see sidebar for traits).

Suggested Modifiers

+2	Recently dead (within an hour)
-2	Dead longer than a year

The Mark of Lucifuge

The mythological Mark of Cain made it so all who looked upon the first murderer would know him. Thus were the wages of sin when angels roamed the earth. A lesser form of this mark is known to the Lucifuge. By laying a hand on the bare skin of a vampire, the Lucifuge brands its flesh with the merest stroke of that original mark. True to legend, once the vampire is marked,

ANIMATED DEAD TRAITS

Attributes: Strength 3, Stamina 3, Dexterity 1, Resolve 1 and Composure 1, otherwise the Animated Dead has no applicable Attribute scores.
Skills: Brawl 1, Athletics 1
Willpower: None
Initiative: None
Defense: 1
Speed: 4
Virtue: None
Vice: None
Morality: None
Size: 5 (average)
Health: 8

nothing can be done to rid itself of it. The char will not wash off long after the wound has healed; its burning cannot be carved out with a blade, nor can its flickering light be covered by any amount of clothing.

Cost: 1 or 2 Willpower (see below), 1 point of lethal damage

Action: Instant

Dice Pool: None

The hunter spends her Willpower and takes one point of lethal damage as she draws the mark across her palm (it appears like a second-degree burn). In many cases, the hunter may first need to succeed on a touch attack or have a cellmate grapple the creature.

Branding causes one point of aggravated damage to the target. From now on, any and all Lucifuge to encounter the marked individual will recognize it and its unholy nature even across a crowded room. What's interesting, though, is who *else* can see the mark.

Other creatures can see the mark. Humans—meaning, most other hunters—cannot. Doubly strange is that hunters of both the Cainite Heresy and the Malleus Maleficarum can see the brand, and in fact the Cainites claim it as a mark quite familiar to them (they often leave the mark at the scenes of their hunts).

This ritual works on other creatures besides vampires, but doing so necessitates spending 2 Willpower points instead of the 1 necessary to "brand" a vampire.

Elixirs

The Cult of the Phoenix is no stranger to the legions of Seth and those that defy Ma'at's judgment. The strange alchemies of the Ascending Ones trend toward broader applications than any one type of monster. Even still, they are not completely uninspired by these abomi-nations. Alchemy is said to be able to turn death into life, then it stands to figure that it could interrupt such a transmutation, as well.

Hunting Sight of the Asp (•)

Vampires might be the loudest offender, but many things go bump in the night. Much of the Vigil rightly takes place in the dark, and for some hunters the tell-tale flashlights and bulky night-vision equipment isn't always the most effective hunting tool. This potent concoction of cobra's venom, fish liver oil, and strong opiate alkaloid (usually filling up a small, nondescript bottle of over-the-counter eyedrops) works upon the hunter's eye to, as one hunter puts it, "open the eyes *behind* the eyes."

The infrared spectrum comes alive to the Ascending Ones, separating the world into hot and cold and removing all other distractions. There is only life and unlife, rodents and serpents, predator and prey. Hunters who have taken this draught tend to hold their eyes open a little too wide and act just a little alien, but their ability to hunt in complete darkness or identify the one vampire in the crowded night club is unparalleled.

Roll Results

Dramatic Failure: The imbiber is struck blind for 24 hours and acts as if taking a dose of poison of Toxicity 3 (see the **World of Darkness Rulebook,** p. 180).

Failure: The hunter suffers as if having taken a mild hallucinogen (-1 to all dice pools and traits) (**World of Darkness Rulebook**, p. 177).

Success: The hunter now sees in the thermal spectrum enabling her to more or less see in the dark becoming particularly adept at detecting the heat radiated by living things. The hunter gains the following benefits for the remainder of the scene:

• Even if a target is attempting to hide, the hunter gains +3 on any Perception rolls made to find a target attempting to hide nearby (heat radiating from a body behind a curtain, for instance).

• This draught is also quite useful for determining if a person is undead simply by noticing the dramatic pitch in body heat. The hunter gains +5 to any roll used to determine if a body is masquerading as alive. Alternately, werewolves (and some demons, particularly those fresh from whatever Hell realm they come from) "run hotter" than humans—the hunter gains only +3 on the roll to discern the nature of such creatures with Hunting Sight of the Asp, however.

• This Elixir can be used to help determine emotional states. The imbiber gains +1 on Empathy rolls.

• Perception rolls regarding inanimate objects—especially those that feature little or no temperature variation from their surroundings—suffer a -2 penalty while the Hunting Sight of the Asp is active. (Think of trying to locate a set of car keys with mystical infrared sight.)

Exceptional Success: As above, but the hunter only suffers a -1 penalty when making Perception rolls regarding inanimate objects.

Suggested Modifiers:

-2   Ambient temperature greater than 98 degrees Fahrenheit (37 degrees Celsius).

Nehebkau Tears (•••••)

Legend tells of an Ascending One whose wife and family was taken as slaves by a clutch of vampires. Unable to bear this fate but also unable to get close to their stronghold, the hunter went to Nehebkau, Guardian of the Underworld and begged him for help in freeing his family. The god acknowledged there might be a way to approach them in the skins of their own kind, but to do so would close Duat (the underworld) forever to him. The man did not care, he said, he only wanted his family freed and the darkness could take his soul if that was the cost. Nehebkau was moved by the man so willing to sacrifice himself. The god cried two tears, catching them in a canopic jar, and instructed the man that if he wished to save his family, then he must drink the mixture as the sun set. Drinking the tears would allow him to move among his enemy for one night. At the end of the night, he would die but his soul would be lost forever without Ma'at's judgment or the mercy of Duat. The man agreed and drank the foul poison at sundown the following day and felt himself die.

True to Nehebkau's word, instead of moving onto the scales of Ma'at, the man was immediately able to open his eyes and walk how the sunless dead walked. He went to their stronghold unassailed. He found his family and found only envy in their warm embrace against his skin, but he knew this was the cost of their safety. He led them to freedom and said a cold goodbye as the sun peeked over the mountains. Choking and retching, the man fell to his knees feeling his life violently tearing out of him. Yet he fought with all his will, all the purity of spirit which moved the god. The man reached down his own throat, grabbing the darkness that he had so willingly swallowed and tore it lose, vomiting forth a single fat scarab onto the sand along with his blood and bile. The scarab regarded him and with Nehebkau's voice told the man that his purity and will would allow him to endure the morning sun. As the sun edged over the mountains, so did the man's heart beat again and again. Only then, as he breathed out the last of graveyard air from his lungs did the man weep for joy for the return of his family.

The Ascending One who is willing to take her chances with this rarely-used draught better have a good reason and peace within her god's eyes before trying. There aren't many calls for the Tears of Nehebkau, but there have been in the past. Almost every part of this potion is deadly or unclean. Particularly religious members of the Ascending One say those that partake in this Elixir will find Paradise forever closed to them. With a steeped brew of pig blood, quicksilver (mercury), natron (soda salt), and formaldehyde, an Ascending One can cheat death in a manner nearly identical to vampirism. If mixed correctly and with proper faith and strength of purpose the process is reversible at the end of one night's time when the imbiber completely but painfully returns to life's embrace. She will know it succeeded when she coughs up the bloody scarab.

The hunter uses this terrible potion to not just simulate, but in all ways join the ranks of the undead for the night. The player and Storyteller should work together to translate the hunter as they would a newly-created vampire for the duration of this effect using the rules as they appear within this book.

Roll Results

Dramatic Failure: The hunter effectively blinds Nehebkau and succeeds in transforming into a vampire as per a normal success. At the end of the night, however, they find Ra's door is closed to them. They are forevermore outside of Nehebkau's (or whomever their god might be) purview and have effectively become a vampire. The Storyteller and player should work together to design a vampire using the rules found earlier in this book.

Failure: The imbiber suffers as if taking a potent (and potentially fatal) dose of heroin (all dice pools suffer -3 for a full 8 hours). Because the dose is potentially damaging or lethal, the Elixir also counts as a Toxicity 3 poison.

Success: From sundown to sun-up the hunter effectively becomes a member of the undead per the rules found earlier in this book. This act against the natural world costs either five Willpower points or one permanent Willpower *dot* at the end of the evening as the hunter undergoes the slow struggle back to life. Note that during this time, the character works according to the rules for vampires in this book (or in **Vampire: The Requiem**). He cannot risk Willpower. He cannot utilize his Endowments. He is similarly out of sync with his cell—he can still be a part of Tactics, but suffers -2 dice to do so. He may need to feed (drinking one blood equates to Willpower, at a rate of one point gained per one point of lethal damage incurred), and is subject to all the advantages and disadvantages of existing in a vampiric state.

Exceptional Success: As above, but the vampire fills up his Willpower pool upon turning—as a result, he may not need to feed during his (hopefully) one long night of undead existence.

What Game Are We Playing?

The Storyteller and player should discuss the full possibility of dramatic failure in regards to Nehebkau's Tears. Everyone should agree and be willing to play through the potential consequences. Any of the results open up a lot of potentially interesting doors within an ongoing story, but has just as much potential to derail a story or at least take a detour that may demand a lot of time. After everyone feels like they know what they're getting into, all that's left is to roll the dice, metaphorically and literally.

Relic

The hunters of the Aegis Kai Doru have sworn a time-honored blood feud against the warlocks and lycanthropes of the world. However, they are not completely blind toward the other threats against humanity that exist beyond the edge of sight. The Aegis may not go out of their way to hunt vampires, but eventually their paths will cross and they try to be on the winning side of the confrontation.

Scale of Scylla (••)

Greek mythology has many monsters of legend within its rich and colorful mythology. Several behaved similarly to the modern *vrykolakas* (i.e. vampires). One figure, commonly associated with vampiric folklore is the poor, cursed Lamia, Queen of Libya, who like so many queens caught the eye of Zeus and the ire of his wife. Hera drove Lamia mad and killed her children save one, whom she made into a monster of the sea. She then drove the Queen of Libya further into darkness as a breath-stealing, baby-killing madwoman. This portion of her story often gets her associated with the likes of the Mesopotamian Lilitu as a mother of monsters (*lamiae* and *vrykolakas*). Whatever the poor queen's true fate, several half-moon plates recovered near the Straits of Messina have become a part of her family's tragic legacy.

This flat plate-like Relic is larger than most adults' hands and is reportedly a scale from Scylla, the sea monster and Lamia's only surviving child. Use of these Relics enables the user to pass unseen among the Lamiae (widely interpreted and more practically speaking, vampires).

Cost: 1 Willpower and blood incurring one point of lethal damage (from any source)

Benefit: Activation of the Scale of Scylla involves drawing blood and polishing the scale with it. Note, this isn't necessarily the blood of the one activating it, but one lethal point of damage must be taken (or given) as part of the cost. Once activated, the Scale makes any who touch it invisible to the sight of vampires. It is possible other creatures may be similarly blinded if mythology is to be believed, however, mortal servants of the creatures have proven unaffected by the Scale of Scylla.

When applied, the blood soaks into the Scale of Scylla's surface, leaving behind an unnatural sheen. The user will have no other indication that the Relic has worked until she walks straight up to a vampire without arousing even the slightest suspicion. The hunter—and any others who touch the scale—simply disappear to their senses, heightened or otherwise. A vampire actively searching for the hunter can make a Wits + Investigation roll, subtracting a penalty equal to the hunter's Stealth score.

While this invisibility is fairly potent, the hunter must still be careful not to disturb her surroundings outside of anything on her person. If she draws attention to herself, any vampires in the area gain bonuses toward searching out the disappeared hunter. Causing a candlestick to wobble back and forth might earn the vampire a +1 from his suspicion, whereas running bodily into the monster might add +5 to the creature's pool.

Worm Pipe (•••••)

This peculiar article was only recently acquired by the Aegis Kai Doru. This long wooden pipe, carved with what appear to be worms or serpents spiraling its length, was long-believed to only be the subject of Native American Prairie legend until the very real thing turned up in a pumpkin patch. Once positively identified, it sent a ripple through the ranks. It is a dangerous item to have in one's possession and carries great temptation. The legend tells of a hunter who lost his wife in childbirth and went on a long journey to the land of the unliving Worms. He hoped to reclaim her life, for now her son was without a mother. Once there, he begged for them to give him back his wife. They agreed, and gave him a small pipe that they said could return her to life—but she would be changed, for a part of her would always remain with the Worms.

At present, this purportedly unique Relic lays hidden behind a series of locked doors in some Aegis Kai Doru cache: they believe it is a power man was not meant to wield, the ability to return life to the fallen. Some antiquarians within the Guardians (chief amongst them, a man named Grellich) believe that this artifact belongs to the vampires, that it is perhaps something they created to curse living man with the taint of death. Some say that Grellich revived a fallen cellmate with the Worm Pipe, but upon seeing what the man had become, ended the man's life once more.

Of course, it's only a matter of time before another Guardian has strong enough cause to seek the Worm Pipe, with or without permission. There also remains the lingering possibility that it is not as unique as the Aegis Kai Doru have been led to believe and there might be other, similar devices that a Guardian could seek.

Cost: 1 point of lethal damage; all of the user's Willpower points (regardless of how many he has in his pool, he must exhaust them)

Benefit: The hunter must burn tobacco in the pipe, but the tobacco needs to be drizzled with her own blood. She inhales, filling her mouth with a sickening sweet smoke—she may blow this smoke into the mouth of a corpse dead for no less than one week to bring it back to life. The corpse lurches forth, sucking in a deep breath—it's said that the resurrected may vomit up a gut full of worms, roaches, even rotted stomach lining. The resurrected individual returns with a Health track full of bashing damage, as all serious wounds and rot mend and appear as a series of intense, dark bruises across the body. The resurrected is normal for the most part, but suffers from the following disadvantages from now on:

> • The resurrected gains one of the following mild derangements (Storyteller's choice): Phobia, Fixation, or Irrationality. This derangement can be resisted as normal, but can never be "cured."

LAMIAE VENERATION

Some vampires form cults. In some such cults, they worship a Mother of All Monsters, a "Crone" figure like Lamia, Scylla or Lilitu. These fiends celebrate their own monstrousness, finding joy in the viciousness of nature and divinity. While some vampires still believe themselves (or at least long to be) human, the cultists that one might call Lamiae (in **Requiem**, we're talking about the Circle of the Crone) care little about retaining humanity beyond the merest masquerade. To them, honoring their awful goddess is all about embracing ones monstrousness, not eschewing it. Ritual sacrifice is not uncommon among the Lamiae; they might pound corn and blood into mash on a stone alter, might bloodlet seven hounds to honor a goddess like Ereshkigal (Sumerian queen of the underworld), or might slit the throats of seven holy men and women to let the blood drain into a sacred marble vessel. These cults offer divergent practices, but the common themes of "spilling blood" and "worshipping a Dark Mother" remain fairly constant.

• The resurrected is "reborn" with one less Morality than when he perished.

• The resurrected returns with no Willpower points in his pool.

• The resurrected is overly susceptible to vampiric Dread Powers. Any mind-altering or mind-controlling Dread Power (such as Alter Memory, Control Emotion, Ecstasy, Impress, etc.) that the vampire uses upon the resurrected gain +3 dice.

• The resurrected has a harder time when locked in combat with a vampire. He may experience flashes of fear or feel burdened with lust; extreme emotions and brief hallucinations distract her. When in combat with a vampire, the resurrected character's Defense is one less, and any attacks he makes against a vampire suffers -2 dice.

The resurrected does gain two benefits, however:

• The resurrected now gains +2 to any Social rolls involving vampires.

• The resurrected now gains the Unseen Sense Merit in regards to vampires, ghosts, the Reanimated, and other unliving entities.

Thaumatechnology

The Cheiron Group has no shortage of vampire parts in the hands of the boys in the back room. Most such parts are hard to graft onto a living body, but some of what they've found useful is listed below.

Voice of the Banshee (• or •••)

Mythology is full of wailing creatures whose voices either lure or unnerve any who hear it (think of the Sirens or Bean Sidhes). Often these creatures are beautiful from afar, but dreadful to approach and they often portend death. These terrible creatures may well be rare off-shoots of the vampire genealogic tree as they've been witnessed preying on desire, breath, or age. When a field agent came across one of these mysterious wailing women of legend—washing what looked to be a Cheiron Group issue field jacket in the Thames—she was quick to tranq it for the fat bonus she knew she could earn. Shame she was struck by a bus only two days after telling the story to the man who came by to pick up the carcass and deliver the check. The Cheiron Group successfully extracted the vocal chords from a rare few of these specimens and found use for them in the field.

Benefit: The stringy tendons of the vocal chords allow the recipient to make a high-pitched keen just outside the range of human hearing. She emits a sub-aural wave of sound that will agitate animals and deafen anyone using supernaturally enhanced senses.

Cost: 1 Willpower
Action: Instant
Dice Pool: Stamina + Expression
Roll Results
Dramatic Failure: The hunter strains herself trying to swallow her tongue and force the sound from her throat. She suffers two points of bashing damage and spends the turn hoarsely retching. Her voice is reduced to a whisper for approximately 24 hours.

Failure: The hunter can't muster the will necessary to emit such sound.

Success: The hunter successfully emits a shrill keening wail. Animals, vampires and other creatures with heightened senses cannot concentrate for the racket, suffering a penalty to all actions for as many turns as the hunter has breath (the hunter can continue uninterrupted for as many turns as she has dots in Stamina or end the effect prematurely if she so chooses). In addition, those affected suffer bashing damage equal to the number of successes gained to active the Endowment. Normal humans are generally untouched by the effects of this implant.

If the hunter possesses the three-dot version, those affected as above also suffer the effects of the Depression or Melancholia derangements (p. 97, **World of Darkness Rulebook**) for the remainder of the scene.

Exceptional Success: The wail is so damaging that all objects within ten yards of the hunter suffer one point of Structure damage.

Suggested Modifiers:

+1	Area is totally silent
-2	Loud place like a factory or dance club

Evil Eye (•••)

The eyes are the windows to the soul, so says the proverb. Field agents who have seen what vampires can do to a man just by looking him in the eye believe those words wholeheartedly. The mavericks of the Cheiron Group thought to prove the expression beyond reasonable doubt, however. Any fool with a scalpel can pluck the eye from someone's head, but to lock the soul inside the eye beforehand? Well, that's why they get paid the big bucks.

For whatever reason, the method used to extract the eye while maintaining the inherent abilities of the creature causes the awful discoloration and unsightliness. They say it's because the twisted soul of the creature becomes trapped inside. The surgeons of the Cheiron Group are still investigating ways to make a more... fashionable version, but so far, efforts have failed.

These sightless milky eyes are able to replicate a vampire's ability to sway the minds of others to a limited

degree. Unfortunately, true to name it has proven difficult to look at conversationally, and is most often politely covered by an eye patch. When needed, the field agent simply flips up the eye patch to reveal to her opponents her awful ocular addition.

Benefit: The hunter has replaced one of her eyes with a bloated and milky abomination; appropriately, she suffers from the One Eye Flaw (**World of Darkness Rulebook** p 219) and -2 to any Social rolls where the eye is exposed. She may choose one of the following Dread Powers at one dot: Confuse, Fury, Hypnotize, Sleep or Terrify (all found pp. 276-283 in **Hunter: The Vigil**).

Special: The character may purchase additional dots of the Dread Power chosen, to a maximum of three dots. The cost is new dots x 8 in experience points. Additional powers cannot be chosen (unless the character chooses to lose the second eye, which would render her totally blind).

Cainite Endowment: Rites of Denial (• to •••••)

Prerequisite: Status (Cainite Heresy) •

This is the truth of the Cainites' magic: they do not understand it. Sometime, a very long time ago, they were granted insight into a kind of ritualized magic (and some writings intimate that early Cainites stole such rituals

from the vampires themselves), and Cainites still have access to and knowledge of these rites today. They even learn *new* rites. But they do not understand them, and frankly? They don't care to.

To be clear, being a zealot of the Cainite Heresy is not about asking questions. It is not about deep understanding. The reality is plain: vampires exist. They are a persistent, septic infection. This menace must be destroyed at any cost, no questions asked. Cainites are encouraged to use whatever weapons are available to them, and the Rites of Denial represent one such weapon. Rites of Denial are just another tool in the arsenal, next to a lead pipe or a rough-hewn stake. Not much to grasp about a stake or a pipe, is there? Not much to grasp about the Rites of Denial, either, at least according to the Cainites.

Bloody Equations

Cainite rituals take a fairly simple form, but one that's odd enough that it probably *should* merit question, even though it doesn't. Every Cainite carries around a small glass phial of blood taken from other Cainites, enough to fill the small vessel. Most hang the phial around the neck or even the wrist, though some choose to protect the phials more stridently (even going so far to keep the glass phial in a small metal lockbox that can sit in one's coat pocket or glove-box).

Every Rite of Denial demands use of this blood—it might be smeared on a lead pipe, drawn upon a wall (usually in the form of the Cainites' own sigil), or up-ended into the mouth so it can be spat out. No Cainite magic fails to make use of the collected blood.

But it's rarely just that. No, usually the strange rituals demand other actions be taken, too—a line of cakey sea salt drawn across a doorway, a bulb of garlic crushed beneath a bootheel, or a splinter of wood shimmied into the skin of the palm.

Think of it like an equation. In a simple equation, A + B = C, and the Rites of Denial are very much like that. Use the blood in just such a way, perform the other actions demanded with the reagents demanded, and a result occurs. No faith is necessary (though one must certainly concentrate and commit to the action, but Cainites are nothing if not committed). No prayer, no entreaties to distant powers. Some religious Cainites might evoke such additional details when casting one of the Rites of Denial, but it's by no means necessary. A plus B equals C. It's that simple.

Straight from the Source(s)

Cainites do not learn the Rites of Denial from other Cainites. They don't gain them through meditation or starvation or prolonged prayer. No, one's access to the Rites of Denial comes from the Sources, those mysterious missives that arrive in one's mailbox, slide under one's door, or ping one's email inbox. When they (excuse us, *They*, capital-T) want a Cainite to learn a new ritual, they get the message to her. The message tells her exactly what to do: "Hammer a bloody nail into the creature's footprint to prevent his escape." It's elegantly straightforward. To most, it would be disturbing, and certainly some Cainites find it so. But, again, most grow to view it in an alarmingly pragmatic way: it's the same as if one's mysterious patron left a loaded handgun in the mailbox or a gift-wrapped hawthorn stake. It's a weapon. It'd be foolish not to pick it up and use it on the creatures of the night. Wouldn't it?

Casting Rites of Denial

Calling upon a Rite of Denial is, as noted, a direct affair. Do as the ritual demands, and it should succeed provided the Cainite is devoted enough to see its result manifest. Unless otherwise stated, casting Rites of Denial goes accordingly:

Cost: 1 Willpower and some measure of blood (see each Rite for more information)

Dice Pool: Resolve + Occult

Action: Instant or Extended (see each rite)

Note that each rite demands certain actions to be taken, and one of those actions involves expending the phial-bound blood of other Cainites. Each phial of the Cainites is the same: a small glass bottle with a cork fitted in the top. A Cainite receives this phial not from others in the conspiracy, but from the Sources themselves—often in an unmarked brown box left upon the doorstep or inside one's car. (Lose the bottle, and one shall be resent within the week in a similar package.)

Each phial must contain the blood of five Cainites (the character counts as one of the five)—and each must contribute approximately one thimble's full of the red stuff, which fills the bottle. Each Rite of Denial necessitates expending some of that blood, and this is noted in cost as how many "thimbles" of blood must be used. If the Cainite does not have the requisite amount of blood, the rite cannot be performed. The Cainite *must* replenish the blood into the phial, fresh from other Cainites (likely those in his cell)—oddly, storing blood anywhere but this glass phial (say, carrying around a blood bag full of the mixture) doesn't help with the casting of the rites. Cainites who try to use false blood—be it the blood of non-Cainites or blood that has been stored anywhere but her phial—automatically suffer a dramatic failure when casting the rite. If the cell is home to a number of Cainites, they can share phials.

Can non-Cainite hunters cast Rites of Denial? Technically, no, because they don't have the phial, and they don't have the blood of Cainites,

VIGILANT IN IGNORANCE

The Cainites willfully dismiss investigation into the Rites of Denial. *We're* not dismissing it, and it's likely that players' characters won't dismiss it, either. But the hunters of this conspiracy do, just as they willfully ignore many things about their group. They receive mysterious messages. They ask a strange question. They don't look deeper than that. Looking deeper isn't encouraged. Those who look for answers find themselves brainwashed, programmed, or waterboarded into keeping their eyes pressed firmly shut on these issues. Those who keep up the poking and prodding are left outside the conspiracy—forever.

It's appropriate, then, that these Rites of Denial involve more than just denying vampires access to their supernatural ways. It's also about Cainites denying their own origins, their own hypocritical ways, their tangle of secrets that drag behind them.

ONLY VAMPIRES?

Do the Rites of Denial only work upon vampires? Technically, no. Actually, they work on any unliving creature—a shuffling zombie, a Reanimated *tabula rasa*, even a manifested ghost. They *also* work on any creature bound to or formed from vampire's blood, which means that the thralls and addicts indebted to a bloodsucker can feel the pain brought on by the Rites of Denial.

But what about, say, werewolves? Changelings? Witches? Nope. However, maybe you're a gracious Storyteller and you want to tell a story about a pack of rampant crow-faced monsters wreaking havoc on a small town, and some of the players are playing Cainites. If you choose to allow the Rites of Denial to operate upon such blatantly non-vampiric creatures, please do so. But an additional cost should be incurred: each Rite of Denial now demands three Willpower be spent instead of the normal one.

and the Sources haven't explained the rituals to her. That being said, a Storyteller might rule that if a character were able to get past these notable hurdles (steal a phial, steal the blood, force a Cainite to explain the casting of one such ritual), it might be possible for a non-Cainite to learn the Rites of Denial. Of course, doing so earns that individual great enmity from those hunters of the conspiracy.

Learning and Buying

The way a Cainite learns Rites of Denial is curious, because technically it means the Cainite is not herself in control of when she gains a new rite. Of course, the *player* still is—when the player is ready to purchase a new Rite of Denial, she may. The character then receives the knowledge from the Sources.

A character may theoretically know as many Rites of Denial as she cares to—it's not limited by Status or even by points purchased in the Endowment. Each Rite of Denial costs five experience points to learn, though the first one's free when the character purchases the first dot (only) of this Endowment. (Alternately, if a character starts play with this Endowment, he can take one ritual per dot purchased in the Endowment.)

The Rites of Denial available for purchase are found below.

Aggravate

The word comes down from the Sources: drizzle some of the phial blood upon a weapon held in one's hand.

Use one's forefinger to swirl the blood into a rough approximation of the Cainite sign. The instrument now feels heavier. More powerful. The Cainite's hand hums, and he hears the rush of blood in his ears. This can only be cast upon hand-held weapons whose use is dictated by the Weaponry Skill (no firearms, for instance).

Cost: 1 Willpower, 2 thimbles of blood

Action: Instant

Roll Results

Dramatic Failure: The weapon in hand suffers immediate Structure damage equal to the Cainite's dots in this Endowment.

Failure: The weapon feels empowered, but gains no bonus, otherwise.

Success: The weapon seems to vibrate in the Cainite's hand. It feels stronger. For the remainder of the scene, the weapon now gains a bonus equal to the Cainite's dots in Rites of Denial. In addition, even if the weapon would previously have done only bashing (a lead pipe, for instance), it now does lethal damage. However, this weapon's bonus only applies to attacks against vampires, their minions, or other unliving (physically manifested) creatures.

Exceptional Success: On the weapon's first attack, half of the damage (round down) is aggravated. However, after the scene is up, the weapon crumbles to ash or dust.

Befoul

This Rite of Denial represents a cruel trick, but what do the Cainites care? Their only goal is to see vampires eradicated from the earth, and if this ritual helps to accomplish that by even a tiny margin, then kudos all around. By sprinkling the phial's blood, a bag of salt and a handful of dead leaves in and around a location, the Cainite has "fouled the nest" (or as some say, "salted the earth") in regards to the vampire. The Cainite symbol must also be marked on every wall, also in blood. The vampire may not slumber in such a place. The vampire may not use Dread Powers in such a place. The vampire can't spend Willpower (blood) in such a place. The locale is cursed, made toxic to the creature.

Cost: 1 Willpower, 4 thimbles of blood

Action: Extended (the larger the area to be "spoiled," the more successes are necessary—a small apartment needs five successes, a warehouse would demand 15 successes, and a sprawling estate would necessitate 25 successes; each roll is equal to ten minutes)

Roll Results

Dramatic Failure: The Cainite traps himself in the location. He finds himself unable to leave: doors will not yield to him, nor will windows. This lasts for one hour.

Failure: The rite does not take hold.

Success: The nest is fouled, the earth salted. This lasts for one night per dot possessed in this Endowment. The vampire cannot slumber here during this time—if the vampire *does* fall asleep here (in other words, the sun rises and the vampire unwittingly tumbles into daysleep), he takes one point of lethal damage per hour spent. The vampire may not activate any Dread Powers while within this place, nor can it spend Willpower (blood) for any purpose (healing, for instance).

Exceptional Success: As above, and now the vampire suffers -1 to Initiative while within the befouled location.

Behold

The Cainite dabs the phial blood upon his skin, drawing the symbol of the conspiracy upon his forehead—it signals revelation. It signals war. With this Rite of Denial, the blood-hungry monsters are revealed.

Cost: 1 Willpower, 1 thimble of blood

Action: Instant

Roll Results

Dramatic Failure: The Cainite suffers a migraine behind her eyes—all Perception rolls suffer a penalty equal to the dots possessed in this Endowment.

Failure: The sigil upon the head grants the Cainite nothing.

Success: All vampires within sight are revealed as what they are, only moreso—they appear truly vile, with gaping maws full of teeth and hands tipped with crooked talons. This doesn't count towards those vampires who are hiding using the Stealth Skill or other Dread Powers—however, it does grant the Cainite a measure of aid when trying to spot such hidden creatures. The Cainite can add her dots in this Endowment to any rolls made to pierce natural or supernatural Stealth.

Exceptional Success: As above, but the Cainite regains the spent point of Willpower. His sight and power is confirmed and it fills him with certainty of purpose.

Deny

A line of sea salt left upon the threshold of a door—and coupled with a drizzling of phial's blood—can prevent a vampire from entering through that doorway. The vampire simply is unable to conjure the will necessary to bring his body through the door (or window or other portal). The Cainite may invite a vampire through, however—at which point the chosen creature may enter freely.

Cost: 1 Willpower, 2 thimbles of blood

Action: Instant

Roll Results

Dramatic Failure: The ritual fails. The remaining blood in the Cainite's phial suddenly boils over; it's all gone and cannot be reclaimed.

Failure: The line of salt and the trickle of blood fail to provide the barrier that the Cainite desires.

Success: The doorway is protected for one hour per dot the caster possesses in this Endowment. No vampire can cross that line of salt and blood. If someone attempts to throw the vampire through the door, the creature rebounds off of it, failing to pass—and, in addition, suffers one point of bashing damage in the process. Some Dread Powers will work across the barrier, however—if the vampire can still see the eyes of someone on the other side, for instance, he could attempt a Dread Power like Terrify.

Exceptional Success: As above, but when the vampire encounters the barrier, he loses one point of Willpower (i.e. stolen blood).

Evade

The creatures of the night can be swift—so it behooves a Cainite to be fast, or even better, fast*er*. The Cainite smears a line of blood on the ground with her thumb, and then steps over it. If her Sources were right, then she may gain preternatural swiftness when dealing with the bloodsucking fiends.

Cost: 1 Willpower, 1 thimble

Action: Instant

Roll Results

Dramatic Failure: The hunter fails to gain any benefit. In addition, her legs seize with terrible cramps for the remainder of the scene. Her Speed is halved, and any rolls necessitating use of her legs (such as an Athletics roll for jumping) suffer -3 dice.

Failure: The Cainite gains no such swiftness.

Success: For the next hour, the Cainite gains a bonus to her Speed whenever involved in chasing down or being chased by a vampire (Foot Chase mechanics are likely to be involved, though not necessarily). This bonus is equal to twice the character's dots in the Endowment.

Exceptional Success: As above, and the hunter also gains +1 to Initiative when in combat with a vampire.

Invoke

Most vampires find the traditional apotropaics nothing more than a trivial annoyance: garlic does not repel them, holy water fails to sear the undead flesh, and silver is nothing more than shiny metal. With this Rite of Denial, the Cainite can confirm the truth behind the stories and force such apotropes to work for a time. The Cainite must choose one traditional apotropaic—it can be a common one such as the garlic noted above, or something more uncommon in folklore such as poppy seeds

or a bundle of wild roses. The Cainite must hold some of the phial blood in his mouth and then spit it over the folkloric apotrope. For a time, the object will repel—and even harm—vampires.

Cost: 1 Willpower, 3 thimbles of blood

Action: Extended (a number of successes are needed equal to 10 minus the character's dots in this Endowment; each roll is equivalent to one turn's worth of spitting or drooling blood upon the apotrope)

Roll Results

Dramatic Failure: The mouthful of blood brings on a terrible bout of nausea. The character suffers -2 to all rolls until she is able to achieve eight hours of uninterrupted sleep.

Failure: The apotrope fails to affect the vampire.

Success: For the remainder of the night—until dawn—the apotrope works to repel vampires. Vampires may not come within 10 yards of the apotrope without succeeding first on a Resolve + Composure roll, and this roll is penalized by the Cainite's dots in this Endowment. In addition, if the apotrope can be held to the flesh of the vampire, it does the creature harm: one point of aggravated damage per turn of exposure. Note that doing so likely to inspire the vampire to immediately enter frenzy (p. 163).

Exceptional Success: As above, but the range is extended to 20 yards.

Mark

The coppery taste of blood and coins in the mouth can, for some unknown reason, give the Cainite a sense of potent focus. Using this Rite of Denial demands that the Cainite let a coin soak in phial's blood for up to one hour. Then, the Cainite must hold the coin *and* the

THE BIG BOOK OF APOTROPAICS

Want a nice (though admittedly non-comprehensive) list of folkloric vampire repellents? Any of the following could be used when casting Invoke (or, alternately, a Storyteller might want to look at this list to create interesting vulnerabilities for some of the more "unique" vampire specimens that could be found in his game):

Amulets (iron, silver, otherwise), bread (especially bread made from flour milled with blood), brooms, dried peas, garlic, grain, grave dirt, holy wafers (communion), holy water, iron filings, lemons or lemon juice (seriously), poppy seeds, river pebbles, rosary beads (or Buddhist prayer beads), vinegar, wild roses (i.e. dogrose), wine.

blood in his mouth. His hand and eyes work with sudden determination and concentration when attempting to waylay a monstrous vampire.

Cost: 1 Willpower, 2 thimbles of blood

Action: Instant (though note that the coin must soak for one hour before casting)

Roll Results

Dramatic Failure: The character swallows the coin and the blood. It burns on the way down, confirmation of her worthlessness. The character suffers one point of lethal damage. In addition, talking is difficult until the wound heals, incurring a -1 penalty to those Social rolls necessitating speech.

Failure: The bloody coin fails to provide the focus necessary.

Success: The character gains a number of bonus dice equal to her dots in this Endowment. These bonus dice apply only to rolls meant to *stake* a vampire or *decapitate* a vampire. The penalty for target rolls still applies, of course, but ideally the bonus dice will lessen or entirely obviate those negative modifiers. The effect lasts for one scene, or until the hunter fails to hold the mouthful of blood and coin (whichever comes first). If, for instance, the hunter is struck in combat, the Storyteller may demand a roll (Resolve + Composure) to determine if the hunter can keep the blood and coin in his mouth without ejecting or accidentally swallowing. The effects end if the blood and coin leave the mouth.

Exceptional Success: As above, and in addition, the hunter gains +1 to Initiative.

Obligate

If a vampire leaves any kind of footprint—be it in mud, on a carpet, or outlined in dirt on a cement floor—then the Cainite can endeavor to fix the vampire to that spot. A rusted nail must be made slick with blood from the phial. When the nail is placed within the borders of the footprint, the vampire—wherever he may be at the time—is held in place, or "obligated to remain," as some Cainites put it. This must be cast within one hour of the footprint being left behind. If the Cainite attempts to use this ritual after an hour has passed, the attempt automatically results in a dramatic failure.

Cost: 1 Willpower, 2 thimbles of blood

Action: Extended (the blood must be rubbed into the rusted nail; this roll necessitates a number of successes equal to the vampire's Speed score, and each roll equals one turn's worth of time)

Roll Results

Dramatic Failure: The nail burns the hand of the Cainite, and the hunter suffers a point of bashing damage as a result. In addition, the vampire gains +2 to his Speed for the remainder of the night.

Failure: The nail sits within the frame of the footprint... and that's all.

Success: The hunter achieves the necessary successes. Wherever the vampire is at the time the Rite of Denial takes hold, its one foot becomes fixed to the ground for ten minutes per dot possessed in this Endowment. The vampire can unmoor his foot by succeeding on a Resolve + Composure roll and spending a point of Willpower, but after doing so the foot still feels numb, as if the animating Blood of the fiend fails to circulate to that limb. The result is the same once the time of "obligation" is complete (numb foot). As a result, even if the vampire frees himself for the remainder of the night, he operates at half of his Speed (round down).

Exceptional Success: As above, but the vampire cannot unmoor his foot. He is frozen in place wherever he is for the duration. After that time, as noted, his Speed is halved for the remainder of the night.

Pilfer

Vampires are creatures of many secrets—lost truths and stolen knowledge lie within the lockbox of the vampire's mind. This Rite of Denial offers the Cainite a chance to extract one such secret from the seemingly impenetrable memory of the fiendish bloodsucker. Performing this rite demands that the Cainite put several drops of the phial's blood into her own ears before asking this question of the vampire: "What do you know?"

Cost: 1 Willpower, 3 thimbles of blood

Action: Instant and contested (vampire rolls Resolve + Potency)

Roll Results

Dramatic Failure: The Cainite suddenly speaks one of her own secrets aloud.

Failure: The vampire's secrets are safe. For now.

Success: The vampire needn't speak aloud, but one of his secrets suddenly is made manifest within the Cainite's own mind. This secret is something the vampire doesn't want *anyone*—particularly the Cainite—to know. It can only be used successfully once upon a given vampire. All subsequent attempts on that vampire incur a dramatic failure.

Exceptional Success: As above, and in addition, the Cainite pilfers one of the vampire's Willpower points. The vampire loses it. The Cainite gains it.

Prohibit

The Cainite drizzles some of the phial's blood on each wrist of one she hopes to protect—then smears each into a forbidding 'x' upon the tender skin. She must ask the target a question, *the* question: "Who is Cain?" After which, the blood within the target grows colder, as if a saline rush runs suddenly through the veins. Vampires

will find no sustenance from that blood, now, and in fact it will do the creature harm.

Cost: 1 Willpower, 2 thimbles of blood

Action: Instant

Roll Results

Dramatic Failure: The blood starts to burn upon the target's wrists, causing the individual one point of lethal damage. Even after the damage heals, scars remain forever.

Failure: The phial's blood fails to offer any kind of protection.

Success: The target—or, at least, her blood—is protected. A vampire who attempts to drink from the victim finds that the blood offers no sustenance. In addition, even a single taste of the blood causes the vampire great anguish: the vampire takes a number of lethal points of damage equal to the caster's dots in this Endowment. This damage occurs only once—the vampire can continue drinking from that vessel without additional suffering, but the blood still offers zero value to the consuming creature. Note that the caster cannot use this Rite of Denial on herself. This protection lasts until the next sun-up or sundown, whichever comes first.

Exceptional Success: As above, but the protection lasts for a full 24 hours.

Question

The question is everything. Who is Cain? They don't know the answer. They don't know why it must be asked—but it *must be asked*. Those who know this ritual can poison the mind of a vampire with the question as easily as a vampire can poison the mind of an unwitting mortal. The Cainite must paint her tongue and teeth with the blood one hour before she hopes to ask the question of a monster. She must also chew a sprig or leaf of mint.

Cost: 1 Willpower, 5 thimbles of blood

Action: Reflexive

Roll Results

Dramatic Failure: The character cannot ask the question: it sticks in her throat, and she suddenly feels woefully unworthy. She gains a mild derangement of the Storyteller's choosing.

Failure: The question bears no metaphysical weight.

Success: The question reaches the vampire's ears. The creature cannot stand the question. It worms into her ear and mind like a chewing maggot. It drives her mad—literally. She gains a severe derangement of the player's choosing (the *character* does not choose; note the distinction), and suffers under this derangement for one month per dot the Cainite possesses in this Endowment.

Exceptional Success: As above, but the vampire suffers -1 to any Resolve + Composure rolls made to resist that derangement during those months.

Reflect

The evil eye—a stylized blue oculus—is thought to ward off evil. For the Cainite, it can. The Cainite whispers the question, "Who is Cain?" and draws the evil eye over one of her own eyes in blood withdrawn from the phial. Before the blood dries, she must fleck it with kohl (ground galena), mascara, coal dust, or some other kind of black dirt or makeup. For a time, she is protected against some of the Dread Powers of the vampire.

Cost: 1 Willpower, 1 thimble

Action: Extended (character needs a number of successes equal to 10 minus her Resolve score; each roll equals one minute's worth of application)

Roll Results

Dramatic Failure: The blood drips into the eye, burning it. For the next hour, the character suffers as if possessing the One Eye Flaw (p. 219, **World of Darkness Rulebook**).

Failure: The evil eye affords her no defense against the dark arts.

Success: Any vampire that tries to use a Dread Power upon the hunter that necessitates eye contact will find her efforts soundly rebuffed. The vampire suffers a penalty to the Dread Power roll equal to the character's dots in this Endowment. In addition, if the vampire *fails* the Dread Power roll, then the vampire actually suffers its effects instead of the hunter. (If the vampire were to use Hypnotism—found on p. 279 of **Hunter: The Vigil**—upon the hunter and failed, then the vampire would perform whatever suggested action it sought to implant within the hunter's mind.) This Rite of Denial works upon the following Dread Powers (even if they don't specifically state requiring eye contact): Alter Memory, Ecstasy, Fury, Hypnotism, Sleep and Terrify. The Storyteller may allow this to work on other Dread Powers, however. This ritual's protection lasts for one hour.

Exceptional Success: The hunter is also afforded a +1 to all Perception rolls for one hour.

Unmask

Vampires are hard to track in this modern world because of the inability of media and reflective surfaces to capture their images (think of the photographic blur or the distortion of the vampire's visage in the mirror). Also, vampires have tricks to force their human prey to overlook the more glaring and obvious signs that they are walking corpses. With this Denial, a Cainite daubs blood from the phial onto his own eyelids. The first vampire the Cainite looks upon is suddenly revealed to the world: the creature shows up perfectly in media and in mirrors (so perfectly, in fact, the creature stands out). In addition—and to some Cainites, more importantly—those nearby the vampire suddenly suffer an inexplicable fear of the creature, unconsciously recognizing it as a walking corpse. They do not instantly panic, but most humans (with Willpower of 5 or below) will hurry away with a steady step.

Cost: 1 Willpower, 1 thimble of blood

Action: Instant

Roll Results

Dramatic Failure: The creature gains a measure of strength. It now gains +2 to any Stealth rolls it makes over the next scene.

Failure: The blood on the eyelids dries and flakes off immediately; the effect is not made manifest.

Success: As above. The vampire now shows up brightly and blatantly in all media and in mirrors. In addition, any humans within sight of the creature will try to escape the scene (most will do so surreptitiously). Those at or beneath Willpower 5 must spend a point of Willpower to remain nearby. Those of Willpower 6 or higher needn't spend any points, but must succeed on a Resolve + Composure roll to remain in sight of the vampire. The Cainite casting this Rite of Denial is unaffected by it, but other hunters are affected as normal humans. The vampire has a difficult time hiding from sight—any attempts at Stealth (including those fueled by Dread Powers) suffer a penalty equal to the Cainite's dots in this Endowment.

Exceptional Success: As above, but attempts at Stealth *require* the vampire to expend one point of Willpower (on top of any costs necessitated by, say, Dread Powers). The penalty to Stealth also remains.

In The Blood

They're out there. With just a passing glance, many of them look like anybody else; a deeper look reveals they're maybe a bit pale, maybe dead behind the eyes. Some of them are suave, polished, gathering in penthouses and nightclubs, admiring each other's artworks and acquisitions and applauding every stab in the back, every callous word. Others look like they were *once* human, perhaps, but now are little more than fanged nightmares skittering about in the shadows and sewers, desperate for the next kill.

And kill, they do. Some want to. Some don't mean to. But they're... thirsty for blood. Hungry for meat. And this insatiable urge sends them forth to feed. They fill their bellies. Their throats. Their dead veins. It gives them power in exchange for some irreplaceable part burned out of their souls (if they even *have* souls, and some hunters consider that a point of contention).

The Dread Powers of the vampire can be found in this section: everything you need to know to build a suitable vampire antagonist in your game. You'll find material that will help you conjure vampires painted every shade of bloody red—icy *strigoi*, cruel *vrykolakas*, the hopping vampires of Asia, the *bhuta* fiends of Hindu lore. You'll find rules for the vampire's insidious powers of the mind, and will even uncover rules to create a vampire that doesn't feed off of blood at all—instead, he's a psychic leech, feeding off of dreams, hopes, and fears.

The Laws of Death

When creating a vampire antagonist, the following rules are generally in-play, though certainly you may have reason to change this subtly or dramatically (in order to keep the hunter characters—and by proxy, their players—on their toes):

• Vampires are nocturnal predators. They slumber—really, a deathlike torpor—during the day. A human regains a spent point of Willpower in the morning upon waking (provided that one's sleep was relatively unbroken), but a vampire *spends* a point of Willpower simply to rise. (See "Daysleep," below.)

• Most vampires consume blood (though in some cases, raw human meat) to survive. In game terms, the consumption of blood translates to Willpower within the undead crucible of the vampire's body. This Willpower is not strictly their own, but rather, it represents the life-force that has been stolen from others. (This also prevents you from having to keep track of both a vampire's blood, called "Vitae" in **Vampire: The Re-**quiem, and Willpower separately.) A point of definition: blood (lowercase 'b') is the stuff that circulates through the human body and that vampire's drink. The Blood (capital 'B') is how the vampires think of and refer to the transubstantiated fluid that mystically animates their accursed corpse-bodies. Rules on a vampire's feeding can be found later in this chapter.

• Hunger taints and pollutes vampires' deeds, corrupting even their noblest actions with a patina of pain and damnation. A vampire cannot regain Willpower from the fulfillment of his Virtue *until* he has fed; until then, he may not experience the fulfillment of Hope or the vindication of Justice. Even then, he may only recover Willpower points up to the limit of his Willpower dots. If he wants more, it must come from feeding. (In game terms, this means that when a vampire is down to three or less Willpower, he cannot gain Willpower through his Virtue: his hunger, driven by the literal or metaphorical Beast within, is the dominant force.)

Merit: Potency (• to •••••)

Effect: Every vampire, whether she feeds from blood, meat or dreams, possesses this Merit. The Merit represents how old or how powerful the vampire is—elder immortals have fed so long on the lives of the innocent that the blood in their bodies is like red sap.

The Potency Merit lets vampires store Willpower above their expected Willpower score. Vampires can also use their Potency dots to resist the effects of other vampires' and other creatures' Dread Powers, and even certain Endowments such as certain Benedictions or Castigations. As Potency increases, vampires' Attributes can even rise above the human limit of five dots.

Potency dots also add bonus dice to contested rolls to resist any Dread Power or Endowment intended to influence a vampire's mind or emotions. This is cumulative with any bonus from enhancing Resistance Attributes; see p. 95 and 133, **World of Darkness Rulebook**. (The bonus equates to the dots held in the Potency Merit.)

Age is how long the vampire has been dead, not the vampire's age was when she was turned. The age ranges overlap, because some vampires are more active than others. Some might spend many nights feeding, fighting rivals, fleeing hunters and testing the physical limits of their dead tissues, whereas others pursue more sedentary unlives and develop Potency more slowly. Potency and Age are not always married: a young vampire sired by a truly puissant elder may possess higher-than-normal Potency for his years in death.

VAMPIRE: THE REQUIEM

For those who don't have **Vampire: The Requiem**, most of this chapter discusses the vampires from that game in broad terms. It endeavors to simplify the systems because, really, the players are likely playing hunter characters, not vampires. Using vampires as antagonists can be made easier (requiring less book reference or rule memorization) when the rules are simpler, as they are here in this chapter.

That said, if you own **Requiem**, feel free to ignore any of what you find below (for instance, you may prefer to keep track of blood—or Vitae—separate from Willpower). However, this chapter does attempt to introduce some new rules—several new "spins" on the vampiric condition—which are helpful in keeping players on their toes. In addition, some of these new rules might even make their way into your **Vampire: The Requiem** game, too...

Potency	Age	Max Willpower/per Turn	Max Attributes
1	0-75	10/1	5
2	25-125	13/1	5
3	100-250	15/2	6
4	200-500	30/4	8
5	400-500	50/10	10

Maximum Willpower/per Turn is the vampire's total potential pool of Willpower; as the vampire grows in power, she is able to transubstantiate the blood of her victims into the will that animates her undead form and fuels her Dread Powers. Note that this different from the vampire's base Willpower score, which remains as a computation of Resolve + Composure. A vampire of Potency • with a Resolve • • and Composure • • • still has five *dots* of Willpower. However, because a vampire at that Potency can store up to 10 total Willpower *points*, the vampire can store five points above her normal Willpower total. This also calculates how many Willpower points the vampire may spend per turn. Vampires of low Potency (• and • •) may only spend one point of Willpower per turn, like most characters—but higher Potency increases this.

Maximum Attributes is the maximum unenhanced levels in a vampire's Attributes. A vampire with Potency 3 can have an Attribute go up to 6, for instance.

Grim Resurrection

How is it that a vampire is born, created or damned into unlife? What curse stirs them to lurch up out of their graves (or tear free from a body bag) and stagger out into the world, hungry for a gut full of blood? Below, you'll find a number of systems that you might use to inform the creation of a new vampire—these are by no means exhaustive, and you are encouraged to come up with your own ideas behind a vampire's bloody genesis.

The Embrace

The majority of vampires—known by and large as the Damned, or the Kindred—create their own progeny through a supernatural process called the Embrace. Upon draining a victim dry of his blood, the vampire places some of his own Blood into the mouth of dead or dying. The victim surges into some rough semblance of life, his undead body now animated by the transmuted curse passed along from his "sire" vampire (and this necessitates that the sire expend a full *dot* of Willpower to achieve this affect).

The Embrace is the "default" style of one vampire creating progeny, and is what you'll find in **Vam-**

pire: The Requiem. It is, of course, not the only option you might consider...

Infection

Vampires are reportedly able to transfer their infection—meaning, their vampiric condition—through a simple bite. If you're bit, the stories say, you die and become one of them. In fact, a few years back a renowned biologist publicly declared that vampires could not exist because, if they did, the rate of infection combined with their nightly predilections for feeding would confirm that we'd all become vampires in a fairly short span of time. This announcement was cold comfort to the cell of Null Mysteriis in New York in June of 2008 who lost five good men taking down a nest of bloodsuckers operating out of Central Park—hunters who emerged from the shadows a few nights later with no heartbeat and a wicked thirst for the red stuff.

Using the infection vector in a story, it's recommended that the vampiric condition not be something that happens immediately after a vampire's bite—the infection takes hold of the victim's body (living or dead) slowly but surely. If the victim is alive after the bite, he suffers one point of lethal damage per day. As the days progress, his vampiric nature emerges in bits and pieces (one day he becomes over-sensitive to sunlight, the next he starts taking his steaks rare, and so forth). Upon assuming the last point of damage (filling his last Health box), the victim dies—and awakens the next night, a vampire. A blood transfusion before this time may save his life (ala the film, *Near Dark*).

If the victim was dead, assume that no decomposition takes place (unless you like your vampire antagonists with a little meat rotting off the bones) and that the

THE BEAST

Throughout, we discuss "the Beast within" with reasonable frequency. Most vampires are given over to what is either a metaphorical or literal demon inside, a raging monster that represents the vampire's most base and vile needs. The Beast is equal parts rabid dog, perverse succubus and uncaring manipulator. It longs to eat, mock and destroy.

Even those vampires that attempt to maintain a high Morality and hold onto their humanity always feel the internal pressures of the Beast rattling the bars of its cage...

corpse will awaken several nights later—probably a number of nights equal to the victim's original Health dots.

The Curse

Sometimes, a vampire's undead damnation seems spontaneous—one night, a fairly fresh corpse struggles free from its grave. It's not a mindless creature, but a hungry fiend with human memories and some semblance of human emotion. How might this happen? And why? This kind of damnation is almost purely story-based, and may make for the genesis of an interesting vampire antagonist. Some options include:

• Suicide. Some suicides are so brutal (and some might say, so selfish) that the victim awakens a few nights later, now cursed to walk this earth.

• Murder. Murder—or any atrocity committed upon another person—might be cause enough for God or fate or some other divine power to curse an individual with vampirism. Any sharp moral decay could thematically be reflected in a person's death and grisly resurrection as one of the undead.

• Improper Burial. A restless cadaver dumped in an unmarked grave or a corpse kicked over the side of a boat (perhaps the victim of a serial killer) may return to this world as a bloodsucking fiend. The idea is of course that the indignity of such a crass burial stirs the body to a new awakening in much the same way that a restless ghost lingers in this world.

• Curse of Birth. A person born with a caul, a tail, teeth (as in, *comes out of the womb* with a full set of teeth or fangs), or born on a diabolical day and at a particular time (seven o'clock on the seventh day of the seventh month) might become a vampire when one day he dies. Or maybe he's a vampire now, born half-dead, womb tissue still fresh in his teeth.

• Curse of Biology. Perhaps a victim suffers an acute, even supernatural form of an existing disease (like the blood thinness associated with anemia or hemophilia or the aversion to light experienced by those suffering from porphyria). Such a sufferer slowly becomes a vampire, either living or dead. Rabies is also a possibility: some might suggest that a rabid animal is somewhat vampiric (driven mad by hunger, occasionally nocturnal). An advanced version or supernaturally-tainted version of the rabies virus could manifest as a vampire-like condition.

Of Demonic Origin

Certainly what vampires do is diabolical—whether they mean to or not, they are driven to feast, fuck, and kill. But are they so truly infernal that their origins are demonic? Maybe so.

If you choose to invoke a hellish origin in regards to the vampires in your **Hunter: The Vigil** game, consider one of two options.

In the first option, upon death, a demon takes possession of the corpse. This isn't a perfect possession; the human's consciousness must make "room" for that of the demon (sometimes called "The Beast"). The demon feeds off of blood, or perhaps the resonant emotions that blood contains, and thus the vampire must feed. Failing to feed the demon only stirs the infernal possessor all the more, driving the vampire mad with hunger.

It's likely that any possessing demon is of the "lesser" variety (demons are described in greater detail on p. 283, **Hunter: The Vigil**): demonic familiars, more or less. That said, it's possible that an Elder demon (an Archduke of Hell, a mad *qashmal* angel, some bloated spirit grown fat on murder) takes up residence within the corpse, instead. Consider the possibility that those vampires possessed by lesser demons are likely to be the followers, or minions, of those vampires possessed by Elders.

In the second option, the vampiric condition comes as a result of an infernal pact. Greater demons (p. 284, **Hunter: The Vigil**) are renown for making offers of information or abilities to those who so require them. Someone desperate for revenge against a loved one—or perhaps a poor soul with terminal cancer who sees the end coming far too swiftly—might make a bargain with the demon that results in the individual giving up his soul. Of course, giving up the soul doesn't mean giving up the body—and, as a result, the fool arises as one of the fiendish dead.

Feeding

Vampires feed. They must; without drawing blood (or whatever it is that the vampire consumes), the vampire cannot animate his unliving body.

The "Drain" Dread Power (p. 278, **Hunter: The Vigil**) is the mechanism by which a vampire can feed. Drain inflicts lethal Health damage through blood loss. Vampires must bite to feed, piercing the

---

ECSTASY OF THE KISS

A vampire's bite is insidious because of the ecstasy it causes in the victim. For some, it's a numbing haze—a heroin lull. For others, it's an orgasmic tide, a constant push and pull to new heights of desire. Hunters bitten must succeed on a Resolve + Composure roll, penalized by the vampire's Potency, to *want* to escape.

---

skin with retractable needle sharp fangs. This requires a successful grapple attack, unless the victim is already helpless. Drain inflicts lethal damage—the victim takes a number of lethal levels of damage per turn equal to the creature's dots in Drain (vampires of Potency 1 or 2, i.e. most vampires, only have one dot in Drain). Each point of damage incurred equals a point of Willpower—transubstantiated from the blood—for the vampire.

Those fangs also deliver lethal damage in combat. See "Dread Attack", p. 278, **Hunter: the Vigil**. A vampire must grapple his victim to apply this attack (see p. 157, **The World of Darkness Rulebook**).

When the vampire is done biting and feeding, it only needs to lick the wound—and the wound is healed. A bruise may remain, but little else. She can only heal those bite wounds she has caused herself.

Feeding Variations

Not all bloodsuckers have fangs. Some feed messily from their victims, tearing into flesh with uneven, rotting teeth; other creatures of the night distend their jaws like snakes to clamp over victims' mouths and noses, sucking the breath out of them. Some vampires have truly bizarre dietary needs: drinking dreams, eating one's luck and grace, consuming memories like a draught of wine.

The following are variations of the Drain Dread Power. All use the same mechanism as "Drain" (p. 278, **Hunter: the Vigil**), but successes rolled inflict the following damage instead.

Leeching Willpower

Psychic vampires' Drain power robs the victim of the will to live. The attack requires sustained eye contact and concentration, during which the psychic vampire cannot perform any other actions. Each turn the victim loses a Willpower point, which the vampire gains on a one-to-one basis. The victim may roll Resolve + Composure to resist, but every Willpower point successfully stolen from the vampire incurs a one die penalty to the victim's Resistance turn after turn (if the vampire has pilfered two points of the victim's Willpower, then the victim suffers a -2 penalty to the roll to resist). The victim *feels* the will being robbed from him. As a result, his mind grows foggy, and he suffers a terrible enervation as a result. The victim suffers a penalty equal to Willpower points stolen (maximum -5) until he can sleep for eight hours.

Dream Eating

Some vampires derive sustenance as much from consuming a person's dreams—and the emotions they feel in slumber—as opposed to consuming their blood. Use of this power necessitates touching the victim; even a finger graced against the sleeper's cheek will do the trick. This is an extended roll on the part of the vampire, though the monster has no target number of successes and may continue draining the victim's dreams as long as it is able to. Each roll is equivalent to one hour. Each success earns the vampire a point of Willpower. In addition, successes earned add up to penalties the victim suffers for the next 24 hours upon waking (maximum of -5 dice).

The vampire actually experiences the dreams somewhat as he consumes them, and may even feature as a presence in the victim's dreamscape or nightmare. The victim's player may roll Wits + Resolve once an every hour—success indicates the sleeper awakens, interrupting the vampire's feeding time.

Those victims affected by Dream Eating do not regain a point of Willpower upon awakening. In addition, overuse of this power can damage the victim's mind. If the vampire feeds on the target a number of times surpassing the target's Resolve score, the victim gains a mild derangement of the Storyteller's choice (a Phobia of sleep or the dark is not unwarranted).

Stealing Breath

The vampire must clamp his mouth over the victim's own mouth—the mechanic requires grappling (provided the victim resists; if the victim is willingly accepting a "kiss" then the grapple may not be necessary) just as with a bite. Here, as with blood drinkers, the consumption of breath incurs lethal damage, which is then translated into Willpower for the creature. Victims suffer respiratory ailments for the next 24 hours—asthma, coughing, shortness of breath—which incurs a -1 penalty to Physical rolls.

Sin-eaters

This ritualized form of vampirism goes back to Biblical times (and possibly earlier, all the way to Ancient Egypt). Sin-eaters take on the burdens of another's sin to ensure that their clients go to Heaven, or the Courts of Ma'at (Heavenly Justice). The ritual requires that bread and salt be placed on the client's chest, and the Sin Eater consumes this. In the undead version, the victim's sins soak into the bread, staining it with blood.

Dice Pool: Manipulation + Occult

Action: Extended; target number is the client's Morality

Roll Results

Dramatic Failure: Both the sin-eater and the client suffer from a severe derangement that lasts for one week.

Failure: The client fails to absolve his sins, and the sin-eater gains nothing.

Success: The client revisits the moment of his worst sin in his soul, and the sin-eater consumes this sin. The client has a chance to reroll his last failed degeneration roll; he must accept the result of this new roll as final. The sin-eater consumes the burden of the sin, gaining Willpower up to the limit of his Willpower dots; however, the sin-eater must also make the same degeneration roll as the client.

Exceptional Success: As above, but the Sin Eater's Morality is considered one higher for the purpose of the degeneration roll he must make.

HUMAN VAMPIRES

Are all vampires dead—or, *un*dead? Not necessarily. This book assumes that, yes, the vampires noted within are all the walking, hungry dead, but it *is* possible that a living human could possess the consumptive Dread Powers of the vampire (and the sin-eater, above, is a good example of this). Perhaps the human is some kind of necromancer, or just a "psychic vampire" leeching off people's minds, or even just a cursed human (those born with a caul, as noted). They could drink blood or any of the "variant consumptives" noted in this section. What do hunters do with a vampire that appears ostensibly human and can be killed with a bullet to the heart?

The Blood is the Life

In the still, small hours of the night, when a human is surrounded by silence, all they hear is the sound of their breathing, the feel of their heart beating and the susurration of the blood in their ears known as "the sound of silence."

A vampire hears no such reassuring sounds. She has no heartbeat; she does not breathe. Her stomach does not grumble. But she hears the song of her Blood—the scream of want and need and Hunger wailing within her, relentless and insatiable.

For most vampires, it's all about the Blood. But what, exactly, can a vampire do with the sweet *claret* within her undead body?

Wounding and Damage

Strangling a vampire, or punching one in the solar plexus, won't have any particular effect beyond the bashing damage incurred. Vampires don't get winded from a punch in the gut; nor do they depend on a steady blood circulation through the carotid artery to the brain, so choke holds have no effect.

The necrotic tissues of vampires don't suffer the same pains as mortal organs and tissues. A bullet tearing through an atrophied lower intestine won't cause much pain to a vampire, beyond the kinetic energy of the bullet's impact.

Similarly, vampires' nervous tissues don't conduct electricity like they used to, and neither the vampire brain nor the unbeating heart suffer any particular harm from electric shocks.

In game terms, bullets and electricity only do bashing damage to vampires. Not only that, vampires can't be stunned or knocked unconscious by filling their rightmost Health boxes with bashing damage. Normal electricity, even from a lightning strike, inflicts no more than one point of bashing damage.

Drugs and poisons have little impact on the flesh of the dead. Corrosive chemicals such as acids burn vampire tissues as effectively as human tissues. Combustible materials like gasoline, of course, can ignite and inflict aggravated damage. However, if the vampire consumes blood tainted with drugs or poisons, she may suffer their full effect.

The Blood Heals

A vampire can expend his blood, urging it toward a wound to supernaturally mend it. The blood may literally manifest and begin to grow into new bone or tissue, or it may instead be somewhat transparent: the vampire simply wipes his hand over the wound, smearing the blood cleanly away, leaving mended flesh beneath.

A vampire can spend one Willpower point to heal two points of bashing damage or one point of lethal. Vampires can't heal aggravated damage easily; doing so necessitates spending five Willpower points over the course of five nights—and that's just for one point of aggravated damage.

The Blood Strengthens

We've already said it: it's the Blood that stirs dead flesh to move. A vampire doesn't need to wish this to be so—he doesn't need to consciously will the sanguine fluids in his body to each limb, finger, and eye. It happens. It's the nature of damnation.

Ah, but a vampire *can* urge the Blood to his body to increase his Physical Attributes. Sanguine puissance pushes to his arms and he can tear a car door from its moorings or throw a bouncer through a closed wooden door. It extends to his legs and gives him a preternatural burst of speed. It gathers beneath the epidermis and toughens him against blades and bullets.

This is best reflected by the Unholy Attribute Dread Power (p. 283, **Hunter: The Vigil**). However, assume that vampires of Potency • and •• only gain the bonus to a Physical Attribute for a single turn. Only those vampires of greater Potency (••• to •••••) are capable of using the Unholy Attribute as written (meaning, bonuses last for the remainder of the scene). Remember that when a Physical Attribute changes, so do other traits: Health, Initiative, Speed, and so forth.

Fuck Breathing

The blood animates the body; vampires don't require oxygen, and if they do (as some Null Mysteriis hunters claim), then they milk it from the stolen blood within them.

The undead quickly learn how "not breathing" can be used to their advantage, launching attacks on their prey as devious as they are devastating. For instance, a vampire can lay an ambush hidden in a body of murky water. When prey walks past, the creature emerges. Because the vampire doesn't need to breathe, no Stamina rolls are necessary on the creature's behalf while submerged.

Plus, when humans run, they get tired after a certain point. Lactic acid builds up in aerobically-exercised leg muscles, leading to cramps and exhaustion. Over a long enough distance, the body's glycogen reserve gets used up and the human reaches what marathon runners call "The Wall."

Vampires don't have this restriction. Over a long foot chase, the vampire therefore has the advantage over a human: the vampire does not need to make a Stamina + Athletics check to keep up the chase (though should the sun soon be rising, that could be a problem).

Another option for a callous creature of the night? She can trap humans in an airtight room with her. De-pending on the size of the party, their exertions and the size of the room, a cell of unprepared hunters may have between 20 minutes and two hours before having to make suffocation rolls, as per p. 49 of **The World of Darkness Rulebook**. Even if a hunter came prepared with an oxygen tank, that supply can't last forever. All the vampire has to do is play the waiting game. (Alternately, he may lure them into a trap, filling the room with anesthetic gas to incapacitate them, or pump nitrogen into the room to kill them quickly and painlessly.)

Mockery of Life

Some hunters think they're so smart. If the target is breathing, can't be a vampire. If the subject is eating food, has a blush to his cheeks, can pop his cookies in sexual intercourse... clearly not one of the accursed undead. Right? Wrong.

Imitating human biological behavior necessitates that the vampire expend a Willpower point to stir the Blood to flush the cheeks, provide an erection, fake a heartbeat, and so forth. Counterfeiting life in this way lasts for one full scene.

Eating food, however, isn't covered by that expenditure, and necessitates its own expenditure of Willpower (one point) to accomplish. Those that do consume food in this way noisily and painfully purge the food from their atrophied bellies once the scene is up.

The Downsides of Undeath

Immortality is not a free ride. Vampires are shackled by their frailties—for as much as the Blood giveth, the Blood most certainly taketh away. Joining the ranks of the Damned comes with a number of notable concerns, many of which are described below.

Frenzy

The heart doesn't beat, and it's been said that the blood fails to rush in a vampire's ear. But for creatures of the night, the blood almost *sings*. Perhaps it hums in the marrow, or whispers indecipherable voices in the ear. And, in a seeming paradox, the less blood a vampire has in his body, the *louder the maddening song*. This song makes it hard for them to maintain self-control in the face of provocations such as being humiliated, suffering starvation or even being in close proximity to the casual lighting of a cigarette.

Sometimes, the song grows deafening. It drowns everything else out. It doesn't calm the Beast within; it only enrages it, and for a time, it leaves its cage.

The vampire frenzies. Frenzied vampires are out-of-control; they rarely use weapons, they can hardly speak beyond monosyllabic utterances of need and want, and humanity is lost beneath a tide of feral compulsion. In this state, a vampire only wants to feed and kill.

Three Flavors of Madness

Three things might set a vampire off the edge and into the spitting, snapping jaws of a blood-hungry frenzy: starvation, humiliation, or fear.

A *frenzy of starvation*—a hunger frenzy—generally only occurs when the vampire has three or less points of Willpower left, thus indicating that his blood has run low. Still, a vampire might be given over to the throes of a hunger frenzy when confronted with a great deal of fresh blood (usually blood that's out in the open, such as what one might find sprayed up onto the walls at a murder scene or coagulating on the floor of a slaughterhouse). Like a shark driven mad by an ocean frothed with chum, a vampire's hunger is dragged kicking and screaming to the fore when witnessing an abnormal amount of the red stuff. (Note that frenzies of starvation are likely among those just-created vampires who stir for the first time—their bodies are often devoid of blood and so they must feed, *and quickly.*)

A *frenzy of humiliation* is when the vampire is debased or disgraced. Generally, vampires are social creatures—as society's parasites, they gather in their families and clans, applauding one another's cruelty and engaging in incestuous blood-soaked tangles of love, lust, and revenge. (Some hunters have likened them to cancer cells: they look like normal cells on close inspection, mimicking certain normal behaviors, but really they're free radicals in society's system causing corruption—and ultimately death—from within.) When a vampire is humiliated in a way that makes him seem lesser to his vicious peers (even if they're not watching because, oh boy, they have *ways* to find out), it may kick him over the edge. The human façade drops. The Beast emerges from its corner.

A *frenzy of fear...* well, sometimes a vampire knows he's licked. Like a frightened rat, he knows the only way out is to scurry away, flee as fast as possible so that the Beast within may feed another night. Out of a *fight-or-flight* response, this is most certainly the "flight" aspect—and a vampire most commonly suffers from a fear frenzy when confronted by flame. Fire and sunlight have the potential to send the creature of the night into a paroxysm of panic and terror.

Resisting frenzy necessitates that the vampire succeed on a Resolve + Composure roll. This is an extended action, and each roll made equals one turn of internal struggle where the Beast or demon within struggles to kick down its cage door. The target number of successes necessary depends on the provocations confronting the vampire. Some elements may incur modifiers, as noted below.

Starvation	Successes
Sight or smell of blood when hungry	2
Taste of blood when hungry	3
Pulled away from feeding	3
Confronted by lots of fresh blood when hungry	4
Less than three Willpower points remaining	-1 die
One or less Willpower remaining	-2 dice

Humiliation	Successes
Verbally harassed	2
Insulted in public	3
Suffer great damage (five or more points of lethal in one turn)	5
Betrayed by ally or loved one	7
Loved one or ally slain	10
Less than three Willpower points remaining	-1 die
One or less Willpower remaining	-2 dice

Fear	Successes
Someone lights a cigarette	1
Sight of a torch	3
Burning building	5
Obscured sunlight	7
Direct sunlight	10
Surprised by fire or sunlight	-1 die
Burned by fire or sunlight	-3 dice

In the Throes

In a frenzy, the vampire has no moral concerns, and will not stop unless stopped. On encountering a frenzying vampire, hunters might have no choice but to stop it permanently, even if that vampire was otherwise an ally.

Whilst in the throes, the vampire will claw, bite, flee, or guzzle blood like it's the last taste the creature will ever be allowed. The human aspects of the creature are lost beneath a surging tide of bloodlust. (Many vampires hiss, spit and snap their jaws when lost to frenzy.)

Controlling a vampire in frenzy is a difficult task. Vampires in frenzy gain +2 dice to resist being compelled or coerced by any kind of supernatural mind altering or emotion-altering power, such as certain Castigations or Benedictions.

During frenzy, a vampire gains +1 die to all Physical rolls. The creature can also ignore any wound penalties during this time.

Most frenzies last for one full scene, or until the vampire has resolved whatever threat or hunger issues confront her.

The Broken Image

Perhaps there's an element of truth to the old adage that a camera captures the soul of the subject, because vampires—thought by some hunters to be soulless—don't show up on any forms of electronic or magnetic media. Any captured visual of a vampire (on a CCTV camera, for example, or a point-and-shoot 35mm) reveal only a distorted blur. Sometimes, the blur almost seems to twist into something monstrous, like the way one might see a face in the clouds or in an old water stain.

For some vampires, this is also true for their reflections, whether in a mirror or even in a polished glass window.

Most vampires can repress this flaw for a scene by expending a point of Willpower.

Sunlight and Fire

Two universally recognized banes of vampires the world over are sunlight and fire. Damage from these two sources inflict aggravated damage to vampires, and can destroy them utterly.

Fire

Fire *really* burns vampire flesh. Where a flame does lethal damage to human tissues, to a vampire the damage is aggravated. Fire, as such, doesn't do any *more* damage to vampire flesh—a flame that inflicts two points of lethal damage to a human only inflicts two points of damage to a vampire—but the severity of fire seems somehow anathema to the vampire's unliving flesh, burning it utterly.

Fire damage is calculated using the system on p. 180 of **The World of Darkness Rulebook**, automatically upgrading the damage to aggravated for vampires.

Sunlight

The biggest source of fire? That giant mass of incandescent gas in the daytime sky. Vampires are cursed creatures, and part of their damnation is that they can only walk this world when shadow reigns during the night-time hours. Some hunters believe that vampires were cursed by God Himself, or maybe by some kind of sun god (Apollo, Ra, the Polynesian Maui), and that's why the creatures of the night are so easily harmed by the sun's rays.

Like fire, sunlight does aggravated damage to vampires. How much damage the creature suffers depends on how bright the sunlight is, and how much of the vampire's body is exposed to it.

Intensity	Health Points/Turn
Faint filtered sunlight	1
Filtered or weak sunlight	2
Direct sunlight	3

Exposure	Damage
Small part of body exposed	+0
Large part of body exposed	+1
Much of body exposed	+2

Faint filtered sunlight includes sunlight through heavy, closed drapes, heavy cloud cover or twilight. Filtered or weak sunlight involves more direct exposure, such as sunlight through thin drapes, being caught outside on a cloudy day, indirect exposure to reflected sunlight in a mirror or through a window.

Having a small part of the body exposed means no more than a hand or foot or part of the face; also, this covers the level of exposure of a vampire wearing top-to-bottom heavy clothing. A large part of body exposed means an arm or a leg or, at most, the vampire's whole head. If much of body is exposed, that means a torso, both legs or arms, or a vampire caught out in the sun wearing only thin clothing.

Wooden Stake

The most famous weapon of vampire hunters is the sharpened wooden stake. Whether the stake is a carefully crafted, sculpted object lovingly carved out of a single hawthorn branch and wielded like a long bladed punch dagger, or a crude sawed-off wooden chair leg with one end whittled to a point, the stake is the most important, and obvious, weapon in any vampire hunter's arsenal.

For rules on staking, see p. 170 of **The World of Darkness Rulebook**. As a staking attack needs to achieve an exceptional success, most hunters find it far easier to plunge the stake into the chest of a slumbering vampire, such as one that sleeps away from the sun.

A stake through the heart won't kill most vampires, and instead places them in a state of deep deathlike sleep called torpor (see below). However, to keep things interesting, the vampires in your **Hunter: The Vigil** game may turn to greasy ash upon having a stake thrust through the chest and into the heart... or it may do nothing to them at all.

Daysleep

When a vampire sleeps during the day, typically in a light tight haven safe from the sun, she enters a state indistinguishable from death. Scientific examination of a sleeping vampire will not be able to tell the difference between the vampire and a regular cadaver, save that the vampire doesn't show signs of decay (most likely, anyway; some vampires live in a constant state of putrefaction or desiccation).

A vampire in daysleep can rouse herself to defend against attacks. The vampire spends one Willpower point, and for the rest of the scene she is free to act, albeit clumsily—all of the vampire's rolls lose the 10-Again property, and every 1 rolled on behalf of the vampire removes a success.

Particularly powerful vampires must also succeed on a Morality roll before waking for the day—those of Potency •••• or ••••• are so likely given over to their vampiric state that their human Morality must be tested to determine if the Beast within may allow them to stir.

Torpor

If a vampire is staked or receives sufficient lethal damage to fill her rightmost Health box with a lethal damage mark, she will enter a torpid state. This deathlike slumber is similar to the daysleep of most vampires, but the inert body will slowly shrivel until entering a mummified state. Another source of torpor is prolonged starvation. If a vampire slumbers whilst possessing no Willpower points, the vampire enters the torpid state.

Torpor is a long-lasting state, but a temporary one. How long the vampire remains in torpor depends on her Morality score. The higher the Morality, the more "human" the vampire is (as she holds to more human ideals of behavior than those "ideals" favored by the Beast within). Use the following chart to determine how long a vampire remains slumbering:

Morality	Time Spent in Torpor
10	One day
9	Two days
8	Three days
7	One week
6	Two weeks
5	One month
4	One year
3	One decade
2	Five decades
1	One century
0	One millennium

WAKEY, WAKEY, BLOOD AND BAKEY

You want a story hook? A vampire's been slumbering in some rubble, away from the sun, for an even millennium. That means the vampire is old. *Crazy* old. And that the creature clings to absolutely zero shreds of his one-human Morality. *And* that the ancient fiend is going to be hungry for blood, and feeding his wretched body will take dozens of exsanguinated bodies, if not more.

When that creature wakes up, the city and its hunters are going to have hell to pay. Stopping a creature like that isn't the job for a single cell. It might not even be a job for one compact or conspiracy. The hunters of the city are going to have to put aside any differences they have to mount an offense on a creature whose nativity might predate the *Biblical flood*.

Other Ways to Awaken

It may be possible to awaken vampires by other means. Whether this means that lesser vampires have chosen to try to rouse a sleeping ancient or it means that a cell of hunters hopes to awaken a vampire to ask him some questions (before staking him again and leaving him for the sun—you know, ask questions first, stake later). Other options include:

• A vampire in torpor due to being staked remains so for as long as the stake remains in place. Removing the stake generally awakens the creature.

• Vampires that have entered torpor due to starvation may awaken when human or animal blood is poured upon lips and down the throat.

• Some vampires will awaken from torpor only with blood from another vampire—a vampire of *higher* Potency.

• Sometimes, demons are capable of awakening vampires from torpor, though doing so often necessitates that the demon possess the vampire or, alternately, procure some kind of favor from the vampire when the creature of the night awakens. However, some Lucifuge whisper of a forbidden Castigation ritual that actually *forces* a demonic familiar into a torpid vampire's sleeping body, allowing the vampire to stir to unlife. The vampire serves the Lucifuge hunter, so the story goes, but at what cost to the hunter's sanity?

I Eat Your Heart

Here's something that might interest hunters: vampires can consume one another's souls and earn great power as a result. Oh, they frown on it, of course, because such a vile action purportedly brings chaos to their orderly nocturnal society, but it happens just the same.

If one vampire drains another dry of blood (Willpower), and then *keeps on drinking*, she starts eating Health dots, instead. Once those are gone, the victim turns to dust—and the victor quite literally drinks the vampire's heartsblood and soul into her own body. If the vampire was of higher Potency, assume that the rewards are that the lesser vampire is now of that Potency, and may claim the eaten vampire's Dread Powers as her own. Of course, here's a creepy question: what happens when a hunter does that to a vampire? Drinks 'em dry, and imbibes the soul? Shudder.

Torpid Dementia

Prolonged torpor can poison a vampire's long-term memories, making them generally unreliable. In general, a vampire who has been in torpor for longer than the sum of their Potency + Morality in years will find recollection of facts and figures from their past increasingly difficult: each decade they have been torpid applies a cumulative penalty of –1 to all attempts to remember details: see p. 44, **World of Darkness Rulebook.**

Of course some memories may be clearer than others; and a vampire hunter hoping to capitalize on an older vampire's dementia may discover to his horror that the vampire quite clearly remembers how it was the hunter's great-grandfather who staked him, and just how closely the hunter resembles his ancestor. It can go the other way, too—a vampire may assume the vampire hunter is some eternal nemesis of his, as opposed to just some poor bastard who crept into the wrong haven.

Such vampires are likely quite frightening—not for what they do remember, but for what memories are twisted and damaged, lost to the degradation and madness of the mind.

Folkloric Frailties

The mythology of vampires is bloated with scads of misleading information regarding how to protect oneself from and destroy a creature of the night. Hunters may come across any number of folkloric "solutions," and strictly speaking, very few of them work. However, given that this section can easily be used

as a "build your own vampire" guide, you may want to examine some such frailties out of folklore to see if they might fit in your game. They may similarly work to keep players and character guessing in regards to the nature of the vampires you've chosen to include as adversaries.

- **Holy items.** Crosses, rosaries, Stars of David, mala (Buddhist prayer beads), and so forth, are sometimes thought to repel vampires. The logic is, of course, that vampires are plainly unholy (possibly the servitors of Hell itself), and so holy items have a measure of power against creatures plainly outside God's design. A mild "frailty" would be that thrusting such an object in the face of or against the skin of a vampire might incur a fear frenzy, similar to what the vampire might suffer upon witnessing a waving torch. A more severe version would have these objects burning the flesh (one point of aggravated damage) of the vampire when pressed against its skin. Another question is: what happens when such a creature is dragged across the threshold of a church? Does it burst into flames and perish? Or is it simply so caught in the grip of pain that it cannot act—it can only squeal and writhe?

- **Alternate stakes.** Some legends have it that stakes must be made out of wild rose, hawthorn, or willow branches. Gypsy folklore demanded that an iron spike or needle be thrust through the heart (and in some cases, between each finger).

- **Invitation only.** Folklore has it that a vampire cannot enter the home unless invited in. One modern spin on it (from the film, *Lost Boys*) offers that once you've invited the vampire in, you lose the ability to harm him.

- **Garlic.** Garlic, thought to be a healing herb (and one that some suggest repels mosquitoes, which are similarly mean little blood-drinkers), is somewhat canonical when it comes to apotropaics that repel the undead. In this case, a vampire within five yards of a bulb of garlic suffers a -2 to all rolls.

- **Silver.** Just as it was thought to harm werewolves, silver has long been considered one of the vampire's vulnerabilities. Weapons made out of silver will have one less die of "equipment bonus," but successful attacks will do aggravated damage to the vampire.

- **Reburial.** In various European myths, if hunters bury a vampire with certain objects (sickle, crucifix, mustard seeds, rose petals, and so forth), then the vampire acts as if staked: it enters torpor and cannot rise until one unearths the creature and removes the "binding" object from the chest of the mummified fiend.

Thralls to the Blood

The vampires have names for their human servants: thralls, ghouls, blood dolls. Some hunters call them "Renfields," after the zoophage asylum inmate who served Dracula. Whatever the name, humans who consume the blood of the Damned find themselves empowered, addicted, and likely enslaved.

Ghoul Rules

The ghoul is still human, but has moved closer to the deathless state of his accursed masters. The effect of vampire blood upon him is subtle to those looking for the stains of death: he might grow pale or jaundiced, he may become more driven by his vices, and he might suffer under the yoke of one or more derangements. Beyond that, the following rules apply:

- A true ghoul—and not just a blood addict—is created when a vampire expends his will when feeding a human subject his blood. This necessitates, for the vampire, the release of *two* points of his Willpower: one for the blood, one for the mystical impulsion encoded in that blood.

- Ghouls can operate both at night and during the day.

- Ghouls exist in a state of suspended age. They are immortal, except...

- ...the ghoul requires at least one drink of the vampire's blood (necessitating the vampire to expend a point of Willpower) per month to maintain her condition. Failing to receive that taste of blood, the ghoul returns to her purely-mortal state: she ages one year per day after she's "overdue," until her suspended age has caught up with her "true age." Yes, this can kill some ghouls if they've lived well past their natural life expectancy. Oh, and strictly speaking, the ghoul needs *a* taste of vampire blood, and it doesn't need to come from the vampire that originally enthralled her—which means that the World of Darkness is home to "hunters" whose sole quarry are vampires filled with the sweet, potent Blood.

Addicted and Enslaved

The Blood is so potent, it's addictive. Consuming it is a rush; for some it's erotic and seductive, for others its equivalent to the peak of adrenalin highs or the nadir of numbing pleasure.

The rule for growing enthralled with the Blood—and, by proxy, the vampire whose body contains such a rapturous draught—might be called the "Three Drink Rule."

Upon the first drink of the Blood, a character (be that character human, vampire, werewolf, whatever) recognizes the feelings of pleasure, but is not mechanically bound to the Damned.

Upon the second taste, the pleasure is only heightened, and the character becomes somewhat enamored of the vampire that offered that taste: the vampire now gains +1 to any Social rolls made to affect the target character.

Upon the third taste, the addictive bond between the blood-drinker and the vampire is likely complete: the character may attempt a Stamina + Resolve roll (penalized by the vampire's Potency dots), and success on that roll means the full addiction and enslavement hasn't happened... yet. Any time the character drinks that vampire's blood, the chance for thralldom to "take" comes up again, with the same roll.

If the character fails that roll? She's officially in thrall to the vampire. Note that this is different than being a ghoul, though most of the unholy Damned are likely to pair the conditions of making a human a ghoul *and* enslaving the ghoul with the mighty and mystical will of the Blood—but, a character could be a ghoul without having become addicted, and a blood addict could be addicted to the vampire without the vampire making that character an actual ghoul.

Empowered

Ghouls gain a measure of their master's power. The following powers and abilities are available to ghoul antagonists:

- A ghoul may have up to three dots in Dread Powers, but these Dread Powers must be ones possessed by the vampire that originally enthralled the ghoul. If the vampire didn't possess Enhanced Senses (below), then the ghoul may not, either.

- All ghouls may spend Willpower to increase one Physical Attribute for one turn (Unholy Attribute).

- A ghoul may spend Willpower to heal wounds, just like vampires... with the exception of healing aggravated damage.

- Ghouls may only spend one Willpower per turn, like any other mortal character.

Dread Powers of the Vampire

Vampires can call upon a variety of Dread Powers to stack the odds in their favor in a hunt. Legends attribute various terrible magics to the vampire: the ability to shapeshift into mist, bats and wolves; to fix the prey to the spot with a glance; to seduce with hypnosis; and many other feats of unholy prowess.

The following are new Dread Powers available to vampires. Note, too, that any of the Dread Powers from **Hunter: The Vigil** can be used when creating a vampire antagonist. (And, technically, the following Dread Powers can apply to any creature of your creation; the beastie needn't be a vampire.)

Alter Memory (• to •••••)

With this power, a vampire can reach into a victim's memories and amend, add to or delete them. This power could be used therapeutically, to help a mortal or vampire overcome a Derangement by visiting the memories of her sins and helping her to come to terms with her actions, and helping vampires recover their memories after long torpor. However, given

GHOULS OF THORN AND CLAW

Both animals and plants can become "ghouls" of a sort. Animal ghouls are subject to the same rules as any other ghoul, except that animal ghouls may not possess any Dread Powers beyond Unholy Attribute. They are still subject to addiction and enslavement, however.

Plants fed vampire blood are ultimately quite different: they grow black and twisted, but still maintain some measure of life. They move, albeit slowly—vines creep along a forest floor, hungry roses open up at the sight of the full moon, a whole savage garden stirs with its leaves and petals whispering. They move too slowly to truly "attack" a hunter, but some vampires bind victims and allow the plants to slowly consume the subject—a tendril works its way into the corner of one's eye while a branch slowly rakes across the flesh, drawing fresh blood. Over time, the agonized human is "overtaken" by the hungry flora. Some say that these "plant ghouls" burst with a milky blood-like sap—rumor is that some Ascending Ones use this sap in a few forbidden Elixirs.

the nature of vampires, this Dread Power is far more often used towards less benign ends.

Altering a victim's memory can be highly useful to a vampire. If the vampire is at the center of a blood cult, she can toy with the memories of all her adherent cultists, turning them against their friends or inserting herself into their pasts as a central figure. If the vampire draws too much attention to herself with other Dread Powers, *this* ability allows her to "edit" their memories so that they forget that they ever saw her displays of unholy prowess.

Note that most vampires do not have the finesse or patience to work this ability perfectly. Those who suffer use of this power are often left with a feeling of improper memories, even if they can't dissect them to find the truth. Incomplete or overly-simplistic memories can actually stir a victim to investigate what really happened, which is surely the opposite of what the vampire intended (and, in fact, many hunters have been called to the Vigil in just such a way).

Use of this power requires eye contact. The vampire acts almost as a hypnotist, asking questions and drawing out memories—memories she soon replaces with her own recalculated recollections.

Cost: 1 Willpower

Action: Extended (1-100 successes necessary, with more simplistic memories necessitating fewer successes, and more complicated successes demanding much higher successes; each roll represents five minutes of manipulation)

Dice Pool: Intelligence + Subterfuge + Alter Memory minus victim's Resolve

Roll Results

Dramatic Failure: The attempt fails: the vampire cannot use any Dread Powers upon that victim for the next 24 hours. Also, if the victim has a derangement, the vampire now suffers from that derangement without the possibility of controlling it for the remainder of the scene.

Failure: The vampire fails to access the victim's memories.

Success: The vampire finds the specific memory he is after; when altering a memory, the vampire manages to perform the procedure successfully. If the vampire has inserted fake memories of herself to gain a victim's trust, the vampire gains +1 to all Social rolls involving the victim per dot in Alter Memory; the same bonus applies as a penalty to Social rolls between the victim and her friends, if the false memories were implanted to turn the victim against them instead.

The vampire can reinforce or weaken specific memories, adding successes rolled as a bonus or penalty to remember specific details of an incident, such as the vampire's apparel or appearance, or to alter the memories of an incident where the witness saw obviously supernatural manifestations of the vampire's Dread Powers; see Memorizing and Remembering, p. 44, **The World of Darkness Rulebook**.

Exceptional Success: Extra successes are their own reward.

Dice Pool Modifiers

+2	Victim is a blood-addicted servant of the vampire (see "Thralls to the Blood," above)
+1	Vampire has hypnotized or altered the memory of the victim before

Beastly Command (• to •••••)

The vampire has mastered the ability to communicate with animals and force them to submit to his dire commands. This ability necessitates the vampire make eye contact with the creature or creatures upon which he forces obeisance. With one Willpower point, the vampire commands only a single creature. Spending two Willpower allows the vampire to issue commands to all the creatures (of one type) within range of sight.

Note that any vampires possessing this Dread Power can also communicate roughly with a creature without necessitating a roll. The two creatures communicate in vague turns of emotion and broken thoughts alongside yips, chirps, growls or however the animal might normally communicate with its brethren. Simple messages are easier to convey and understand than more complex ones.

Cost: 1 or 2 Willpower

Action: Instant

Dice Pool: Manipulation + Animal Ken + Beastly Command

Roll Results

Dramatic Failure: The animal either attacks the vampire or does the opposite of the vampire's command.

Failure: The command fails to register.

Success: The animal obeys its orders to the best of its ability.

Exceptional Success: The animal develops a strong affection (some might say obsession) with the vampire.

Beastly Summons (•••)

This power works to summon animals. A vampire using this power is an eerie sight; crouching, hissing or howling into the night as a horde of beasts flock to him. The vampire can only choose one type of animal to summon: rats, for instance, or cockroaches. The summoning act is usually an attempt to communicate with that type of animal—a vampire calling to wolves might howl, while calling owls might necessitate bird-like shrieks.

Cost: 1 Willpower

Action: Instant

Dice Pool: Presence + Animal Ken + Potency

Roll Results

Dramatic Failure: The vampire summons the animals desired... and on arrival they turn on him, attacking. Rats bite. Birds stab at the eyes with jabbing beaks. Insects swarm and sting.

Failure: The vampire fails to summon any beasts.

Success: The vampire summons all the creatures of the type desired—the area of the call is 100 yards per success rolled. Only those animals appropriate to the area will show up in meaningful numbers: thousands of cockroaches might skitter out of the walls of a run-down tenement, but summoning wolves or vultures in such a place is unlikely to yield results.

Exceptional Success: Any Animal Ken rolls to communicate with or command the creatures gain +2 dice.

Control Emotion (• to •••••)

Vampires sometimes like to induce certain emotions in their prey, theorizing that such intense emotions add flavor to their blood. Others simply induce lust or pleasure in their victims, making the job of seducing them into a position where they can be fed from that much simpler.

The most insidious use of this Dread Power is its application as a tool of brainwashing and conditioning. By judiciously applying emotional pressure to the victims—bursts of despair and self-doubt, followed by waves of emotional fulfillment and a sense of joy and of being loved, as well as love for the vampire—the vampire can secure long-term loyalty from his herd of followers, bypassing the need to gain their trust the hard way.

Cost: 1 Willpower

Action: Contested; victim rolls Resolve + Composure

Dice Pool: Manipulation + Persuasion + Control Emotion

Roll Results

Dramatic Failure: The victim sees right through the vampire's manipulations. The vampire can't affect the victim with this Dread Power for the rest of the night.

Failure: The vampire fails to affect the victim.

Success: The vampire controls the victim's emotional state, making her feel the desired emotion. She feels anger, grief, sexual arousal, anger, fear or similar emotion, and believes it to be her own. The effect applies as

a Social penalty to the victim's Composure in all Social rolls involving that emotion for the rest of the scene.

Used for conditioning purposes, successes rolled for this Dread Power are added to the vampire's extended action rolls to brainwash the victim.

Exceptional Success: The emotion is inhumanly intense, causing the victim strain: any attempts to perform an action contrary to the emotion felt (i.e saying kind words while angry) suffer a -2 penalty.

Enhanced Senses (• to •••••)

The power to track their prey by scent, or by following the sound of their frantic heartbeats, is a thrilling Dread Power for vampires. This Dread Power also enhances the rush of feeding for the vampire beyond any pleasure experienced by a human.

Cost: ~

Action: Reflexive

Dice Pool: None. This power is considered on when the vampire demands it.

Effect: The vampire's senses expand far beyond human capacity. She can hear the worms turning in the ground beneath her feet, identify a song being played on an MP3 player across a room, or track a particular human through a crowd by their scent.

The vampire gains night vision such that he can read by faint moonlight; his scent tracking is as accurate as that of a wolf; his hearing is as acute as a bat, and can pick up sounds at frequencies which lie beyond the range of human hearing.

All Perception rolls and Wits + Composure rolls to react to surprise gain +1 bonus dice per dot of Enhanced Senses.

Drawback: Loud sounds, bright lights and pungent odors stun the vampire when this power is active, inhibiting her actions as long as the stimuli remain; in such an environment all her actions, including Initiative and reacting to surprise, are penalized by -1 per dot in Enhanced Senses.

Mist Form (•••••)

Legends tell of vampires turning into an icy, fine mist that moves of its own accord, even against the breeze. This Dread Power verifies the myth.

Cost: 2 Willpower

Action: Instant

Dice Pool: No roll is necessary

Effect: The vampire concentrates and uses an action to turn into a cloud of fog or vapor, which can travel at his natural Speed in any direction—even against the breeze. Changing back into solid form necessitates the expenditure of another Willpower point.

Normal weapons cannot harm a vampire in this state, while mystical attacks (or damage suffered from fire or sunlight) do one less damage to the vampire.

Unholy Grace (••••)

A vampire equipped with this Dread Power is a feared foe in combat, her senses honed with a powerful kinesthesia, moving with inhuman grace, her every step planned and executed precisely, never putting a foot wrong.

Cost: 1 Willpower per bonus die

Action: Reflexive

Dice Pool: No roll is necessary

Effect: The vampire moves with inhuman grace. Each Willpower point spent grants the vampire bonus dice to use in any Dexterity dice pool based on Athletics, Brawl, Firearms, Stealth or Weaponry. Furthermore, if the vampire needs to make a Dodge maneuver, each Willpower point adds +1 to her Defense before being added to the Dodge dice pool. Finally, the vampire may abort an appropriate dice pool if the result is a failure: the vampire merely does not take an action that turn. All these benefits apply for the duration of an entire scene.

Bloodjackers (The Owls)

Take a flip back to p. 172—first chapter, "Love Birds." Poor Randolph and Janey. It was the owls, you see? Dark shapes in trees. Screeching calls. Quiet whispers. Those awful owls, *they* made poor Randolph do the things he did. And they made his girlfriend get up and walk again, at least for a time. What's going on here?

Truth is, nobody knows. Sometimes, a mist creeps in through the window. Owls alight upon branches. And when that happens, the dead walk, and when the dead walk, they commit vile atrocities and embrace life with grotesque pleasure.

These are the Bloodjackers, the Owls, the *Strix*.

Body Thieves

The Bloodjackers are without form, at least in their default state. They appear in a variety of ways: one looks like a shadow, another like a roiling carpet of fog. All of them can appear as owls, though—large owls with tufts of feather like a demon's horns. Even

then, though, they aren't really manifest—the swipe of a blade or a swiftly-speeding bullet simply goes right through the bird, as if the creature's flesh is purely ephemeral. That's because it is.

They do not delight in this form, though. No, the Bloodjackers like to steal bodies. Corpses. They possess the dead flesh and force it to rise, and then they puppet the body out into the world. There, they commit the body to the vilest of actions—gluttonous acts of consumption and horrifying feats of lust. When they're in a body, they gain the five senses, and they use those senses to their uttermost—taking in every smell and sight, every feel be it pleasurable of painful. And when the body is destroyed, they leave it behind, moving onto the next corpse, and the next after that.

Thing is, the Owls? They really *love* to steal vampire bodies. Vampires may be up and walking around, but they're still dead. Which makes their blood ripe for the taking.

Truly Alien

The Owls don't seem to have human natures. They can communicate in human ways—whispering from the shadows or using one of their puppet-bodies to speak—but they are themselves not human. May never have been human, really. But they're not animalistic or incomprehensible. They're just cold. Calculating. And most certainly cruel.

Dread Powers

When the Owls are disembodied, they have no Health score—each has 10 Willpower, and if damage is done against the ephemeral parasite, the damage is done to its Willpower, not its Health. If the creature is reduced to zero Willpower, the creature dissolves, leaving behind little evidence of its existence. However, mundane attacks do not work against such a creature. Blessed items (p. 214, **World of Darkness Rulebook**) do damage, as do hunter Endowments. Abjurations and exorcisms also work to cause the Strix anguish and damage.

Possession

Owls possess a version of the "Ride Corpse" Dread Power (p. 280, **Hunter: The Vigil**), except the Bloodjacker version is far more complete. It costs a Willpower point, but requires no roll—only a single turn to complete.

Story Seeds

- A local vampire—someone low on the totem pole, maybe even a loose ally of the hunters—goes on a rampant *bender*. He gorges on blood. He leaves a trail of bodies. He even takes down his own sire, the vampire that made him. The hunters track him down, but find his eyes shine like a bird's, and there's something different about him. He's possessed by an Owl, of course—is there value in saving him? In trying to extricate the Bloodjacker from the stolen body? What happens when the Cheiron Group gets involved, certain that such a unique specimen can be of use to them no matter the cost?
- The Owls seem to show up *en masse* after a disaster—like Katrina, or the San Francisco earthquake that's probably soon to hit again. One such disaster comes, and the Owls arrive in frightening numbers. The dead start walking left and right. The Lucifuge get the message from the Lady in Milan: *the gates of Hell are open*. These are demons. They must be purged. Violently. In total. Many will die. Other hunters can't have that. Plus, the disaster has thrown off the vampire hierarchies, and now it's pretty much chaos—can order be restored?
- One disembodied Bloodjacker communicates with a hunter: it offers its aid. It hates the vampires, too. It wants them all gone. It speaks of revenge. Of some lost "family." It opines about Ancient Rome. It wants to help. Will the hunter let it? What happens when it starts to ask him for favors of its own? For him to provide it with a dozen bodies—"costumes" for it to wear? Certainly the vampires seem afraid of these things… is that a good thing? Or a bad thing?

The Strix takes on the Physical Attributes and Skills of the body, but otherwise uses its own traits (see sidebar). The Strix also keeps any Dread Powers it already possesses.

A body decays as normal. Every two days, the corpse loses one dot from a Physical Attribute as lividity and rot take hold. (Note that as it loses these Attributes, other traits—Health, Speed, Initiative, etc.—also go down.) Once the creature has no Dexterity, it

SAMPLE BLOODJACKER

Mental Attributes: Intelligence 2, Wits 3, Resolve 4

Physical Attributes: Determined by body

Social Attributes: Presence 3, Manipulation 4, Composure 2

Skills: Investigation 3, Occult 3, Intimidation 4, Persuasion 3, Subterfuge 3 (Physical Skills determined by body)

Merits: None

Willpower: 10

Morality: None

Health: Use Willpower as Health

Initiative: 9 (or as determined by body)

Defense: 3 (or as determined by body)

Speed: 20 (or as determined by body)

Size: 2 in disembodied form (otherwise determined by body)

Dread Powers: 8 dots in Dread Powers

Variants of the Blood

Hunters investigating vampires come to a swift realization: the folklore is pervasive, conflicting and confusing. Trying to figure out what you're fighting from reading Wikipedia entries or *The Vampire Encyclopedia* seems an exercise in frustration—especially when the "normal" vampires stalking the streets don't really seem to fit in with a lot of what the world believes true about the bloodsucking throngs.

As a Storyteller, though, you might be engaged by the myriad bits of crazy vampire folklore around the world, and might hope to use some of that in your **Hunter: The Vigil** story. Well, we've got you covered. Below you'll find a handful of vampire variants from around the world (though the list is far from exhaustive). For the most part, such creatures can be created using the Storytelling rules and various Dread Powers. Still, you'll find some rules tweaks where appropriate—otherwise, simply choose the right stats and Dread Powers that seem appropriate to the antagonist you so desire. Assume that for the most part, a lot of the standard vampire rules are the same unless otherwise noted (drinks blood, can't go out in sunlight, and so on).

Adze (Ghana)

Disembodied vampire spirit—sometimes appears as a bright red firefly. Feeds on children (as so many vampires reportedly do). Potentially teaches arcane secrets to sorcerers and warlocks. Assume that this is another version of the Bloodjackers, above.

Algul (Middle East)

Vampire bound to cemeteries and places of death—potentially cannot leave such places. Thought to be a *djinn*—one of the lesser demons of the desert. Some are thought to feed from dead infants, but some hunters report that the *Algul* actually can animate such deceased babies and call the hollowed-out infants to serve them.

Bhuta (India)

The Bhuta are created not by the embrace of another vampire, but crawl out of graves after suffering a truly violent death (such as a brutal murder). They feed on any kind of fluids—blood, semen, feces. They often lurk along dark pathways and forgotten roads. As demons of the crossroad, they love to waylay travelers and feed upon them. (Also: Rakshasa.)

can no longer move. Once it's lost all of its Physical Attributes, the body erupts in a gassy heap and collapses in upon itself, leaving a mash of corpse-flesh.

Possessing a vampire is a bit different. No roll is required, and one Willpower is still necessary. But the vampire body doesn't rot as noted above. The puppet vampire still needs to feed and can still spend Willpower (blood) in all the same ways. Such a vampire is not vulnerable to staking anymore (as arguably, the puppet-body is already torpid). To excise the Owl from the body, either an exorcism must be completed or the body must be destroyed. If the Owl leaves the body prematurely (forced out or leaves of its own volition), the vampire does not recall what happened.

Fire and Sunlight

In both forms (disembodied and puppet-body), the Bloodjacker is trapped by fire and sunlight. It cannot move past them—it literally freezes in the sunlight, unable to make even the tiniest motion. Sunlight doesn't hurt the Owl, and when the Owl is possessing a vampire it fails to hurt the vampire's body, as well. Fire still causes a puppet-body aggravated damage, but does no damage to the disembodied form.

Owl Eyes

When possessing a body, the puppet-form's eyes shine like an owl's. The Bloodjackers can see quite well in low or absent light, suffering no Perception penalties in such conditions.

to this world as a screeching demonic blood-sucker.)

Incubus, Succubus (Western)

The term *incubus*, meaning "nightmare," reveals a creature that only shows when one sleeps. The creature consumes dreams as well as sexual fluids. It engages in intercourse. It rarely kills the victim immediately, often taking months or even years of nocturnal visitations to slowly drain the victim of its life-force. Children can be born of this infernal coupling—most that are born are deformed or insane. Some become hunters. (Lilith is a popular "succubus" figure throughout Sumerian and Hebrew myth. The demoness—associated with owls, uh oh—is said to steal the seed of sleeping men so she can fertilize her fallow womb. What kind of spawn might crawl from just such an act? Fertile ground for new antagonists, right there.)

Empusa (Greek)

Out of Greek myth come the Empusas: they can take any face (possessing the New Face Dread Power, p. 280 of **Hunter: The Vigil**) and are accomplished liars (Subterfuge at five dots, always). Some have been found serving demons, while others are found serving witches. They're usually serving *someone*, though.

Hannya (Japan)

Sometimes, women die in childbirth. And sometimes, those women rise from the grave. These wretched harridans (clad in flowing robes and gathering together in roving cabals) scream when they approach—a sound so unnerving, one who hears it must succeed on a Resolve + Composure roll not to collapse and cover one's ears. The Hannya is most vulnerable to the attacks of the child she bore whose birth ended her life—when that child grows up, he can be very effective in eradicating that particular creature. (Some hunters have been made in just such a way, actually, dragged into the Vigil when learning that one's mother has returned

(think cholera or tuberculosis) if they survive. She moves swiftly (Speed 20), floating about. She has no hands and cannot perform actions that require hands. If you can find the headless body (the creature often keeps it hidden—think a cellar or barrow somewhere), shoving broken glass into its heart kills it. Otherwise, it's got to be destroyed like any other awful creature of the night. You'll find a Penanggalan on p. 45 of this book, actually.

Revenant (Western)

The Revenant is a curious type of vampire. It rises from the grave after dying through great violence. It drinks blood, but generally doesn't do so to hurt people. It also seems to have little interest in hurting the innocent, and instead is obsessively focused on waging a war of revenge (and sometimes, yes, innocents get hurt indirectly due to such violent reprisals). The Revenants do not suffer bashing damage. Once a Revenant's revenge is complete, the creature immediately returns to a state of death. Revenants can be an interesting conundrum for hunters—on one hand, they're clearly

Kiang-Shi (China)

Tall corpse. Pale white or jaundiced flesh. Seemingly mindless, totally inhuman. Has vicious claws (+2 to Brawl, lethal damage). Doesn't suffer from a vulnerability to fire, but lightning (or any form of electricity) does the creature aggravated damage. Oh, and did we mention it can leap great distances? That's right—this is the "hopping vampire" of Chinese legend. Assume that the creature gains +5 to any Athletics rolls and has a Speed of at least 20.

Ohyn (Poland)

The Ohyn is a child born with a caul over its head. The caul is removed, and the child is alive... but it's a vampire. It can be killed by normal, mundane means, but the child must drink blood to survive, and possesses a wide range of Dread Powers. The Ohyn do age, but do so at half the rate of humans (a 40-year-old Ohyn looks only 20).

Penanggalan (Malaysia)

Unique because, ew, it's nothing more than a head, neck, and a trailing bundle of bloody intestines. Almost always a female, and seems hellbent to feed from children and infants. Those she bites seem to contract some manner of wasting disease

dead and monstrous, and innocents might get hurt. On the other hand, it's possible the Revenant is doing some good, and certainly revenge is a motive many on the Vigil understand.

Ubour (Bulgaria)

Mindless and swollen, the Ubour only rises after 40 nights in the ground. When it rises, the skin is largely intact, but it bulges—the insides have liquefied, turning to a kind of blood-colored jelly. The Ubour eats anything. Roadkill, garbage, dead bodies, and most certainly blood. The creature often has very low Dexterity, but higher Strength and Stamina. Even with higher Strength, though, assume that its Speed is configured by pairing only Dexterity + Strength (no species modifier added). The Ubour lurches about, only attacking when something stands in the way of its food. It cannot speak. It cannot reason. Here's the kicker, though: kill the creature, and a black cat emerges wet from its throat. An indication that somehow, black cats or demonic familiars are somehow responsible for the animation of these bloated carcasses? Most hunters kill the cats, just to be sure. Nothing personal, felines.

Vrykolakas (Greece)

The Vrykolakas represents a breed of vampire that makes the hunters of the Lucifuge less than happy (and the Lady of Milan is quite clear about what to do with this monsters). The reason? Demons. These vampires are possessed by lesser demons, who quite literally merge with the soul upon dying. (The bonus is, of course, that Castigations sometimes pack an extra oomph, and in addition, exorcisms, blessed items and abjurations are effective against these vampires.) A few things make dealing with the *vrykolakas* tricky, though. First, they know your name. Always. They also know not insignificant details about anybody they meet—the name of one's wife, the hospital where a hunter was born, the age of his trusty hound. Second, and altogether more troublesome, any that the *vrykolakas* kill through feeding rise the next night as one of them. These are "second generation" vampires, however—they have only a fraction of the power of the sire, and cannot themselves sire new fiends. Plus, if the progenitor fiend is destroyed, then all of his unruly progeny turn to ash, as well.

"All right, petal?"

Bianca Crowe stops dead. She thought she'd seen it all, evaded all kinds of terrors. But this... this she is not prepared for.

The last time Bianca saw her father, he had named the sainted Pauline, and it had been the final straw. It was hard enough for her to slam the door and break it, to stride down the path, nearly tripping over as a stiletto caught in the cracks in the paving, to turn on a penny and to walk without stopping to the railway station in the rain. She registered the sign engraved on the paving in front of the station entrance — *Ambition is Critical* — as if for the very first time.

"Too fucking right," she thought. She hadn't got very far that first trip. Her intent was to get as far as she could from her lovely ugly pretty shitty godforsaken hole of a town. She got to Cardiff. She ended up on the streets. She sold some coke. She got caught. She'd been sent to the detention center. Frank hadn't come to the hearing.

And then she got away again.

She remembers hitching a lift along the M4. She remembers the possibilities that filled her world as the lights of the fading town sunk beneath the glowing hills. She switched on a stolen iPod and made the techno the soundtrack to her life, drifted off to sketchy, excitable sleep.

The dream she had stayed with her: the bright lights of the city danced with her, and gave her a glass of distilled freedom to drink. She drank the freedom into her veins stickily, guiltily. It tasted like blood.

⌘

> The dream she had stayed with her: the bright lights of the city danced with her, and gave her a glass of distilled freedom to drink.

> She drank the freedom into her veins stickily, guiltily.

> It tasted like blood.

"Dad. What the fuck are you doing here?" She is icy cold.

It isn't turning out as Frank expected it to. He reacts in the way he always did, realizing he isn't helping matters, even as he says, "Bianca! Mind your language! What would your mother say?"

"She's not here," says Bianca. "She's never gonna be here. She's dead. Sorry, but she is."

"Can I come in?"

She looks at her front door, looks up and down the street. "I don't think so. You can say what you want to say here and now."

Frank accepts the judgment with a sad nod. "What've you been doing? I heard you were in some kind of trouble. I got a call."

"It was Wayne, wasn't it?"

"I don't know. A bloke."

"Wayne. He confessed that he did it."

"Who's Wayne?"

"I work with him. Look, Dad, it was a stupid practical joke. I'm all right. Really."

"So this Wayne was just having me on?"

"No. No, Dad. I'm fine. Really fine. I think you should go home. This isn't a good place to hang around in."

"I can handle myself." Frank flicks his cigarette away. "You're hiding something from me, aren't you? What is it? Is it that young boy who phoned me, cos I don't mind saying, Bianca, those of us in the Force, we develop an eye for things. We can sense things, you know? And I got this feeling, this inkling, like, that there's something not quite right with him..."

He stops short, aware of a small, buzzing insect crawling along his daughter's hairline.

"Stop! I've got it! Stay still!" He swats with his hand; his daughter's face twists into something he doesn't understand, and before he touches her, she has his wrist in her right hand.

"Leave it, dad!"

"There was a wasp or something. It was crawling in your hair."

"It's nothing." Bianca's expression — click — changes like someone flipped a switch. Anger becomes absolute blank calm. "It's just a bug."

Frank looks his daughter up and down. She looks like a doll or a mannequin, her make-up expertly if heavily applied. She has hardly aged since he last saw her (she was sixteen. Now she is twenty — *God, she's twenty,* he thinks). She is wearing a suit. The skirt is too short and the jacket too tight, but it is not anything he could have imagined the old Bianca — with her heavy gold chains and pink tracksuits — wearing. She looks well enough to him, but there is something wrong. Something different.

"What have you done to yourself?" says Frank. "You're not on drugs, are you?"

"Don't be stupid."

"What, then? Is it that Wayne? Is he treating you bad?"

"Wayne? Nah, Wayne's okay."

"Are you seeing him?"

"Don't be ridiculous, dad. He's just a mate."

"I'm only trying to protect you. I'll bet he's into drugs. Has he offered you anything?"

"Dad. I've told you. I'm not into drugs and I'm not seeing Wayne."

"Christ. You're not on the game."

"Dad! *Stop* it!"

Frank finds himself momentarily seized by an unseen force, as though his entire being — thoughts, dreams and actions — are frozen or switched off.

Bianca releases a breath, and the force's grip on Frank relaxes.

He shakes his head.

"What— "

"You're tired, dad." She turns around and takes her key out, to open her front door, to walk indoors, to shut him out. "I'm not on drugs. I'm not seeing Wayne, I'm not pregnant and I'm definitely not on the game. I'm fine. Now shut up and go home. Go back to your crap little life in sodding Swansea and leave me alone."

"You're tied up with some terrible things, princess. Even if you don't think you're in trouble, you are. You're in so much trouble. Please. I just want to help you get out of it."

"Dad — for the last time. I'm not in trouble."

"Why are you buying blood from the Hallam feed factory? Why is there a basement room with your things in it under a *children's home*?"

"What?"

"I went to those places. I saw... things. Fucking terrible things."

The streets of London were wild and brand new. They glittered like stars — so much to see, to do, and to be. The question was: who to be today? The wild runaway? The tragic teenager? The *femme fatale*? On that night, Bianca had fancied a note of tragedy, a father who did not care and a mother who had died early of cancer (but a different sort of cancer with all the unpleasant bits removed, fading into a gentle tragic emptiness, a murmuring of sweet nothings to the white angel-foldings of her pillow, and skin so soft, so soft).

She remembers how she had thought she might play the part of the abused child — cruelly torn and tormented by a domineering father. Forced to live up to a role she could never attain. It was always, "What would your mother have said?" or "Pauline would never have done that" or "When she was alive, your mother used to say to me..." so that, sometimes, she wishes, for a moment, that her mother had never even existed, and left her the space to grow up to be who she wanted to be. Whoever that was.

She decided that on this night she would be the clued-up city girl, out for adventure and a wild time, excitement and sex — and music and lights and clubbing.

Except that she hadn't any money, or food, and it was cold, and it was dark and maybe even frightening, and not at all how she had imagined it to be. The gold under the street lamps that night looked like only rain, the sort of rain that seeps in under your skin until you shiver, like a creeping death.

She had a fright: but no, the coming shadow she saw in the shop doorway was slender, a woman not much older than her.

The shadow asked her what she was doing out, and offered to take her inside, and used a tone of voice

that gripped Bianca and made it impossible to say no. And then she showed Bianca the hive that lived in her bed.

Bianca remembers spending the night with her, their bodies covered with bees, their blood and honey mixing forever and becoming something dead like an empty wasps' nest, made alive by the tiny emotionless occupants. Who know each other, who exist for the good of the hive, of their hive mother.

The vampire offered Bianca a job. Bianca said yes, and the woman then hollowed her out, made her into a new hive for her bees and her wasps, and showed her how to make people behave in orderly patterns, like the insects.

Bianca proved herself talented and enthusiastic. Callousness and coldness came easy to her; she had never really taken enjoyment in living, but now in death, hollowed out, she has the jittery, fluttery feeling of the insects crawling inside her. It is ecstasy.

She was in business for a while with Wayne, but he lost his nerve. He was never cut out for this sort of thing, for the deals, for the brokerage. He still had a conscience. He might have had an apprenticeship on the streets, but he was soft. Bianca was brought up to be tough. Dad ensured that she is cut out for this.

Bianca closes her eyes briefly, fantasizes about catching up with Wayne and talking to him. She will kiss him and make him drink from her blood, and she'll work on him, shackle his tiny, weak little mind. She'll make him...

do things. He'll be her own little dress-up doll, forever and ever, and he'll never fuck up and do anything as stupid as this ever again.

⚬━╾╼━⚬

Bianca suddenly feels very hungry.

"I don't know what you're talking about," she says.

"Let me stay, pet. Let me buy you a decent meal, at least. You look half-starved. We can talk about what you've got into and we can try to find a way to get you out of it."

The thought of feeding causes Bianca's stomach involuntarily to clench. She thinks of blood. Her blood, her father's blood. She looks at the red flush in her father's face and almost considers making him her puppet, bending him to her will, and then tearing his throat out. And then she thinks, *no, there are limits.*

A wasp crawls out of her ear, down her neck and into her jacket. It stands on her breast and stings her repeatedly; the poison makes her make an involuntary, ecstatic *aah* sound.

"Are you all right, petal?" says her father, taking a step forward.

The wasp injects its proboscis into a blemish on her skin, sups on her blood a little. The insects love her more than her father ever could have done. She makes a little twitch with her perfectly painted red lips; she composes herself, stares her father in the eye.

"Tell me here. Tell me now."

"This isn't the place, princess."

"*Tell* me."

And he has no choice. He must tell her. He does. He tells her everything, about the Frenchman, and the orphanage, and about what happened to Mrs. Polak's body even though he doesn't want to think about that.

And when he is done, she says, "I don't think it went like that."

And she tells him how he imagined what happened to the Night Manager, because he was tired, and how she has been working in logistics, and how she had arranged for the buying and selling of animal feed, and had no idea about the factory, and about how she will make sure someone knows...

And then she tells him it is time to go home.

And Frank cannot do anything else but nod, and turn to go, although he has the strength of will to say, entirely naturally, "Take care, pet. You were always my weakness."

Bianca stands outside the door for some time, looking at her father's receding figure. She notices, at her feet, a small, shiny piece of paper. She picks it up:

DI Frank Crowe

Area Headquarters
New Swansea Central Police Station
Grove Road
Swansea SA1 5EA
Tel: 01792 456 999

She puts it in her handbag and snaps the catch shut. She goes inside. An insect is buzzing around the hallway light.

She thinks that maybe she should go out again and get a bite. She's starving.

⊶——⊷

Frank gets in the tube and lights up, ignoring the silent, angry stares of the other passengers.

He reaches into his pocket and takes out the princess drawing, unfolds it, folds it up and puts it back. Then he pulls out his wallet, and stares through the now almost brown plastic window at the tiny faded picture of Pauline.

"If only you were here," he says to the photo. "You would have known what to say."

Idly, he picks up a copy of the *Evening Standard* that happens to be lying on the seat next to him and scans the headlines:

Woman dies in children's home blaze.
Nameless child abandoned at hospital.
Gang violence in Highgate Cemetery claims ten lives.

He reads the stories without fully comprehending their content. His memory of the last few days is vague, and beginning to fade, as if he were sleeping the whole time. He doesn't know how he gets through the changes of line, or from the final station to his guest house.

He sits alone on the bed in his room until the dawn, wondering how he's going to make the drive back home to Swansea.

"Could have been worse, Frank," he says aloud, as the sun sends its first rays through the window. "Could have been so much worse. At least she's still alive."

Vampire stories may be old, but they're not antiques. They never go out of style. Modern movies borrow from earlier films and novels—and those come from even earlier legends. Every vampire tale is a bastard born of a chaotic mating between past and present.

Storytellers are a part of this tradition. You can give any story a vampiric twist, but in a **Hunter** game, where we are able to choose any antagonist, we want to give vampires a distinctive place in the chronicle.

Examine the state of the vampire mythology today. Read books. Watch movies. Make connections in your head as you prepare your story. Whatever you end up with, remember that the vampire mythos is *dense*—there's a lot to explore. Unlike many monsters, the theme of losing humanity runs through centuries of legends. Old *vrykolakoi* and revenants were people once. They inspired fear because of an evil transformation that turned them from friends and relatives into hungry things, outside the rule of nature.

A compelling vampire story explores that transformation and the deep mythology that springs from it. Like most people, hunters have preconceived ideas about vampires. They examine legends for facts and victims' wounds for clues. They get to know the enemy, almost to the point of empathy—and then the stakes come out.

Beyond that, vampire legends are highly mutable. They'll fuel any story you want to run. This section explores classic reference points, but they aren't the only ones available to you—and let's face it, we just don't have the room to cover every aspect of the modern vampire mythos. Everyone has a favorite core legend, a taxonomy of the undead, even if they've never said anything about it. Use any idea you choose but above all, engage the players.

Tier and Genre

You can do so much with vampires that as Storyteller, your primary challenge won't be to find ideas, but to carve away the conceptual excess until you've got a powerful, consistent plotline. Are the characters tangling with an ancient conspiracy or standing against a lone horror? Are your vampires Hell's willing servants or weird-science medical curiosities? Make a choice.

Genre's an effective way to whittle all that potential down into a working plan. Use it to set general story goals, but remember that it shouldn't restrict your imagination. Map out an action, horror, mystery, crime drama and so on, but think about ways to challenge each genre's assumptions. Start with derivative elements, but make the final product your own.

The figure turns half round, and the light falls upon its face. It is perfectly white—perfectly bloodless. The eyes look like polished tin; the lips are drawn back; and the principal feature next to those dreadful eyes is the teeth—the fearful looking teeth—projecting like those of some wild animal, hideously, glaringly white, and fang-like. It approaches the bed with a strange, gliding movement. It clashes together the long nails that literally appear to hang from the finger ends. No sound comes from its lips.

—James Malcolm Rymer, Varney the Vampire, Volume I

Hunter: The Vigil's tiers provide another way to cook some vampire stories out of the mélange of options. You can run any tier through any story, but some tie to a given genre better than others. A streetwise cell working the docks isn't likely to tangle with elite, undead assassins. A Task Force: VALKYRIE group might, but won't necessarily pay attention to small time predators. On the other hand, you might have a really *cool* idea that explains why your first-tier barflies head to West Africa to destroy the root of the vampire race. Pick that option over anything you'll read below.

Beyond the Requiem

This book is designed to allow crossovers with **Vampire: The Requiem** but doesn't force you to use that game. This Storytelling advice in section takes a particularly broad look at vampire myths. You can fit most of its advice into **Requiem**'s structure but you don't have to. The World of Darkness has room enough for any kind of vampire you like as long as you don't add so many that it would break the already relaxed assumptions behind the setting. (Note, too that even though **World of Darkness** books include many, many kinds of monsters, no objective canon states that says they must *all* co-exist. This stuff is supposed to add options, not boost the supernatural population beyond your comfort level.) Some archetypes hint at alternative possibilities. The possessed, for instance, draw from myths and fiction about vampires as shells for malefic spirits. Go with that idea, use it as a metaphor for the creature's personality, or slot it into an existing **Requiem** concept.

Look beyond **Vampire** whenever you want to surprise experienced World of Darkness players. Change vampires' powers and vulnerabilities to give players the chance to authentically uncover secrets, instead of saying, "My character doesn't know this, but we're definitely hunting a Mekhet." Then again, if your players have fun saying just that and they're good at separating player and character knowledge, go with **Vampire: The Requiem**'s take on vampires— but take a look at this section to get a better handle on what they look like from the outside.

First-Tier Cells

First-tier stories begin and end with individuals. Without overarching organizations, hunters encounter vampires through personal ties. They track vampires who attack their neighbors and friends—or *were* those people. Low power and a local, intimate focus lends itself to the following genres:

Psychological Horror: This genre's disturbing themes and images have been tailor-made for particular characters. Fear comes from intimate sources. If a hunter has a miscarriage in her background, the antagonist is an ever-pregnant vampire who's "eating for two."

Vampires arouse disgust because they remind characters of their own failings. They spark fear by reminding characters of their past traumas and dark secrets. The hunter's abusive father is mirrored by the vampire who torments his blood slaves—or the hunter *was* the abuser, and the vampire is his daughter turned monster, come to reap a price in blood.

Survival Horror: The vampire isn't a schemer here, but a straightforward physical threat. Survival horror's filled with flight or flight scenes (see the Hunt, Abduction or Chase or Be Chased scene outlines for examples). The environment's a critical factor because hunters will be on the run, looking for a crucial doorway or bit of scrap to help them prevail. They can't beat the vampire right away. They'll have to find a solution in mid-flight: a desperate plan that evens the overwhelming odds.

Survival horror works well with packs of vampires, due to a certain resonance with modern "fast zombies" and as an extension of the psychological horror concept. If you make the pack a dark reflection of the players' cell, it reminds them that the hunt *can* go too far, making them like the monsters they fight.

Compacts

Compact-level stories open a window to greater supernatural secrets. Characters learn that vampires aren't singular freaks of nature who've crossed their paths by chance, but members of a conspiracy of the damned. Compacts decrypt their secrets and oppose their plots.

Crime Drama: This ventures a touch beyond the horror genre but in the World of Darkness, crime dramas are excellent models for citywide vampire conspiracies. The average vampire fiefdom is half Renaissance principality, half Mafia family. It loves ancient rituals but walks hip deep in modern avarice. Hunters might be the "cops" in this equation, or a competing "crime family." When Union members fight vampires for control of the docks, what do they really want to do: protect normal people, guarantee their cut of the business, or strike some mad balance between both?

Weird Tale: Compacts have just enough power to learn *too* much. Members have an inkling of the bigger picture. They know that strange, secret laws govern the universe. A weird tale reveals a maddening fragment of the truth about vampires. It lays bare a hideous truth about their origin or secret nature. It's is a broader version of psychological horror. Where that genre makes the vampire a personal foil, the weird tale reveals why the vampire plagues everyone—and the implications of the answer inspire madness. Compact members find the mad god that made them, or discover that the God they thought they knew created the undead to slake his terrible hate for mortals. Or every vampire is an intrusion from some being that would destroy the universe, were it permitted to fully manifest. Vampirism is the anti-god's invasion.

Conspiracies

Hunter conspiracies have powerful resources and profound secret lore at their command. They're prepared for extreme stories that blur the edges of horror, fantasy and pure action. At lower tiers, events center on individual hunters or dueling local conspiracies, but at the level of Aegis Kai Doru and the Cheiron Group, stories lay bare the ultimate secrets—and wake them from their restless slumber. Plots unleash elder blood-devourers on an unready world, or they might hold some hope of destroying the undead forever. Don't explore extreme stories right away—give them time to grow. Build vampire epics over time to present the world in all its complexity. If the players don't appreciate the World of Darkness' scope, they won't take the threat of its destruction seriously.

Action Horror: There's a time to brood over the predators in our midst and a time to shoot them with silenced HK MP5's packed with specially-irradiated, vampire-burning ammo. High technology and supernatural powers justify extreme action sequences. Vampires run along walls twirling swords from their medieval youth. Endowments give hunters the ability to stay in the game and maybe even perform a few cool tricks of their own. This genre splits time between plot exposition and action set pieces—but the action's the main thing.

Epic: The fate of the world's on the line. Your hunters might destroy or transform nearly every vampire, everywhere. These stories evolve from sober investigations to intense exploits with global implications. The Dead Who Rise at the Sun's End rip their way out of secret crypts. Hunter task forces search for the mother of all vampires and command her to betray her bloodthirsty children. You don't have to knock over buildings or blot out the sun—but you can. Apocalyptic stakes are the key, whether they play out in public or not.

Vampire Archetypes

Vampires are psychological landmarks, born of legends flexible enough to accept any significance we give them. There's no "true" vampire legend. Some classic aspects (such as a vulnerability to sunlight) are the products of celluloid, not medieval legendry. Culturally speaking, a vampire is a loosely defined monster that readily accepts any significance we attach to it. That's why they're flexible antagonists, able to play almost any role without breaking some literary-mythic rule about what they *should* be. The 21st century has already broken all the rules; there's no such thing as a "traditional" vampire nowadays. This is a fantastic opportunity for Storytellers, because their vampire—no matter how they choose to conceive it—has as strong a claim to authenticity as any other.

Nevertheless, even though vampire myths are easy to customize you still have to limit yourself. Vampires mean many things to many people, but they really do *mean* something. Few people want to roleplay a life-or-death struggle with vampires who are wise-cracking rodeo clowns, for instance. (Though for sanity's sake, maybe you shouldn't let your players read this passage, because some wit among you will decide that *she's* the exception.)

Look to your group and the local culture to guide you. They determine the basic vampire archetype based on what they read, watch and talk about. It's easy to go on your gut feeling (you probably belong to your players' culture, after all) but if you want to fine-tune a vampire antagonist try to step away from your immediate impressions for a moment. Look at the vampire from an outsider's perspective, think about the characteristics you observe and customize them to fit the story you want to tell.

Of course, if you're reading this you're probably familiar with vampires as they manifest in the English-speaking world, so we can get a bit more specific. The Western, postmodern vampire myth mixes tradition and mass media to produce a creature with a few common characteristics. Vampires are born of us, but they are *not* us. They need blood. They don't age. They turn *us* into *them*. Something sinister, above and beyond their unusual needs, influences their thoughts. Once a vampire brings him into undeath, our best friend, brother or lover can't be trusted. This book is about those vampires, but even when we take these characteristics for granted, vampire mythology's protean nature gives us the power to customize them. So let's look at some common vampire concepts for your **Hunter** game. Use them to customize vampires for your chronicle or portray individuals in a variegated group of undead.

The Addict

The vampire addict can be sympathetic or sinister, depending on the situation. He's a victim of his thirst for blood. Maybe he was turned against his will or without getting all the facts. Whatever the reason, he hates being in thrall to his needs. He doesn't want to hurt anyone, but he has to. He might even help hunters take down fellow vampires. He doesn't want to be a part of an undead conspiracy!

On the other hand, he's absolutely ruthless about getting his fix. He'll say or do anything to satisfy the hunger. He feels it more intensely than most vampires—and he won't wait until he's starving to satisfy it. Even one night without blood is painful—two is utter agony. Human addiction turns your best friend into someone who'll steal your laptop or rip the copper piping out of your neighbor's house. A blood addict will drug your family and lock them in a closet to secure his source. He'll finish off sick or wounded friends while saying he doesn't want to do any of it, but *has* to.

The addict probably knows his prey. He doesn't like to take chances, so he sticks to people he knows. He might have a circle of repeat victims, scarred from his clumsy feeding. He only hunts the streets if he's desperate enough to be sloppy and dangerous. He'll drain strangers completely, but he might to leave a lot of evidence around. The blood-high makes him careless.

Most addicts don't last long. More disciplined vampires take their territory. Their mistakes attract hunters. Some addicts make it through the gauntlet, though, and they're dangerous to hunt. They've developed an iron will and meticulous nature. After surviving vampire "adolescence," they learn to keep the thirst in check and employ practical, carefully-planned hunting methods.

Appearance: The addict's unkempt, too focused on his next feeding to care about how he looks. He'd be filthy if he sweated like a human, but on his undead body the

ALL VAMPIRES KNOW KUNG FU

Vampires are so popular that they've attracted motifs that aren't exactly horrific. If you go by television depictions, lots of vampires are martial arts experts. Some of them even belong to black ops squads that have custom weapons and armor. These things scream "action flick," not "desperate horror," but they'll influence your players' point of view even if your chronicle is a low key affair.

You've got two ways to deal with this. You can set the tone of the story early on and show players that your vampires go for savage, streetwise violence: ambushes, feral bites and rusty pipes. If you don't want to show the monster yet, let his victim's testimony (or autopsy) do the talking.

The other option is to embrace the action film stereotype, but twist it for your own purposes. Movies and TV shows use martial arts to set up interesting fights, but you can take the same martial arts skill set and use it to showcase a vampire's physical prowess and sadism. It's not a kung fu fight; it's a monster toying with its prey in a one-sided conflict. When it comes to the neo-cinematic vampire's gadgets, there's one plausible way to get them in a **Hunter** game: third-tier conspiracies. The average vampire pack isn't going to tool around in an armored van while they prep nightvision gear and assault weapons, but one that's broken into a Task Force: VALKRIE safehouse might. Even though the action film vampire might not to be what your chronicle's all about, you can still use him to inspire you. Don't be afraid to throw on *Blade* or *Buffy the Vampire Slayer* to mine ideas, but filter them through a vision of the world you want to share with your group.

dirt dries out, leaving him dusty looking and superficially, more sanitary. He occasionally sorts himself out long enough to look good in front of a more powerful vampire or to infiltrate a group that might get him a rich feeding. His eyes look a bit blank; he splits his thoughts between matters at hand and plans to get blood. He's in denial about being a predator so he's rarely armed with anything more sophisticated than a sharpened screwdriver. The total effect might make him look like a loser but he knows how to turn on the charm, especially when it comes to eliciting sympathy.

Traits: An addict usually has high Social attributes, especially Manipulation, which he uses to portray himself as a victim or scam his way into someone's confidence. His Skills are focused on the fields that support his preferred feeding tactics. Many addicts are familiar with Medicine, to help them find veins quickly, treat peotheple they victimize repeatedly and to infiltrate blood storage facilities. The addict often has a human "herd" to feed from. These people might well be friends and family from his human life, who believe that somehow, if they all help and support him, they can cure him. These are either Allies or if he's turned them into blood addicts, loyal Retainers.

The Aristocrat

She represents the upper class: old money, the boardroom, the exclusive club. She's a parasite, but not just because she drinks blood. The aristocrat is a vampire who exploits the weak using exactly the same methods as the executives and other modern gentry she resembles. Mortal blood is her natural right, her reward for being superior to the human "cattle" around her.

Aristocratic vampirism is a metaphor for class struggle, populism versus elitism and political corruption. The vampire destroys lives like a cruel boss or venal politician—blood is just another form of power to be hoarded and wasted on selfish ends. An aristocrat usually feeds discreetly, leaving little more than a muffled scream emanating from the guest room of her huge mansion. When she slaughters a mortal in a more accessible venue, it's a gesture of contempt that affirms her superiority. She gets as much satisfaction from the fact that she can get away with it as she does from the blood itself. Servants clean up the mess. She might toy with some victims over several nights or go "slumming" to take them from the streets, out of boredom or the belief that she needs to cull the "herd."

The aristocrat rarely feels guilty. Mortal culture helps; she's just one master in a society that breeds haves and have-nots. She's beyond human, part of the (un) natural elite; mortals exist to satisfy her needs. Some aristocrats toy with meritocracy, or at least tell themselves that anyone who didn't deserve her fangs would be strong enough to resist her. She might even turn someone into a vampire to "reward" him for loyal service. To her, most humans are food or serfs. If she's kind to the latter it's out of pragmatism, for abuse can breed dangerous resentment. She'd hate to admit it, but her thralls know some of her vulnerabilities. Some aristocrats aren't so careful; their retainers get sick of the horror show and help hunters dispose of "Mistress" for them.

Modern nights support two kinds of aristocrat. The first is the classic noble, thriving on an inheritance or the spoils of a long unlife. She has anachronistic tastes in everything from fashion to social mores. She yearns for an imagined era when people appreciated luxury and treated their "betters" with respect. Old clothes rarely give her away, however; servants keep her up to date on vulgar modernity. Other aristocrats are thoroughly modern: ardent capitalists, made bolder by traits that money *can't* buy. They lair in upscale penthouses, not rotting country estates. The modernist fancies herself a master of human nature, but she assumes that *everyone's* selfish. The classic aristocrat sometimes acts out of a twisted sense of noblesse oblige but her modern counterpart holds weakness in contempt.

Appearance: It would take the average person a year to buy what the aristocrat wears for a night, but not because she's gaudy. Her bespoke outfits and antique ensembles tend to be understated. An educated eye recognizes the utter wealth—and the ability to send that message to anyone capable of noticing it is a kind of power, too. It says that she's part of high society, not some nouveau riche invader. Immaculate grooming makes it hard to tell whether her artificial appearance is makeup or death's mark.

Traits: The aristocrat has high Social Attributes and Skills. She gives effective orders. She'll often have some expertise related to her wealth or an obsessive pastime. Mind-affected Dread Powers reflect her will to rule. Aristocrats have high Resources ratings and enough Status to bend mortal and undead institutions to her will. Retainers are practically mandatory, too. She'd never soil her hands by moving bodies herself. They're often older vampires who've accumulated wealth just by surviving. They might have game traits representing old interests: parts of her history that hunters might exploit.

ARCHETYPES, CLASSIC VAMPIRES AND THE REQUIEM

This section presents archetypes as if they were discrete types of vampires. You can look at one, pick suitable character traits and use the result right away. The archetypes are artificial, however; they break down the fictional vampires into narrowly defined categories that are convenient, but hardly essential. Don't be afraid to mix and match them for a distinctive antagonist. Dracula is both aristocrat and outsider; some interpretations give him incubus and nightmare traits, too.

If you're crossing **Hunter** over with **Vampire: The Requiem** you should know that archetypes don't *exactly* map to vampire clans and covenants. Many Invictus are Aristocrats and Daeva are even nicknamed "succubi," but vampires from both clans exist that don't fit either archetype. **Vampire** and this book both use the same cultural mythology, so overlaps are unavoidable. For creativity's sake we suggest that you try contrasting the way each book uses the source material. If you make a Daeva a succubus you're painting by the numbers— why not explore an addict from that clan? Design a Mekhet succubus or an Invictus nightmare who *isn't* a Nosferatu for a change and see what happens.

The Blood Witch

Vampire lore has always been linked to magic. In some legends, witches become vampires when they die (and hey, maybe that's even true). Other myths don't distinguish between black magicians and the undead. Learning occult lore is enough to turn a careless mortal into a vampire, or vampirism is no disease, but a black magic spell. No matter the truth, the blood witch represents a magical take on vampirism. He's an occultist whose devotion to the dark arts transcends death. Vampirism is only one offense against the natural order. His other crimes are powered by weird chants and vile sacrifices—and they get horrible, supernatural *results*.

A blood witch hunts for more than sustenance. Magic demands blood—his own or a sacrifice's—and he can always use other parts of his prey for occult experiments. He divines the future with human entrails or captures victims for ritual sacrifice. Hunters might be able to save a blood witch's captives before he does something horrible to them, but they have to find his inner sanctum first. Blood witches' penchant for ritual extends beyond the mystic arts. Some feed in a ceremonial fashion to honor prey the way traditional hunters thank the kill, or dedicate a soul to dark gods. These feeding patterns might give a blood witch away to investigators.

Blood witches always have a lab, tabernacle or other hidden place of power. It hosts solitary blood-rites or cult gatherings—whichever the witch prefers. Either way, his methods belong to a particular school of magic. He's a Satanist, a pagan with a sanguine approach to his ancient faith, even a Taoist mystic— whatever his choice, his blood magic relies on it. His philosophy determines the rituals he learns, the experiments he performs and his ultimate goals. One blood witch aspires to godhood; another hones his art in the hope of freeing unspeakable creatures from eons-old prisons.

Anyone on the trail of a blood witch has to ask which of his beliefs are mad superstitions—and which are equally insane, but *true*. Many Blood witches ascribe even instinctual vampire powers to their occult discipline. This is probably a delusion, but elder blood witches master eldritch powers that go far beyond a vampire's basic capabilities. If a vampire says he can command animals because of some patron demon, this begs the question: Does the demon exist? If so, the blood witch might foreshadow a greater threat to come.

Appearance: Blood witches save their gore-spattered ceremonial robes for private occasions. Some care nothing for material pleasures and dress practically, in clothes scrounged from victims. Most blood witches use their powers to get the finer things in unlife and go for an upscale look. In both cases, the vampire carries a token of his devotion with him: an old necklace, a fetish hidden in his breast pocket or even a pouch of ingredients to support spontaneous magical workings.

Traits: The blood witch has high Mental Attributes and Skills. A high Occult rating is mandatory; other Skills help him research the dark arts. He has the Resources to fund a ritual space and Contacts in the occult community. His network might even extend to other supernatural beings. If he has Retainers, they're cultists who trade blood and obedience for magical favors. His most distinctive traits are his Dread Powers. They're numerous and strange, even by a vampire's standards. Some of these abilities might rely on rituals, or inflict dark stigmata on the users: derangements, deformities and other unnatural alterations.

The Decadent

The decadent is an esthete. She fancies herself a painter, musician or poet, but her real art is unlife itself. She lives in a moral universe where right and wrong takes a back seat to sensation and entertainment. To the decadent, evil is the superstitious relic of frightened, spiritually moribund religions. Human morality gets a sardonic wink and chuckle when she bothers to confront it at all. The decadent believes she's more than human; vampirism opened her senses to experiences mortals can't conceive. Artistic pretenses can't hide her callousness, however. To her, pain and pleasure are just two more colors on the merciless easel of existence. She uses them to "brighten" dull moments. Death is theatre. Human beings don't have a say in the drama because their perceptions are too limited to appreciate her artistic aims. Her "vision" is more important to her than almost any human life.

The decadent stalks people she thinks lead beautiful lives. She might turn them into vampires or initiate an affair that ends in madness and blood addiction, but she'll just as often watch from afar while she secretly manipulates their lives. She loves them just as they are and never wants them to change—even if *they* want to change. If her struggling musician wins a record deal she'll sabotage it, just so she can keep watching him wrestle with hardship. Human frailty fascinates her; she secretly envies real pain. She sees, hears and feels things undreamt of in her mortal days but her ordinary passions are as dead as her flesh. She creates art to try and trigger her old emotions but it rarely works; it only reveals the emptiness in her heart. She learns to resent human beings as time goes on, all while she claims to embrace the best in humanity.

A decadent is usually a socialite in and out vampire society. She entertains her peers with tableaus of blood and pain using victims culled from her favorite mortal communities. Some decadents haunt a specific subculture: ravers, performance artists, even food connoisseurs (though this last is tricky, to be sure). Others drift wherever their whims take them. These groups are filled with artists to inspire her—or human "raw materials" for her own work. She uses her Social Skills to establish herself as an influential figure: a rich patron, teacher or master artist (in the technical, rather than creative sense, because her work rarely matches truly inspired mortal creations). The decadent bends the scene to her will. She thinks herself more creative and enlightened than her mortal "children" and recruits them to support her own art. Her influence tests her companions' moral limits; some kill for her art, but others won't. The latter group is a likely source of informants for hunters who've set their sights on her.

Appearance: She dresses for effect, in *haute couture* or carefully studied street fashion, in tune with the creative pulse of the times. She wears cutting edge fashion unless irony or tradition demands a more conservative style and even then, she can't resist putting her own spin on things. She's beautiful, but rarely looks like a model. Even though she aspires to aesthetic perfection she wants to be treated like an authority, not an object. She chooses accessories with a similar degree of care, balancing the latest trends with a suggestion of executive power.

Traits: The decadent has high Mental and Social Attributes. She's a witty conversationalist with a working knowledge of several creative fields. Accordingly, her Skills balance academic knowledge and artistic crafts. She's rarely a skilled combatant, but might be surprisingly athletic if she's taken an interest in dance. Dread Powers focus on extrasensory perception and emotional influence.

The Immortal

The immortal is more a monument to time than a person. He protects a potentially endless existence with melancholic stoicism. He knows that that nothing in this world can endure the ravages of time. Lives, philosophies and nations are fading notes in the unending dirge of his unlife. Ironically, for all his meditations on impermanence, his hold over mortals is the tyranny of an inescapable legacy. He's the secret grand-father of a debased aristocratic bloodline, the master of decrepit cults and the ruler of shadowy networks that no human lives long enough to build. He's almost never a street-level antagonist. Instead, he's the enemy at the end of a chain of crimes and clues. The immortal isn't as overtly bloodthirsty as other vampires but he's indifferent to mortals and their ephemeral passions. People die all the time; it makes no difference to him whether their end comes now or later.

An immortal wants to "live" comfortably until the stars wink out. He cultivates slow, steady schemes for safety, wealth and power. Centuries of observation have given him a keen insight into the human psyche. He masterfully exploits his servants and society itself. He doesn't care about the latest philosophical fashions but looks to the underlying psychology beneath them. To him it's as constant and predictable as the sunset. The immortal prefers loyal humans to vampires. He holds some modest but unquestioned influence in the world of the undead, but he doesn't interfere in nightly affairs unless they threaten his interests. And aside from self-preservation, his interests are deep secrets.

At least one of those secrets keeps him from greeting the sun out of boredom or despair. It could be his mortal family, a prophecy he's tracked through time or another immortal—a lover or enemy. This is his weakness. If something should threaten his hidden passion it forces him to throw caution to the wind. He has considerable resources at his disposal but he's not used to improvising or thinking at a mortally quick pace. He underestimates short-lived enemies, expecting the same fearful, venal attitudes he's manipulated over many lifetimes. Unpredictable situations amuse him as much as they frighten him, however. They might inspire him to offer his assailants immortality.

Appearance: The immortal projects conservative affluence. There's always something a bit blank about his expression. He assumes modern disguises with staid boredom. He might reveal some sign of his true age, if he's thinks nobody will notice. The most obvious tell is something he's hard-pressed to hide: his still, emotionless face and body language. If he didn't go through the motions of twitching and moving like a human or young vampire he'd look like a statue, not a man.

Traits: An immortal has high Attributes in all categories. Even if he was never a warrior sheer age toughens his body. He has a broad array of Skills and isn't ignorant of contemporary technology (if he couldn't adapt to the times, he'd be dust) but he's not likely to be an IT expert either. He has considerable Resources and loyal Retainers, including families who have served him for generations. His Dread Powers are potent, diverse and include abilities that younger vampires are incapable of learning.

The Nightmare

The nightmare is a straightforward monster. She's the closest thing to the old mythic vampire: strong, impulsive and *hungry*. Maddened by her transformation, she seeks out familiar elements from her old life, but thirsts for blood all the same. Thus, she usually feeds from family first. She isn't subtle; if the authorities never hear about her it's either because she's preying on people in a remote location or someone—another vampire, hunters or even guilty family members—is covering up for her. Some nightmares erupt from the shadows for an extended feast but many hunt in cycles, creeping from their lairs to kill after some infrequent trigger event.

You can't reason with a nightmare; she's not even remotely human any more. She might have some vestigial emotional attachments but they can't replace human love—or even hate. Maybe she won't touch her own children, or she only feeds on people she hated while she was alive, but she's still a creature of instinct. On the other hand, that doesn't make her stupid. Rather, her intelligence is the slave of bestial impulses. She could read a newspaper or carry on a conversation if she didn't lack

the desire to perform such simple, human tasks. The monstrous soul inside her harnesses her intelligence to hide, hunt and kill. She uses her powers with surprising sophistication. She might haunt her prey's dreams for several nights in a row to tire and frighten them before she actually attacks, or could use unnatural strength to block a country road with stones and logs.

Nightmares rarely survive long; hunters and more sophisticated rivals destroy them, or madness inspires them to jump in a fire or expose themselves to the sun. A canny nightmare falls into a working routine through luck and cunning. It determines when she hunts, when she sleeps and how she deals with enemies. A nightmare is potentially a predictable enemy, but few people get a chance to examine her moments— she kills them the first time around. Many of them feed on animals or enter long periods of hibernation. The oldest nightmares enter local legends. Some communities even form a symbiotic bond with the monster among them. She protects them from intruders and leaves the townsfolk alone. They give her slaughterhouse blood—and sometimes the odd tourist, too. A few of these arrangements have gone on so long that nobody can remember where the customs come from, but if they forget, they'll reap a violent reminder.

Blood Children

In modern vampire stories, children typically stop aging once they become undead. They lose their innocence to the thirst for blood. Years pass; the vampire child's psyche twists under the strain of a lifetime's experience coiled inside an immature shell.

Add any archetype to a vampire child but avoid using it for cheap shock value. A good vampire story builds interest in the antagonist—not pure revulsion. Take particular care with sexual themes like those implicit in the succubus archetype. Even though the vampire only *looks* like a child the superficial effect is, to put not too fine a point on it, utterly disgusting. The image of a child coming to harm in any context can be just too unsettling for many people. Don't fall into the trap of judging horror by how extreme the situation is. If you make the scenario totally repellent your players won't want to get involved. In gaming, effective horror comes from *willingly* exploring a frightening situation, not being dared to be a party to something you really hate.

Appearance: Nightmares are inhuman and ugly. Unless they need to blend in they'll wear tattered clothes or none at all. Their bluish limbs and pointed nails are signs of a blasphemously transformed corpse; their faces have oversized fangs and sunken eyes. Some nightmares have been hideously transformed by vampirism itself. Their bodies have funhouse mirror distortions or animalistic features.

Traits: A nightmare has high Physical Attributes. She masters Brawl and Stealth by instinct. She may have intellectually-demanding Skills but she's rarely in the right state of mind to use them. Dread Powers augment her physical abilities. She may have other powers as well but uses them infrequently if they depend on speech.

The Outsider

The outsider archetype has evolved through the ages. He was originally a foreigner whose language and customs evoked fearful speculation. The modern outsider can spring from different social classes and cultures inside a more familiar society. He's an undead gangbanger or hides inside a closed religious community. Like the succubus (see p. 194), the outsider is a traditional element of vampire horror that needs to be treated carefully. He's frightening because he's *different*. He speaks an unfamiliar language and surrounds himself with servants from his own culture. In a better world, we wouldn't be afraid of mere difference; the outsider wouldn't be that scary. Used correctly, he's effective because he's unpredictable, not because of specific cultural traits. It's very easy to unwittingly weave racism into your story by misusing this archetype. Thus, the description here isn't *quite* traditional, as it provides alternatives to the racist subtext in classic examples.

The outsider isn't from the same culture as your hunters but he's interested in their community. If his people are the majority, he wants to dominate or destroy the characters' small community. If hunter characters are a part of the majority culture, he uses his own community as a shield and cloak to enhance the hunt. He doesn't have the broad connections of some vampires but he does have ironclad control over some members of his native culture—and rarely with that group's consent. Family members are hostages; community leaders are blood addicts. He exploits traditions when it suits him and breaks them when it doesn't. If he's arrived with an occupying army, for example, he abuses the chain of command to quash rumors of bloody "interrogations."

The outsider uses his relatively exotic ways to misdirect and intimidate enemies. His actions throw a wedge in between his community and the people that might help get it out from under his thumb. He discourages cross-cultural contact, because some of his "countrymen" might appeal for outside assistance. When he thinks enemies are on his tail he hides in the local enclave or smuggles himself back to the "old country." If hunters follow, they find the outsider well-prepared to deal with any threat. He presses others to do the fighting for him or sets his lair up in a hard to find location.

He takes his blood in one of two ways. The outsider might set up a blood-giving custom in his community. If it's a gang, new members give him a cut of their blood along with their drug money, letting it drip into a goblet as part of a contrived ritual. He might target a particular family or social group—only priests perhaps, or the poor. He rarely hunts his own, but outside the enclave he's a remorseless killer. Every time he mutilates people outside his group it demonstrates what will happen to members who try to leave. The insiders are the "lucky ones."

Appearance: The outsider dresses according to his culture, but closer to stereotype than everyday fact. This is posturing on his part, designed to provoke xenophobia. A real gang member adds a few signs and symbols to his normal dress; the vampire OG *starts* with the symbols; he combines them to turn himself into the kind of character that only exists in movies. Some adapt traditional dress from various cultures in a fashion that looks more contrived than spontaneous, but not everyone who sees him can tell.

Traits: Outsiders have high Social and Physical Attributes to back up the two ways they keep their enclaves in line: intimidation and violence. His Skills follow suit, but he also has some knowledge of the law via the Academics Skill. Politics help keep his community isolated and easy to control. He has Allies and Retainers from his enclave and mind control powers to keep them loyal.

The Possessed

She's not the person you knew. She's got the same face and memories but her personality, her *soul* is gone, replaced by a malevolent *thing* that wants you to suffer. We call her possessed, but the real reason she's turned into a demon in the flesh is for the Storyteller to decide. Is there an alien spirit animating her body, or did turning undead rip out the decent parts of her psyche? No matter the answer, the effects speak for themselves. The possessed targets friends and family. Sometimes she kills them right away, but one of the possessed might look upon her former confidantes as slaves or potential vampires themselves. In the last case, she turns them into a parody of a family. They hunt and lair together like a pride of psychotic lions. Bloodjackers (see p. 172) are the epitome of this archetype.

The possessed vampire is pure psychopath. There's nothing human to redeem. She's good at pretending to feel love and compassion though, especially when she deals with people who knew her when she was human. She wears the façade to get close to victims so she can stab them in the back. The flavor of fear meshed with betrayal intoxicates her because she wants her prey to suffer. Ironically, this offers them some hope. She'll avoid a quick kill or a quiet feeding whenever she can get away with it. She would rather play with her "food" over a half dozen nights then snap a neck in a second.

Some vampires fill even the most hardened hunters with doubts about their mission. The possessed is not one of those. Once they know what she really, is only a complete pacifist would argue against driving a stake through her heart. Possessed are suitable antagonists for toe to toe action because they're willing to confront hunters head on. They love the thrill of the fight. It gives them a chance to destroy the most confident, hopeful humans. Possessed are more than heartless and cruel. They're *evil* in the classic sense and love to inflict suffering for its own sake. This makes the archetype a tad two-dimensional for some chronicles, but a touch of classic black-and-white morality can drive a refreshing change for even the most subtle, shades-of-gray **Hunter** games.

Some myths say that you can cure a possessed vampire, but it's never an easy task. You have to kill the vampire who made her, use an occult ritual to give her a soul or sacrifice yourself for her out of perfect love. Only mighty interventions such as these can halt her monstrous sadism without actually destroying her.

Appearance: The possessed looks human on the surface. She's even good at feigning normal emotions, but a few telltale signs give her away. Her clothes are a bit shabby and disordered. The social instincts that tell her how to make herself attractive are gone, so she uses habit and imitation to fake it. Her face is eerily blank or twisted in a snarl when she doesn't think anyone's looking. Some possessed undergo physical changes when their vampiric instincts take over. Their fangs grow and faces distort, evoking the appearance of angry wolves trapped in human skin.

Traits: Possessed vampires have strong Physical Attributes and Skills. Some have a high Manipulation score that helps them lead naïve humans into the inevitable betrayal. Fighting and athletic ability leap forward after her undeath. A monster's intuition guides her every move. Her Dread Powers give her supernatural speed and strength. Unless she's enslaved friends and family she doesn't have many valuable ties to the human world. It makes no difference to her whether she sleeps in a sewer or a mansion.

BY BOOK OR BY TYPE?

If you own **Vampire: The Requiem** you can portray most of the archetypes in this chapter as standard Kindred, but you don't *have* to. The possessed is an example of an archetype that ultimately owes its existence to legends that contradict the default assumption that a newly-Embraced is in some sense, the person she was before she crossed over.

Basically, you have two choices when it comes to using vampires in your personal World of Darkness. You can aim for depth, by giving vampires a complex secret history and common traits (and not necessarily those found in **Requiem**), or you can choose variety, where every vampire is a unique monster, with its own supernatural origin, strengths and weaknesses. In one chronicle, wooden stakes paralyze all vampires. In the other, a stake that kills one has no effect on another. A third vampire keeps his heart sealed in a canopic jar, guarded by mummified cats.

Aiming for depth is suitable for crossover games (somebody might be playing a vampire and needs a good background to start with) or chronicles where vampires are the primary antagonists. This gives you the means to gradually reveal one secret after another, until hunters piece together an accurate picture of the undead. Variety is good for episodic chronicles, where telling the difference between one "monster of the week" and the next is part of the fun. Just remember that your hunters have to be able to gather *some* intelligence about their foe. Switching around the rules for no reason other than to confuse the players isn't really entertaining. Even if your vampire antagonist is the only one of his kind on earth he should be some clues about his history and characteristics.

The Predator

The predator is "Nature, red in tooth and claw," incarnate. His bloodlust trumps all morals, though he doesn't feed excessively fill his vampire's hunger. He hunts intelligently, for survival's sake alone. He feigns kindness or channels murderous aggression according to the situation, never pausing to think how it affects his prey. To him, human beings have the same rights as cattle. The predator's disciplined nature and minimalist tastes make him hard to hunt. He has an unbreakable will to survive that manifests in contingency plans, deceptive tactics and cold-blooded murder.

Predators adapt to their environments in many ways but for discussion's sake it's easy to think in terms of rural and urban varieties. The rural predator is usually a nomad. Even counting animals, the countryside doesn't have a high enough population density for any single area to support him long. He feeds on animals if he can, leading to rumors of alien cattle mutilations and *El Chupacabra*. He doesn't care if he's draining a stray dog or a lost child; anything with blood is fair game. Animals help the predator keep a low profile but it's not a viable long term solution. Even domesticated creatures flee vampires on sight or smell. Predators have to chase them down—a time-consuming process for relatively little nourishment. Older predators can't drink from animals at all. Eventually, he'll take human prey or starves himself with a long, deathlike sleep—and few of them are willing to do that. Instead, they wander from town to town, feeding with as much stealth as they can manage before moving on.

Urban predators can afford to stay put. They have a rich hunting ground but need to approach it with social sophistication. An urban predator develops specific routines for hunting: scripts he uses to talk prey into vulnerable positions, specific ways to quietly kill a man without spilling his precious blood and ways to dispose of the bodies afterward. His methods are hard to crack, but they're habits nonetheless. Hunters who learn them can track him down. Predators restrict their social lives to the hunt. Some hunt in packs, but collective bloodthirst generally outweighs the advantages. When prey's thin and hunger's high, members separate or turn on each other. They stay on the fringes of vampire society and do just enough to protect hunting grounds from competitors. A predator only talks to a human as part of the hunt; otherwise, they have no reason to talk to their food.

To a predator, mortals are just another prey species in a world filled with those who eat, and those who are eaten. Vampires are part of nature; even they are vulnerable to its cruel laws. Many predators systematically hunt other vampires. If a predator drinks another vampire's heart's blood he believes he's improved the undead "breed." The strong survive on the blood of the weak—and his victim was *weak*. To prove he's one of the strong, a predator concentrates on survival. There's no room in his Spartan existence for entertainment or egotism. But despite a pretense of discipline, his vampire's rage seethes just below the surface. When his plans fail and pursuers trap him reason flies out the window. He lashes out like a cornered animal.

Appearance: A predator dresses to camouflage himself and provide pockets and straps for his tools. He wears fatigues or three piece suits depending on the hunting ground, but in each case, he opts for a style that won't bind his movements or keep him from carrying a weapon. A few predators have unkempt long hair, but most go for cropped hairstyles or tight braids that require minimal attention.

Traits: A predator develops abilities that suit his hunting style. If he ambushes victims he develops strong Physical Attributes and Skills like Stealth, Brawl, Weaponry and Firearms. His Dread Powers enhance physical prowess. The urban predator hones Social abilities. He masters mind control to pacify his prey and cover his tracks. Few predators have Allies, Contacts or Retainers. Money is just a hunting tool, so his Resources are minimal.

The Succubus

The succubus (or incubus, if male) is the vampire as demon lover, whose unrestrained sexuality strides the border between honest passion and exploitation. She sees no difference between feeding and sex. She not only treats bloodthirst like a sexual passion, but treats sex like a fundamentally selfish act. If her partners don't take what they want from the experience they never deserved the pleasure in the first place. She might seduce her prey or even carry on an extended relationship, but it's casual play at best—never true love. If she wants to take her pleasure by force she will. Her sexualized personality conceals a lack of empathy, but she's not always aware of that. If she feasts by force or kills her "lover," she blames the victim without a second thought.

A succubus' proclivities inform her hunting strategy. She seduces prey, feigning sympathy when necessary. Sometimes she picks a victim based on her tastes: older men, dark-haired women or anyone who'd be receptive to certain fetishes. Hunger makes her preferences more flexible. If she goes without feeding for long enough she'll make almost anyone her victim. Serious bloodthirst leaves her little patience for romance. If she's starving, she'll take any sign of affection—even a glance—as a pretext for attack. Most succubi feed when they're somewhere between desperate hunger and slow seduction. This makes them look like exciting, dangerous lovers; low-level hunger drives risky behavior and quickens the affair's pace. If the victim survives, the succubus might lose interest because she's sated and can now afford to be choosier about assignations. More than one's vampire's been killed by a jealous lover, though, so many dispose of old lovers. The succubus might keep a stable of these short-lived companions. They live brief, pleasure-filled lives until they fall to blood-frenzied intercourse or the succubus' cold, pragmatic need to cover her tracks.

Her lovers are the heart of her mortal network. She often recruits them through sexually open subcultures, but unless she can get a group of swingers or fetishists utterly under her thumb she'll eventually abandon them and take a few members with her. These groups have tight-knit social networks and some safeguards against abuse, so they don't suit the more extreme manifestations of her hunger.

It's easy to draw parallels between vampirism and rape. They're both forms of intimate violence. Storytellers should use this symbolism with caution. The succubus explores a boundary between sex and immorality that's inspired by Victorian mores, but the border has shifted in the modern era, where consent and free will are at the center of sexual ethics. Make sure you know your group well before scratching the surface of this archetype. Some players won't want to get anywhere near even fictional depictions of sexual violence and exploitation. In all cases, respect the fact that this subject matter cuts close to real life, without horror's usual cloak of symbolism.

Appearance: She's the definition of the word "vamp:" aggressively beautiful and arousing. If she preys on a particular sexual subculture she'll wear its symbols (collars for bondage, or handkerchiefs colored and placed according to the local queer culture's

"code"). She knows how to present herself for potential prey. Her behavior's as subtle or overt as necessary, but it's always meant to lure her target to an intimate encounter. Her apparent wealth also varies from encounter to encounter. Many succubi keep mementos of their former lovers: stolen jewelry, clothing . . . and body parts.

Traits: Succubi have high Social Attributes and Skills. Her many Retainer Merits represents an ever-shifting group of lovers (often blood addicts) who compete for her affections and protect her from harm. She keeps a bedchamber separate from her normal haven or controls a nightclub that gives her access to a steady supply of uninhibited companions. This costs money, so she's usually at least moderately wealthy. Sex, wealth and supernatural powers give her Status in everything from a swingers' club scene to a cabal of sexually voracious politicians. Dread Powers control her prey's behavior and emotions.

The Good Vampire

The vampire archetypes here support **Hunter**'s point of view. Vampires are monsters. **Vampire: The Requiem** has a different take on the undead. Its Kindred have been thrust into a terrible moral dilemma where they do a little evil to keep greater horrors at bay. This situation's exemplified by the quote: *Beast I am, lest Beast I become.* Some vampires search for a balance between their human compassion and monstrous needs. A few succeed, but these bodhisattvas and messiahs of the Damned are as rare as the mortal articles.

You can modify any archetype by adding a truly human conscience. Each entry is an example of the vampire at his worst, so pull back to a more charitable point of view. The "good" succubus *does* experience true love, but her instincts compel her to feed during intimate moments. Possessed vampires and nightmares have episodes of inhuman behavior, triggered by circumstances beyond their control. Some vampires restrict hunting to immoral, human "monsters" or stick to willing companions and blood banks.

This option won't stall your **Hunter** game. Good or bad, vampires drink human blood and need to account for it. Even if they only hunt "evildoers," that begs the question: Who are they to define good and evil?

Tales of Blood

This section outlines typical vampire story scenes. It shows you how you might employ classic motifs and surprise twists to make them your own. You can use them to tell almost any story, but we've based our selection on the fact that vampires *need* victims. This sets them apart from most other monsters. Werewolves eat trespassers and ghosts possess people to slake deathless passions, but the undead must feed or perish. Tell a story about the hunt for blood and you'll go a long way toward telling a true vampire story instead of a generic monster tale that happens to involve fangs.

Develop the following scene outlines into complete stories, add them to an existing plotline or use them as side events in a long-running chronicle. Maybe vampires haven't come to the attention of your hunters yet, but an abduction scene tells them that the threat is real. Like vampire archetypes, these scene templates are really just a useful way of looking at vampire stories for the sake of your chronicle, so feel free to merge, split and warp them to taste.

Abduction

In a classic scene, the vampire invades his victim's home and spirits her away to be his meal, paramour or both. This has become something of a rarity in modern stories with as it's been largely replaced with nightclub seductions and back alley blood-muggings. Even though it's appeared in countless *Dracula* adaptations it might actually inject some novelty into your story.

You can use this scene to begin a story. A friend or relative asks hunters to find the missing victim, or the hunters know her themselves. Alternately, the characters know the vampire's out there and who he's after, so the scene turns from a simple kidnapping to a siege. This sets the stage for a battle of wits between your hunters and the invader. They prepare defenses for the monster to confront. If this is the situation, remember to portray the vampire with enough verisimilitude to make well-planned defenses effective. You might be tempted to treat the abduction as a given by assuming that the vampire can evade every precaution, but the vampire doesn't have your Storyteller's omniscience. Barring extrasensory powers or an informant on the inside, he doesn't know what to expect.

Ask yourself what would motivate a vampire to go so far as to transport his prey across town. Does he love her? Does he want to turn her into a vampire? Does she possess some kind of dangerous knowledge? The answer will inform the vampire's strategy, along with what he'll risk to succeed.

Motifs

A strange entrance: The vampire uses shapeshifting powers to get to his victim. He pours into the bedchamber as a mist, flaps in as a bat, or savages the doors in wolf form. Some vampires do this to pass through locked doors but others use an alternate form to hide and trick the opposition. He transforms into a shadow or wears the face of a trusted companion. If the latter, the vampire might dispose of the original first.

RATING AND ORGANIZING SCENES

White Wolf's **Storytelling Adventure System** features story planning methods that might help you use scene templates more effectively. Two key concepts are scene layouts and ratings systems. Take a look at any **SAS** story to get a heads-up on these concepts, but for completeness' sake, here's a condensed version.

Treat scenes like mini-stories that you can place in any order that fits the characters' actions. Note possible ways to trigger each scene. When characters hit a trigger, slot in its scene, run it and ask yourself which of the remaining scenes would follow.

Next, give yourself a rough idea of what sorts of things will happen in a scene. Give them the same 0 to ••••• dot ratings you'd assign to characters for Mental, Physical and Social aspects. The ratings describe how prevalent and difficult those events will be. The dramatic fight at the end of the story could be a Physical •••• scene, while routine research might be Mental ••. Some scenes will feature dots in all three aspects. It's not an exact science, so don't worry if your players find a 2-dot Social solution to a 4-dot Physical scene. These are just rough guides to the coming action.

She goes to him: Some vampires can summon their victims from afar. The creature infects his target with a subtle, unnatural attraction and calls upon it later. Of course, not every victim needs supernatural compulsion. What if she's fallen in love with the strange, pale man who now whispers at her door? Either way, the hunters must block her path, or track her back to the vampire's lair.

Snatched from the shadows: Not every vampire takes his prey with a dramatic entrance. In this variation, he relies on surprise and speed to kidnap his victim. Perhaps he cuts the power to his victim's apartment or sets the building on fire. He eschews subtlety, creating the chaos he needs to grab her by force.

Complications

Competition: Anyone who's worth taking instead of just killing might be valuable enough to attract competitors. Maybe she's a charismatic blood doll who's been stringing along half a dozen vampire suitors. If the victim's an occultist or psychic, she might be a valuable to several factions. Once others catch wind of the vampire's plans they'll intercept him, throwing hunters in the middle of a bloody supernatural brawl.

She Escapes: The victim gets away. The vampire's enemies (including the players' hunters) interrupt the kidnapping or the victim's smart or lucky enough to escape on her own. The scene changes into a complex chase. The vampire's after errant prey and hunters have to chase them both, but keep them apart.

The Wrong Victim: Even vampires make mistakes. Avoid simple name and address confusion because it's either boring or silly, but there are more serious alternatives to consider. He's come to take an author of some disturbingly accurate vampire fiction, but he doesn't know it was actually written by ghost writer. Perhaps the target's a witch who's impersonating the vampire's lover. She can steal his blood for occult purposes or infiltrate undead society.

Dice Modifiers

Aids/Bonuses: Closed circuit cameras (+2 to detect intruders), guard dogs (+1 to detect or slow down intruders), security guards (normal guys who provide a +1 to +3 bonus to detect or slow down an intruder), security system (+1 to detect with a basic system to +3 to a comprehensive, high-tech system)

Obstacles/Penalties: Shadows and darkness (-1 to -3 to detect intruders), target's moving around (-1), they don't know the vampire's coming (-1), they don't know who the victim is (-1)

The Hunt

This scene's about the core of a vampire's existence. She feeds on the living to fuel her unlife for another night, another year, another century.

Every vampire develops a distinct hunting strategy based on her personality, territory and powers. A succubus hunts through seduction, but a nightmare just rips her victims off the street. Use the environment to set the mood, too, so that one vampire blends into a fetish club and the other haunts rain-slicked fire escapes on moonless nights. (Playing against type is fun, too. What happens when a filthy, raving monster bursts into a genteel private club?) Blood isn't the sole objective of every hunt, either. The line between murder and feeding is vanishingly thin, so vampires often use the same tactics to do both.

You can set up a hunting scene a number of ways. If hunters investigate the vampire, drop clues about her habits that leads to a hunt in progress. If the vampire's wise to your hunters, she might initiate the scene by stalking them. She can do this for several nights gathering intelligence to strike when she thinks the characters are most vulnerable. Hunters could settle things with a vampire once and for all or see the foreshadowing of a greater confrontation to come. Either way, the hunting scene says something about the vampire's psyche and tactics, provided they're smart enough to pick the information up.

Motifs

Blood Dolls: Some mortals want to be fed on. They've been conditioned with mind control or have a fetish for it. If hunters intervene (and should they?) the "victims" insult or attack them. Thanks to vampire patrons, blood dolls often have the resources to make a hunter's life hell. They warn vampires about local cells and use their social ties to harass the cell. Blood dolls form a subculture with its own clubs and code words. Your hunters might have to go undercover in the blood doll scene to find the vampire they're after.

Disease: As vampirism is a plague, so too do vampires carry plagues, spreading them with every bite. The victim usually lives to spread the disease but a virulent corpse isn't out of the question either. Hunters might be able to track a vampire through the plague but this is cold comfort, because the disease is as potent a threat to humans as the vampire itself. Some supernatural plagues might *only* affect vampires, however, and spread through human carriers. Is this a powerful weapon for the hunt or a manifestation of some new, dark power?

The Damned Ship: Nobody on the damned vessel called *Demeter* could escape Dracula's hunger. The same thing might happen on another ship, in an isolated mansion or trapped anywhere else that's filled with shadowy corners. Hunters have to find the monster before it takes them out, one by one.

Complications

Bait: Hunters, other vampires and occultists lure the vampire with planted "victims" that appeal to her particular tastes. It takes a brave person to knowingly take this risk, but the bait doesn't always know he's being set up for an attack. A member of the Cheiron Group dupes an appealing first-tier hunter into patrolling the target's hunting ground or a vampire dresses up a blood addict just the way the vampire likes her prey, but never tells him why. If unknowing bait survives, he might seek revenge.

Calling Cards: An arrogant, insane or suicidal vampire leaves a poem naming each victim or puts their corpses in elaborate poses. She wants investigators to know the attack was *her* work, though she might otherwise delight in giving pursuers the slip. This gives hunters insight into their enemy or, when the calling card leads to greater cruelty, emphasizes the horror of the act.

Supernatural Prey: Vampires rarely blunder into other supernatural creatures (and those that do don't often get a chance to repeat the mistake) but some hunt unnatural prey by choice. One vampire drinks the blood of witches to induce prophetic hallucinations; another hunts her own kind to steal their mystical strength—a high crime among the Damned.

Dice Modifiers

Aids/Bonuses: Home turf advantage (vampire or hunters have known the area for a generation; rote quality, re-roll failed dice)

Obstacles/Penalties: Darker than city streets (-1 or -3 to find the vampire when streetlights are out, for example), interfering blood dolls (-1 to -3 to find the vampire, depending on the number)

Research (Mythology and Folklore)

Smart hunters dig for all the information they can find. Vampires are a strange case, however, in that the problem isn't too little information, but too much. There are innumerable novels, films and legends to go on. You can't even discount fiction because in the World of Darkness, many factions use popular media to transmit secret messages. A movie that alludes to a vampire's existence accurately is a warning from one elder to another: *I know everything about you and I can expose you whenever I wish.*

Even if they restrict research to occult literature and mythology, the characters still have to slog through a huge, varied collection of lore, filled with false leads.

This is a problem for characters, but helps Storytellers because it makes vampire research accessible to almost everyone. Comic books and movies are obviously less reliable than academic works (but see the complications section below) but most characters can find research material.

Present research in stages. Easy to find, popular works refer to obscure texts; these in turn lead to even more accurate—and difficult to find—resources. Hunters raid private collections, mislabeled university library stacks, or other hunter cells for information. The Academics and Occult Skills help characters filter real facts from a murky sea of fantasy and disinformation.

Storytelling Research

The stereotypical research scene skips past reading and note taking to get to the facts. In a movie, you'd see a brief montage, followed by the results, but in a game you might end up in a tedious scene filled with Storyteller exposition. You can compensate a bit by tying the facts to character-driven events. Put guards on a useful library or link it to a Storyteller character who wants payment or flattery before he'll ever to give your characters a look.

In addition, consider the following techniques. These will minimize straight exposition, but might require a bit of a shift in thinking.

Character-Detailed Outlines: Nothing's more boring and preparation-heavy than writing out every word of research. Instead, write out the facts in point form and ask the *player* to flesh it out. You can let her define the source and describe the results in as much detail as she'd like. You say she learned that vampires can die by fire from a black leather book, but she writes it out in stanza form and calls that book *The Vengeance of Mithras*.

Seeded Research: Instead of dumping all the facts on players during the research scene, let the players know you'll be "seeding" it: leaving it unspoken until story events make it relevant. For instance, there's no need to mention that vampires can heal feeding wounds until your hunters encounter an unmarked, bloodless corpse. The characters know it, but the players don't need to know until it would matter to the story. This might seem a bit backwards, but consider this: Theoretically, your character already knows lots of trivial things that your players don't bother with. What's on her car's license plate? When's the last time she went to the bathroom? The seeds have that status until story events turn them into things the players really need to know. Decide what the seeds are when you give them to researchers or leave them open so that you can define them on the fly—either way is fine.

VAMPIRES AND CULTURE IN THE WORLD OF DARKNESS

What's vampire fiction like in a world where vampires really exist? The answer is up to you, but our assumption is: "It's the same, but for different reasons." Bram Stoker wrote *Dracula* in the World of Darkness, too, but he might just be the mouthpiece for a rebellious undead novelist. Even though real (as in, World of Darkness "real") vampires obey some consistent supernatural laws, the World of Darkness is still full of contradictory legends. Part of this is mistaken identity, since the average person doesn't know the difference between a vampire, a fresh, ghost-ridden corpse and a number of other strange things. Vampires add lies to accurate myths to protect themselves.

If there's one difference, it's that in the World of Darkness, some people sense but can't articulate that there's something *real* behind the movies, books and whispered stories. A vampire flick doesn't make them believe in the undead. It frames vampires in a fictional context so that people can reassure themselves that their intuition is *wrong*. Plastic fangs and overwrought prose give them a chance to hope that there aren't ancient, malicious things stalking them in the night. It doesn't always work, though—and your **Hunter** characters are evidence of that.

Motifs

Dangerous Knowledge: The more accurate the source, the more likely it is to have a dangerous minder: vampires, an occult conspiracy or rival hunters. They protect rare books and imprison people who know too much, or just watch them from a distance, afraid that showing their hand will only reveal more.

"It's Not Like the Movies, Man:" Everyone knows what vampires are, so it's research's job to separate truth from common knowledge. One mainstay in vampire films and novels is the point where a protagonist or informant tells you which legends are true or false.

The Informant: The characters' research source is a person, not a book. She could be a rogue blood doll, a vampire who wants to reveal just enough to help hunters destroy his enemies, or a mysterious "Deep Throat" figure from a mortal conspiracy, including a third-tier hunter organization.

Complications

"It Totally *Is* Like the Movies, Man:" An *accurate* pop culture source raises more questions than it answers. Who wrote it? Where'd he get his information? Why hasn't a conspiracy suppressed it yet? The answers can influence your entire chronicle. Plus, it's a refreshing change of pace for a vampire to be *exactly* what your hunters saw at the movies. You can even pick a real movie your players have seen, tailor vampires to match, and send your hunters investigating Hollywood figures—or protecting them from retaliation. The epitome of this twist can be seen in *The Lost Boys*, where the Frog Brothers learn pretty much everything about vampires from comic books—and they're right, more often than not.

Lies: If the source is a deliberate deception instead of an inaccurate rumor, ask yourself what its purpose is. Don't use it to hinder the characters without providing an interesting plot development in return. If a book says vampires can't cross running water, (and in your game, they can) add another passage that mentions the location of a vampire-killing sword. That forgotten crypt may or may not contain a useful weapon, but it furthers the agenda of the book's author somehow, and adds a new twist to the ongoing chronicle.

Networking Opportunity: Your hunters aren't the only ones interested in vampire studies. If they cross paths with other cells and supernatural creatures of the course of their research they won't always make enemies, either. A library meeting leads to a new hunter organization or it creates powerful friendships that last the entire chronicle.

Dice Modifiers

Aids/Bonuses: Assistant to sort material (+1 to research), previous research in the same field (+2 to research), information searchable by computer (+2 to research)

Obstacles/Penalties: Odd form of the language (Ancient Greek to someone who knows the modern tongue, the bastardized Latin of Dark Ages Europe that produces terms like "Lancea Sanctum;" -2 to research), damaged document (-1 to -3 to research), studying under duress (knife at your throat, library on fire; -1 to research)

Dossier, Interview or Autopsy

Smart hunters won't pass up the chance to study a vampire's victims. These kinds of scenes come in three basic flavors.

Some hunters study the vampire's victim from a distance. They assemble information about several victims to unearth a common thread or zero in to learn as much about a single victim as possible. This minimizes the cell's public profile but can't provide the same depth as close-up research. A detailed dossier also creates documents that could land the characters in hot water. Hunters who don't have the Eidetic Memory Merit shouldn't get away with memorizing more than a quick outline.

Hunters who interview victims might expose themselves to the authorities and vampire conspiracy agents. Unless they're prepared to be honest about their agenda (and few cells would be) they have to come up with some sort of cover. Interviews give characters a chance to play up Social Skills and get closer to true, first-hand knowledge.

If the victim's dead, interviews are impossible unless the cell knows how to conduct a séance (which invites its own complications). Characters with medical skills might be able to determine a rough time of death and inspect the body for clues but past that, it's time for an autopsy. In large cities, coroners are quick to examine any apparent murder victim. Hunters have to possess or fake the appropriate credentials to look at autopsy files or get into the morgue itself.

Smart vampires take measures against leaving dangerous clues behind, so hunters not only have to gather information intelligently, but defeat the enemy's precautions. He might watch his victim for several nights afterward, or keeps a blood-addicted mole inside the local crime lab.

Motifs

Fang Marks: Vampires often hide feeding wounds, but some can't or won't. A vampire can't heal large, vicious fang wounds (including those that inflict damage). Victims of repeat feedings might suffer the same complications as injection drug addicts, such as collapsed veins and subdermal scar tissue.

"His Blood is Gone—I Just Can't Explain It:" Puzzling autopsies are an established part of modern thrillers or supernatural fiction. Vampires avoid leaving strange corpses behind as much as possible but pristine, drained bodies turn up in alleys from time to time. Frozen expressions of horror and ecstasy or a strange mix of other people's blood flowing through the body are also possible signs.

Madness: The attack drove him insane. Some victims are "Renfields;" their vampire masters broke their minds with Dread Powers and now influence them from a distance. Other victims go mad out of pure trauma. A powerful memory runs through their thoughts again and again, or they blanked out the attack (or had it blanked out for them), but have disturbing dreams that clue hunters in to what really happened.

Complications

Repeat Attacks: The vampire attacks the victim again. She might be his habitual blood doll, a family member or someone he's *really* loves or hates. She might even be an enemy who the vampire was really trying to kill.

FORENSIC VAMPIROLOGY

Vampires don't leave the same clues behind as human criminals. To call the forensic study of vampires a rarefied field is an understatement; third tier hunters, vampire society enforcers and a handful of scholar-witches might know it. This doesn't mean your first and second tier hunters *can't* learn the ins and outs of vampire forensics—just that it won't be easy.

A vampire leaves signs of itself behind in accordance with its nature as a supernaturally animated half-corpse. We can't list every effect this has on forensic analysis, but as a general rule, treat any body sample as if it belonged to a corpse that's as old as the vampire's true age. Older vampires leave behind a fine ash or desiccated fragments. Nothing larger than a lock of hair or a sizeable chunk of skin survives in one piece for more than a few minutes. Outside the body a vampire's blood turns into a mix of blood from all his recent victims. Nothing marks it as supernatural, though it might seem a bit odd to investigators.

Vampires don't have significant skin oils so they don't leave fingerprints unless the point of contact records impressions on its own. For example, you can't if tell a vampire touched an ordinary window unless he had bloody fingers at the time.

Tainted Love: The victim is the vampire's ally, so she won't cooperate with hunters. She might play the traumatized victim to help her master trap unwary hunters. The vampire might be a lover who came back to her after being turned. She doesn't really want to be fed on but figures it's the best way to protect him—and protect other people *from* him.

The Corpse Gets Up: The vampire botched an attempt to turn his victim. Something frightened him away right after he passed on the curse. The victim appears to be truly dead for an unusual amount of time. It's a supernatural oddity or a psychological quirk. Maybe she was just too traumatized to move. In any event, she wakes up on an examining table or in a body bag and either sneaks or fights her way out. Now hunters have to deal with *two* vampires, one of whom doesn't have a clue about how to adapt to her new existence.

Dice Modifiers

Aids/Bonuses: Victim is friend of family (+2 to interview), investigated previous hunt from the same vampire (+1 to find information), witnesses (+1 to +3 to find information)

Obstacles/Penalties: Victim has minimal paper trail (homeless, criminal; -2 to find information), victim, witnesses or officials (police, CSI) are from a different culture (-2)

Chase or Be Chased

This traditional chase scene features the vampire as pursuer or pursued. Older vampires don't stand and fight unless it's absolutely necessary. Immortality means you can just wait for mortal enemies to die. Unless hunters plan carefully they'll have to corner their quarry. Sometimes, though, the hunters have to run instead. The vampire either draws out the chase for "sport," or concentrates on capturing or killing every member of the cell as quick as she can, but in either case she unleashes her full power to handle the task.

This is an action scene. Characters should avoid attracting undue attention but if you want an all-out pursuit you have to use your Storyteller privileges to help them. No matter how much you want it, hunters won't go in with guns blazing if they're afraid of getting caught by the cops. Set these scenes in warehouse districts, industrial parks and slums where people habitually look the other way.

Thread the chase through populated areas to add "beats" of stealth between action sequences. Alternately, your chase could be a subtle affair, weaving in and out of crowds. Locations determine the character of a chase scene, so plan them out ahead of time.

Motifs

Amazing Feats: The vampire shows you what she's really capable of. She jumps from the ground to a second story balcony, runs up the side of a wall or whips a manhole cover at pursuers. Use these moments to show the vampire's strength and escalate the action.

Cornered: Like a trapped animal, a cornered vampire summons a burst of rage to finish off her enemies. She throws caution to the wind—survival trumps the risk of exposure. Her actions might make enemies in the local vampire conspiracy because secrecy is its supreme law. Conversely, she might corner the characters. That might actually delay the *coup de grace* if she lets herself take time to savor her victory. She might give hunters enough time to get away—or for the cavalry to come riding in.

The Darkened Warehouse: Similar to the abduction scene's "damned ship," the warehouse (or country estate, abandoned cargo vessel and so on) is a confined location that's easy to hide in but hard to escape. A vampire might lead pursuers here to turn the tables on them. She knows the location but the hunters don't. She uses that fact to pick them off one by one. Then again, smart hunters might draw a vampire into *their* home turf, too.

Complications

Allies: Vampires summon servants and undead offspring to help them pin down a group of hunters. Of course, a vampire's allies aren't always totally loyal; they might fight amongst themselves for the master's favor. Hunters could use that to their advantage. They have friends too, and while many cells are loath to put people in danger for selfish reasons there might be an allies ready to storm the scene. If you go for the last option be careful to link it to the hunters' past dealings—otherwise, it looks like you're arbitrarily saving the characters, making their actions look meaningless.

Bystanders: Unless you're in the wild it's hard to find places that are guaranteed to be free of people. Vampires and hunters blend into crowds to gain an advantage. The vampire might take a hostage when the opportunity arises or feed on someone to keep herself fresh for the chase. Some bystanders aren't easily manipulated, though. Cops, security guards and exceptionally determined individuals might join the fray. They'll try to take out the cell or fight back when the vampire advances.

Interlopers: There's a third party watching the chase, ready to intervene for reasons of his own. He's a Cheiron operative bent on capturing the vampire, a monster who takes offense when the pursuit bursts into his territory or some other interloper who adds an extra level of complexity to the chase.

Dice Modifiers

Aids/Bonuses: Home field advantage (rote quality—re-roll failed dice—for the side that really knows the territory), lots of debris (+2 to create a makeshift tool or weapon), crowds (+1 to +3 to hide by blending in, depending on the crowd's size)

Obstacles/Penalties: Dark (-1 to -3, depending on how dark), rooftop chase (play "chicken;" the chased party can impose a penalty of up to -3 to be chased, but suffer that penalty themselves to rolls to keep from falling)

Storming the Lair

When hunters track the vampire to his lair they trigger one of vampire fiction's signature moments. In traditional gothic fiction, the vampire's lair is a ruined castle, decrepit abbey or decadent estate. In modern stories, the undead carve havens out of the urban landscape. Vampires sleep away the day in places like sewers, condominiums and secure basements, but their needs don't change. They look for places to hide from the sun.

Vampires take the sun seriously; many sleep on normal beds in windowless rooms, but just as many won't take any chances, and stick to something that resembles a traditional coffin. Vampires with bestial or minimalist tastes make the raw earth their daytime beds. A nomadic vampire develops a routine to protect himself from the light. He brings along black curtains, doorstops and reinforced body bags to lightproof hotel rooms, or modifies trunk storage in his car to accommodate his daily slumber. Unless the vampire just digs himself a hole, his choice of method has material requirements. Smart hunters can trace these. Funeral directors remember people who order coffins *sans* memorial.

A typical vampire wants as much security as he can manage without leaking his lair's location. If he wants a modern security system he needs reliable servants who can install it without tattling. Secrecy is the first line of defense. Some lairs might be difficult for normal humans to crack. The door is a half-ton slab of rock or lies beneath the ocean, for example. Supernaturally stealthy vampires might even sleep in the heart of someone else's security zone. They sleep in military bases, police stations and government buildings.

Some lairs are nothing more than bare rooms with coffins, but others have all the comforts of home (though the kitchen and bathroom are often unusually clean). If he feels secure about his inner sanctum he'll leave clues about his true nature: journals, refrigerated blood and hunting trophies.

Motifs

Bursting from the Coffin: Vampires sleep deeply but they might still sense intruders. Hunters might have enough time to creep up on the sleeping vampire, but once they stand above him, stake and blade in hand, they're in for a startle. The vampire leaps up to defend himself. (See "Daysleep," p. 165.)

Not Dead Yet: A motionless vampire is virtually identical to a corpse. Inexperienced vampire hunters don't know about a vampire's death-rot so they might assume that any vampire with a stake in its heart is done for. A few vampires can trick even knowledgeable hunters with supernatural illusions. No matter the tactic, the vampire feigns death for a moment and then launches a surprise attack.

Servants: Blood addicts, offspring and occasionally, sympathetic "normal" humans guard the vampire's haven. Hunters have to get by them before they'll get a chance to confront the vampire himself. Servants will probably wake him and even provide a quick, revivifying meal to ready him for danger.

Complications

Captives: The vampire has one or more prisoners. There might be cages, or he might give victims a locked, furnished apartment to provide the illusion of normalcy. Most prisoners are frightened and desperate to escape but a few might have the equivalent of Stockholm Syndrome, as due to shock or mind control, they've come to identify with their captor.

The Pack: Hunters who've been tracking a lone vampire are in for a surprise: He's just one member of a pack—and they're all sleeping in his haven. Members either have a collective bond that allows them to trust each other, or one vampire reigns supreme, keeping others as his slaves. When one awakens, the others aren't far behind.

Traps: The vampire equipped his lair with devices to trap, incapacitate or kill intruders. Unless

Dark Humor

Gamers like to tell jokes at the table and for good reason: It defuses tension, comforts players who blow dice rolls and covers for awkward moments. Humor can be fun, but if you want serious horror, it might bar the way. If this happens, have an honest talk with your players. Don't ban joking from the table completely, but establish a clear time and place for it.

On the other hand, vampire stories *can* be funny. Let's face it: the undead are kind of silly, from a certain point of view. Their urges lead to hackneyed behavior and exaggerated passions. Every "meal" is High Gothic Romance; every failure leads to snarling rage. *Innocent Blood* and *Vampire's Kiss* are dark comedies that never completely shed their horror. *The Lost Boys* is an example of a vampire story that leavens the horror and drama with a good dose of levity, from unlikely hunters like the Frog Brothers to, "One thing about living in Santa Carla I never could stomach. All the damn vampires." If you want to channel your group's constant wisecracking into useful play, add a heavy dose of black humor to the plot.

he has a trusted expert working for him he's built them to whatever specifications his knowledge, money and supernatural powers can manage. Some traps take advantage of a vampire's supernatural physiology. For example, a room filled with carbon dioxide protects him from fire and hinders enemies who need to breathe. Even crude vampires might drop a bear trap for unwelcome visitors or set up a crude security airlock.

Dice Modifiers

Aids/Bonuses: Security system (+1 to +3 for vampire to detect intruders, though he might still have trouble waking up for an alarm), hammer (+2 to use stake on an immobile vampire), heavy coffin lid (+2 for vampire to awaken when opened)

Obstacles/Penalties: Lair in restricted area (military base; DEA warehouse, etc; -1 to -3 to sneak in, depending on security level), improvised lair (hotel room, etc; -2 for vampire to detect intruders)

Philadelphia by Night

Throughout its history, the city Philadelphia has frequently served as the backdrop to conflict. Wars, political skullduggery and social unrest all played parts in molding Philadelphia into what it is today: a city of districts and neighborhoods with well-defined boundaries. The vampires that burrow into the soft underbelly of the city like so many maggots are just as divided. While many (if not most) cities are ruled by a single vampire or a single group of vampires, in Philadelphia, history and circumstance has created a three-way battle for dominance. Hunters may or may not know about the vampiric factions that continue their struggle every night, but they deal with the fallout. In cities where all vampires owe allegiance (or at least pay lip service) to a single rule, the undead can more easily turn their attention to stamping out hunter cells that prove bothersome. In Philadelphia, a faction that turns too much of its attention to battling hunters risks opening itself up for attack by one or both opposing factions. Hunters in the know have a vested interest in ensuring the three-way battle continues.

While the presence of the factions makes it less likely that vampires will focus for too long or expend too many resources on fighting hunters, it doesn't make the process of hunting vampires any easier. Individual vampires, or groups of the undead, are likely to be veterans of the constant struggle. They're likely to be more proficient combatants, more adept politicians and warier predators than others of their kind. That wariness has become second nature to those vampires that have managed to cling to its unlife for longer than a few months, meaning that hunters have little chance of catching a vampire wholly unprepared.

Theme: Eternal Struggle

Peace is an unknown to both the hunters and the vampires of Philadelphia. For as long as the city has stood, the vampires have battled with each for supremacy and hunters have, likewise, either battled in turn with the forces of the night or have been forced to deal with the overflow of blood into the streets. The conflict has no end in sight and the battle-lines are drawn in the blood of mortal and vampire alike. The vampires, especially, have become so inured to conflict that they even seem to, at times, unconsciously attempt to sabotage efforts that might actually lead to a lasting resolution.

Mood: Paranoia

As a result of the eternal struggle, vampires are *entrenched* in this city. The factions cast their nets of influence and control wide to gain some small advantage that might give them final victory. It seems foolish, even impossible that they have such an intense control—could they truly have their hands in every pie? Is it possible that the clerk in that 7-11 could be the lookout for a nest of vampires lairing in the rear of the store? That police detective that seems to take an unusual amount of interest in the activities of a cell… well, might he be acting on orders from the undead? How far up does the corruption go? To the city council? The mayor's office? The mayor himself? It seems foolish, this paranoia. Impossible, even. But hunters have seen the reality too many times, now. Many assume it's better to expect the worst rather than be caught unprepared for the damning truth. All eyes are watching.

Coming to America

Most, though by no means all, of the early vampire colonists that ended up in Philadelphia came to America for the same reasons as mortals. They came looking for new beginnings or they sought to escape the rigid domination of the well-entrenched system of rule that had developed over the centuries in Europe. Most arrived by boat, either passing as reclusive travelers to the new world or by packing themselves in crates to sneak out at night to feed on drunken sailors or solitary immigrants. When they arrived in Philadelphia the vampires found a small, thriving city; and, true to their natures, immediately began to fight among themselves for territory and dominance. These struggles brought the attention of humans who, to the surprise of the vampires, were more coordinated and vigilant than their counterparts in the old country. The city of Philadelphia was (and still is in many ways) a city of neighborhoods where the people of each smaller community watched out for each other and responded rapidly to a perceived threat. Vampires that made themselves too obvious or fed with impunity were rapidly tracked down and destroyed. In response to the unexpected organization of mortals, groups of elder vampires began to assert dominance over all the undead in their territory in an attempt to hide their activities. Unlike other cities, no one group managed to take firm control of the city and these groups formed the base of what would one day become the vampiric factions of Philadelphia.

THE SCARLET WATCH

Hunters with a scholarly bent have come across mentions in documents dating to around the turn of the 18th century of a night watch apparently formed as a response to the activities to the predators of the night. There are repeated references in various letters and diaries that refer to this group as "The Scarlet Watch." The author of one of these diaries specifically mentions the Watch hunting down the slayer of his sister, whose body was found, drained of blood. The Scarlett Watch is referred to by name in a letter penned by a different author, who makes mention of the curious wooden truncheons carried by the Watch that were all sharpened to a point at one end. It certainly seems reasonable to assume that the Scarlett Watch was one of the first hunter cells in Philadelphia.

Story Seeds:

Minutes of the Scarlet Watch: *For Whom the Bell Tolls*, one of the local tabloids, recently printed an article entitled "Proof of Vampires Found!" The article goes on to say that a journal with entries dating from 1696-1698 that was recovered from a grave disturbed by a construction dig. The entries in the journal describe a secret society he dubs "The Blood Watch" that was formed in the early days of the city that hunted and killed vampires. The author of the article, one Clayton Davis, claims to have bought the journal from the foreman of the site. If the article isn't a hoax, Davis may have found a treasure trove of information gathered about vampires (and local ones that may still be up and walking around).

The Purloined Letter: A letter that was supposedly written by one of the members of the Scarlet Watch has gone missing after a burglary. The letter listed names, descriptions and locations of suspicious characters under investigation by the Watch. The theft could be just another random act of crime or it could be that the descriptions or locations listed in the letter are still pertinent today, given the fact that vampires are, essentially, immortal. The ability to establish approximate ages for elder vampires (like the Curator, for example) would give hunters a sort of barometer of how powerful an elder might be.

The War for Independence

The tensions leading up to the American Revolution forced early hunter cells to focus more attention on mundane matters of importance. For nearly two years before the war formally began in 1775 attacks on vampires or their blood slaves dropped to virtually zero, which gave the leeches some breathing room to consolidate their holdings. Without the threat of constant attack by mortals, the vampiric groups that had formed earlier were able to consolidate their positions and think about expansion. At this point Philadelphia played host to at least a half dozen different vampire factions, each claiming a different part of the city. When war finally came to America, the vampires used the backdrop of confusion to war among each other as well, each faction attempting to eliminate potential rivals. Alliances were formed and broken on an almost nightly basis as the proto-groups battled for supremacy.

Other than freeing up the vampires to squabble among themselves, the first five years of the war acted as a boon for the blood sucking population of Philadelphia in a different way. Even the hunters that hadn't entered into the war in an active role in the Continental Army found their ability to stand the Vigil greatly diminished by the desperation and deprivations of war and during the 10-month occupation of Philadelphia by British troops their efforts were further curtailed by the martial law imposed on the city. The vampires took full advantage of this situation. They became more brazen with their night time activities, even taking some time out from their attacks on each other to seek revenge on the hunters and their families, effectively clearing the city of organized mortal resistance. With mortal resistance stymied, the nightly battles began at last to see some progress. By 1780 it seemed certain that one of the proto-factions would soon succeed in claiming the throne of Philadelphia, ushering in an era of "peace" between vampires that had been unknown in history of the city and would likely spell doom for the remaining mortals that opposed them. Then the tide turned.

Throughout the war a number of new British and European vampires had taken up residence in the city, lured to Philadelphia by violence and chaos. (War and bloodshed always attract scavengers and parasites—and vampires are essentially both). Grieving widows, wounded soldiers and orphaned children left to fend for themselves were easy pickings for vampires. The social chaos also made it easier for vampires to carve out niche kingdoms in the affairs of mortals. This second wave of vampire colonists intruded on the domains of the more entrenched "native" vampires with predictable results. The newcomers banded together for mutual protection against the power bloc of the American vampires and

their numbers were further swelled by leeches from the ranks of British soldiers and personnel or Tory loyalists. Unwilling to be ruled by vampires they viewed as barely a cut above peasants, the European faction feigned loyalty to various factions while they subtly chipped away at the foundations of the mundane power held by American vampires, even going so far as to aid and shelter known hunters. Eventually the deceptions of the Europeans were discovered and the city exploded in an all-out war between the vampire groups, with little in the way of subterfuge involved to hide the battles from mortal eyes. This surge of open warfare forced the human citizens of Philadelphia to take notice and soon monsters throughout the city were under siege. By the time the war was officially ended by the Treaty of Paris in 1783, Philadelphia was home to five warring factions of vampires and the hunter presence in the city was firmly reestablished.

Fading Glory

For the next two centuries the importance of Philadelphia as a city of national leadership slowly declined. Boosted by the industrial boom of the 19th century, the city continued to attract new citizens and faced the same problems of immigration and modernization as other large US cities, but Philadelphia never regained the position of prominence it held during colonial times. This was a time of nearly constant upheaval for the vampire populace as their numbers rose with each wave of immigrants and the creatures that followed them, then fell again due to near constants skirmishes with each other and the mortals that hunted them. In the relative peace enjoyed by the United States as a whole directly following the Civil War, the undead of Philadelphia also came to a bloody stalemate, no single faction able to achieve dominance over the others. This lull was aided in no small part to the diminished numbers of hunters, most of who had turned from the Vigil to concentrate on their families and stake out their claim to the growing industrial abundance to be had in the city.

This period of mortal stability and undead stalemate led to a (mostly) bloodless merging of vampire factions and the emergence of possible contenders for leadership over the whole of the city. The more complex webs of mortal societal, business and governmental groups to be influenced and controlled in the late 19th century required the vampires turn more of their attention to dealings with mortals than fighting with each other. Rule by brute force alone was no longer an option. In order to claim the city, vampires were forced out of the shadows and the more they made their presence felt, the more humans began to band together to fight back against them. The small, local hunter cells

didn't make much of a dent in the sophisticated vampiric networks that could count human judges, policemen and politicians among their allies and it seemed only a matter of time until one of the factions finally gained dominance over his fellows and brought the iron grip of vampiric rule to bear on Philadelphia.

History has a tendency to repeat itself and the oldest vampires were aware of what had happened the last time they had nearly gained ultimate control of the city. The four largest vampire factions set on a ruthless campaign of terror against the local hunter cells, determined not to fail a second time. No one knows (or will tell) why it happened, but as a response to this pogrom, hunter compacts and conspiracies appeared in Philadelphia in greater numbers than before and began to fight back. One possible explanation is that hunter compacts and conspiracies already in the city appealed for outside assistance, though it is just as likely the organizations in the city finally began to recognize each other for what they truly were.

The first to exert its influence was the Ashwood Abbey in 1903. With its own broad range of high level social, political and business contacts the Abbey began to slowly push the vampires out of high society, riding their corpses to bloody ash and laughing all the way.

The Lucifuge followed shortly thereafter, attacking the creatures of the night on their own turf, asserting dominance with the aid of their grim Castigation rituals. Last was a zealous order calling themselves Cainites that took over the church of St. Peter and turned the largest faction of leeches against the others, using their intimate knowledge of vampires to sow dissension and disorder in the ranks of the Damned. In short order, the plans concocted by vampires over the last 60 years were reduced to rubble and the factions were once again, literally and figuratively, at each other's throats.

That *Other* Vampire Game

Troupes with access to **Vampire: The Requiem** are welcome to use the wealth of information presented in that game to add to anything shown in this section. To facilitate this, we present information in sidebars and in the main text on how to translate vampire antagonists or agencies shown here into concepts more easily used following the standard **Vampire** rules. For simplicity, any listing or sidebar that begins with the word **Requiem** will be followed with information pertinent to that system.

Modern Philadelphia

Today, hunters in Philadelphia belong to both local and larger international organizations. The war among the vampires continues with three major factions battling for dominance and dozens of small, unaligned gangs claiming parts of the city for themselves. Though the hunters are forced to work together from time to time, no one group has emerged as the supreme leader against the vampire menace. Many of the hunters eye each other with nearly as much suspicion as they do a bloodsucker walking down the street and outright violence between hunter groups isn't unknown. Below is an overview of possible hunter organizations in the city along with their outlook on vampires.

Ascending Ones: *Aggressive.* Ever since the creatures of the night destroyed the Cult of Set, the Cult of the Phoenix has carried light into dark places. The Ascending Ones interpret the well-known vampiric weakness to sunlight as a divine message that, as representatives of light, they are meant to battle these fiends to the last.

Ashwood Abbey: *Moderate.* The Philadelphia branch of the Abbey has been dealing with vampires for over a century and they have learned plenty in that time. Unfortunately, this includes large numbers of Sybarites who have learned to associate the taste of vampiric blood with intense pleasure. So while the Abbey would like to be out and about destroying every leech they see, they must first put their own house in order. The exception to this are those bastards that claim Eastern State Penitentiary. Those leeches must fry.

Aegis Kai Doru: *Aggressive.* Some of the vampires in Philadelphia have been here for centuries (and a few are even older, having come over from Europe). The Aegis Kai Doru believe they must have, or know where to find, Relics that rightly that belong to the Guardians of the Labyrinth. Accordingly, the conspiracy follows up on any rumor it hears about the location of a vampire in hopes of uncovering lost treasures. Most vampires don't survive their interrogations. Then again, some hunters don't survive them, either.

Cheiron Group: *Growing.* It used to be that most TCG field agents won't go out of their way to chase a vampire, unless that vampire seems somehow unusual for its species. But now the word has come down from On High: *if you see one, bag it, bring it in.* Some new initiative at the top seems to think that vampires *en masse* (meaning, lots of their monstrous blood in supply) is going to help the conglomerate make bank.

The Long Night: *Moderate.* Members of the Long Night think vampires could be a sign of the coming Apocalypse. The bible says in Revelations 20:13 that

"*Death and Hell gave up their Dead.*" If vampires are a sign, the Long Night wants to know. Cells attempt to capture and interrogate vampires whenever possible. Some members hope that if they can turn (or remove) enough of the undead from the path of wickedness there still be hope for the rest of the world. God's glory is great, after all.

The Loyalists of Thule: *Aggressive.* Much like their Aegis Kai Doru rivals in the city, the Loyalists believe that vampires, especially older vampires, must know *things.* Secrets that might give them an edge in their occult struggles. Competition in Philadelphia between the Loyalists and the Aegis Kai Doru has been restrained, for the most part. Recently, though, hunters of the two groups have come to blows over resources.

The Lucifuge: *Restrained.* Sure, some people think vampires the spawn of Satan, but the real spawn aren't impressed. The vampires in Philadelphia seem to spend more time fighting with each other than they do trying to seduce chaste maidens by moonlight. The Children of the Seventh Generation generally deal with vampires in Philly by *dealing* with vampires. The hunters make short term alliances with opposing factions and play them against each other.

Malleus Maleficarum: *Aggressive.* The Shadow Congregation seeks out the children of the night with a special fervor and intensity. Vampires form the blight that slowly eats away at the spiritual purity of the world. In theory, the merest rumor of a vampire should bring the full might of the Malleus Maleficarum out in force. Unfortunately, Philadelphia is a godless town filled with heathens and the unrepentant. This means that the Shadow Congregation usually has more leads that it can realistically follow.

Network 0: *Moderate.* The efforts of Network 0 to record the antics of vampires in Philly have met with limited success, mainly due to their inability to capture a clear picture of one. Without YouTube style videos to expose vampires to the public, Network 0 has instead begun to track members of the Philadelphia elite that the vampires have frequent contact with, which has been easier than other hunters might think. See, even if cameras don't capture vampires properly the blurry images they produce *do* make it pretty easy to pick a leech out of a crowd. The Philadelphia community that backs the Secret Frequency hasn't decided what to do with the information they've gathered, though they pass tidbits on to other hunter groups in the city from time to time.

Null Mysteriis: *Aggressive.* The Philadelphia branch of this compact has a small contingent of scientists dedicated to proving that vampirism is just another type of disease to be studied and rationalized. Decades of experimental pathology research has yet to determine the underlying cause of the disease, but with new technology comes new hope. Study of some recent patients does show an unusual pathogen in the bloodstream of some haemovores that a few members of the Null Mysteriis believe might prove to be the key to unlocking the mystery.

Task Force VALKYRIE: *Moderate.* As much as they would like to investigate every report of vampiric activity that comes their way, TF:V just doesn't have the manpower (blame the beancounters). What they have done is quietly put out the word to other hunter groups that backup is... "available." These alliances are generally temporary and VALKYRIE members are careful to never identify themselves or their parent agency to other hunters. Lately, rumors have sprung up in Philadelphia that vampires supposedly captured by TF:V members have shown up other cities—undead and unharmed.

The Union: *Restrained.* Philadelphia is still a city of neighborhoods and small groups of Union hunters exist in many of those 'hoods. Unless a vampire is threatening the families or businesses of Union members, these hard working folks don't go out of their way looking for trouble. Currently the focus of Union activities in Philadelphia is centered on the Walnut Street Theatre, which is under economic attack by one of the major vampire factions of the city.

The Factions

Out of the conflict of the previous centuries, three major vampiric factions have emerged in Philadelphia. Not every vampire in the city belongs to one of the factions, but even these "independent" vampires must deal with them. The factions aren't themselves homogeneous: vampires from all the major "families" have a presence in each faction, much like how mortal families might be related by blood but have different political ideals. In the case of vampire politics, relations of blood take a backseat to political identity and brother will fight brother to achieve political supremacy. Changing factions isn't unheard of, but it isn't highly regarded either. Vampires that move from one political circle to another are likely to be branded as traitors by their past acquaintances. Each faction claims roughly a third of the city as their territory and are constantly on the lookout for ways to increase that territory through fair means or foul. The only section of Philadelphia not under solid control of any one faction is Center City, which is a hodge podge of territories and is the area most likely to host nighttime skirmishes over turf.

Snakes

The oldest faction in the city, with sub-factions that were first formed in the 17th century, is called Serpents or, more commonly, just Snakes by hunters. This nickname resulted from a tattoo common to vampires of this faction depicting the Glasden flag with its famous rattlesnake drawing and caption that reads, "Don't Tread On Me." Alternate versions of the tattoo with captions that read, "Liberty or Death" or, "Join or Die" share common historical links to the Glasden flag. The majority of this faction is made up of younger vampires that were born and raised in Philadelphia and, oddly, this faction seems to be the least deadly to humans. Although they still waylay people walking home by themselves at night, they are (as a whole) less likely to kill a human during their feeding than the other factions (though mistakes *do* happen). The Serpents control the northern and northeastern parts of the city and one of their major strongholds is the Eastern State Penitentiary. Currently, the Snakes and the Wyrms are battling for control of the Rittenhouse Square area.

THE BLOOD BOIL

The local vampires call it the Blood Boil—a sudden agitation within the blood, a furious and unexpected rise to hunger or violence. It doesn't happen often, but when it does... it comes fast and furious, and here's the worst part, *without provocation*.

Some of the vampires that experienced this "boiling of the blood" have seen a shadowy figure standing distant. It's the same figure some 'banger have seen at drive-by shootings or gang skirmishes. The thugs call this figure Thirty-Eight, because of the medallion shaped like a .38 special that hangs from his neck.

The Blood Boil is actually the result of the spirit named Imakillya (see **Hunter: The Vigil**, p. 353), using his influence and the energies of decades of bloodshed to drive the vampires and their human servants insane. Any character with even a single drop of vampire blood in their system that encounters Imakillya must succeed at a Resolve + Composure roll with a -5 penalty or immediately fly into a killing frenzy. Local vampires (probably the Snakes) are keen to discover the truth about this phenomenon, and may attempt to set hunters on the path to doing their work for them.

CARLEE BRISTOW

Mental Attributes: Intelligence 4, Wits 3, Resolve 4

Physical Attributes: Strength 4, Dexterity 3, Stamina 3

Social Attributes: Presence 3, Manipulation 3, Composure 4

Mental Skills: Academics 1, Investigation 3, Occult 3, Politics 5

Physical Skills: Athletics 4, Brawl (Dirty Tricks) 5, Firearms (Pistols) 4, Larceny 2, Stealth 4, Weaponry (Knives) 5

Social Skills: Empathy 2, Intimidation 3, Persuasion 3, Socialize 2, Streetwise (Gangs) 5, Subterfuge 4

Merits: Allies 3 (City Hall), Allies 5 (Gangs), Allies 3 (Police), Allies 3 (Northside Businesses), Contacts 5 (City Hall, Gangs, Northside Businesses, Police, Local Media), Fast Reflexes 2, Language (French, Spanish), Potency 3, Status 5 (Snakes), Resources 5, Retainers (Ghoul Gang Leaders) 5

Max Willpower/per Turn: 15/2

Morality: 5

Virtue: Fortitude

Vice: Pride

Initiative: 9

Defense: 3

Speed: 12

Health: 8

Dread Powers: Crushing Blow, Dread Attack •••••, Impress •••, Terrify •••, Unholy Attribute (Strength) •••••, Unholy Grace ••••

Weapons/Attacks

Type	Damage	Range	Dice Pool	Special
Bite	9(L)		15	Target must be grappled
Knife	2(L)		11	
H&K Mk. 23	3	30/60/120	9	

Requiem: Carlee is likely of clan Daeva.

Antagonist: Carlee Bristow

Quote: *"You won't take orders from a 'bitch,' you say? Fair enough."* (sound of pistol cocking)

Background: Carlee Barstow was born on April 11, 1760 in Plymouth, England. Poor daughter of a dock worker, when young Carlee caught the eye of an English soldier on his way to America, she jumped at the opportunity to travel to the Colonies. After a hasty wedding service, Carlee boarded ship with her new husband and landed in Boston Harbor. Scant months after arriving in the Colonies, America declared its independence from England and soon the fledgling nation and the Empire of Great Britain were at war. Carlee followed her husband when the British Army moved to put down American troops at Bunker Hill and it was during that battle that any hopes she might have had for a happy future with her husband ended. Although the British Army declared victory at the Battle of Bunker Hill, their casualties were appalling. In all the Army suffered 800 wounded and 228 dead, by far the highest casualties suffered by the British for the entirety of the war. When the battle was over and her husband didn't return, Carlee found him dead on the battlefield.

The wives and children of men serving in the British Army were rationed from the public stores that were made available for use by all soldiers. With her man dead, Carlee was denied access to the stores and left to fend for herself. Gathering together what little money she had saved, Carlee made her way to Philadelphia, hoping to avoid the war and looking for honest work. With anti-British sentiments running high in the city, thanks to her accent Carlee could barely find enough work to make ends meet. Late one evening as she shuffled home, weary from a day of washing laundry, she was dragged off the street and into the one of the modest dwellings on the north side of town. The vampire that attacked her surely hadn't intended to make the bedraggled woman he'd snatched of the street his undead progeny. Maybe it was the taste of fury in her blood or the way she struggled to the last that impressed the creature. Whatever the reason, instead of pitching her empty husk aside, the vampire fed her a bit of his own blood and in 1776, Carlee became a vampire.

No one has ever been able to question Carlee's sire as to his motives. His surprise must have been absolute when she staked him and drained him of blood the following week. From there, Carlee fell in with the nascent Serpents, impressed by their determination to rule rather than be ruled. As the years passed Carlee fought her way through the ranks, with a ruthlessness that wouldn't have surprised her sire if he'd still been around to observe it. Falling into torpor only briefly at the end of the 1800s, when Carlee reawaked she continued her drive to the top and in 1957 she toppled the leader of the Serpents and took his place. The Snakes have prospered under Carlee's guidance and expanded their territory deeper into the cen-

ter of Philadelphia. The other factions fear her not only for her physical prowess but also for her political acumen and the social ties she has made with the gangs that rule North Philly.

Description: A wee slip of a girl, Carlee appears no older than 16 years of age and stands a modest 5' tall. Her hair is a dirty blonde color and falls in gently clinging ringlets to her shoulders. Her pale complexion is lightly brushed with freckles and she prefers to dress in loose, comfortable jeans, a sweatshirt and broken-in athletic shoes. Carlee plays down her English accent most of the time, though it tends to come out when she gets angry or excited.

Storytelling Hints: Carlee has a backbone of solid steel and doesn't back down from confrontations. More than one gang leader has underestimated her because of her size and apparent age. The lucky ones survived with impressive scars. Carlee's grip on the North and Northeast is absolute. She routinely blood bonds prominent gang leaders to her to ensure their loyalty. Carlee counts mortal politicians, policemen and successful businessmen among her allies in North Philadelphia which proves her capabilities in dealing with mortals as well as vampires.

CARLEE'S GANG

Carlee leads a pack of her closest allies as well as the Snakes as a whole. The other members of this gang include (potential **Requiem** clans in parentheses):

KJ (Mekhet): KJ is a rat liked by few others. If not for Carlee's protection he'd be a cloud of fine ash by now and he knows it. There's nobody he won't sell out, with the exception of Carlee herself. (Some rumors suggest he's addicted to her blood.)

Tourniquet (Nosferatu): Gained his nickname when, upon first sighting him, Carlee said he should tourniquet his neck cause his face was killing her. Tourniquet acts as Carlee's bodyguard regardless of how many times she tells him she doesn't need one.

Milton (Ventrue): Slightly manic, Milton nevertheless serves Carlee well with his contacts in the business world. He's a genius at playing the markets, but his obsessive focus ruins most attempts at being social.

Location: Eastern State Penitentiary (ESP)

The Walnut Street Jail was the first penal institution built on the grounds of what is today the Eastern State Penitentiary. Constructed to relieve the overflow of other Philadelphia area jails, the original structure was demolished in 1821 to make way for a much larger structure, designed in a radial wheel plan that was so successful, the prison's architecture saw duplication in hundreds of jails around the world. ESP was in active use from 1829 until 1971 when it was closed and largely abandoned until the jail was purchased by the City of Philadelphia in 1980. While in operation ESP housed famous criminals the likes of Willie Sutton (an accomplished bank robber of the 1930s) and Al Capone.

When restoration was finally completed in 1994, a brief, albeit vicious, struggle broke out among the factions for control of the prison. In the end the Serpents arose as the victor, binding the mortal night shift employees to them. Originally claimed by the Snakes to serve as a strongpoint and fallback position for Center City skirmishes, a problem with the locale quickly became apparent: namely the proximity of the Museum of Art, an Ashwood Abbey site. When the Abbey noticed vampires skulking around ESP, they sent their thrill-seekers and jaded debutantes to clear out the newly restored penitentiary. The resulting skirmish ended when mortal authorities arrived on the scene in response to reports of gunfire, but that battle was only the start. The Serpents retaliated for the attack with ambushes and assaults of their own on Abbey members and the tit for tat battle between the Snakes at ESP and the Abbey at the Museum of Art continues to this day.

Story Seeds:

The Escape Tunnel: In 1945 twelve inmates escaped the Eastern State Penitentiary through a tunnel that Willie Sutton claimed to have engineered. The warden ordered the tunnel collapsed and sealed, but rumors persist that a second tunnel out of (or into) the prison was never found. If this is true, the second tunnel is probably how the Snakes enter and leave the building undetected.

Blood Slave: News reaches one of the characters that a cousin has recently begun work at ESP on the night shift as a guard. After working at the penitentiary for only a short time, the cousin has begun to show signs of illness that is marked by chronic fatigue and a low white blood cell count. Every attempt by other family members to convince the cousin that the jail is probably

FAIRMOUNT

Once, the Penitentiary was a brilliant stronghold in a rougher part of town. That's why the Snakes wanted it. But those advantages have slipped away: the Penitentiary has become a tourist attraction, which forces the Snakes to the margins of the admittedly huge prison (basements, unused wings, storage, tunnels). In addition, the neighborhood was once a bastion of local gangs, but recent gentrification efforts have driven the Snakes' urban allies out of this neighborhood.

So why do they keep it? That's the $10,000 question. Is something there that's simply too valuable to give up, something that cannot be taken away from the prison? Or, are vampires simply so stagnant and stubborn (death is unchanging, after all) that they refuse to see the lost utility in keeping the prison as their base-of-operations?

the cause of the illness has failed and he (or she) continues to visit ESP every night, even when not working.

Antagonist: Copperhead

Quote: *"The fuck you looking at?"*

Background: The vampire known as Copperhead is one of the major movers and shakers of the Snakes, frequently spotted hanging around the Penitentiary. Unwary hunters have learned that Copperhead is never as alone as he appears. Four or five of his fellow Snakes (or blood slaves) are always hiding within earshot if he yells out for help. Copperhead has developed a particular hatred for members of the Ashwood Abbey and will sometimes take his gang on high risk hunts for members he has spotted. A few of the mortal gangs in Philadelphia are friendly with Copperhead and he uses his contacts with them to gather information on the other factions, hunter cells and to keep an eye on the pulse of the streets.

Description: Tall and gangly with a sparse stubble of red hair, Copperhead gained his nickname from hunters that observed he was unable to draw in his fangs as far as other leeches. Even with his mouth closed, the tips protrude ever-so-slightly past his lips. Usually decked out in a scuffed leather biker jacket, faded blue jeans and clunky boots, Copperhead keeps an eye out for Abbey hunter groups coming and going from the Philadelphia Museum of Art.

COPPERHEAD

Mental Attributes: Intelligence 3, Wits 3, Resolve 3

Physical Attributes: Strength 3, Dexterity 4, Stamina 2

Social Attributes: Presence 3, Manipulation 2, Composure 3

Mental Skills: Investigation 3, Occult 2, Politics 1

Physical Skills: Athletics 3, Brawl (Dirty Tricks) 3, Drive 1, Firearms (Pistol) 2, Larceny 1, Stealth 3, Weaponry 2

Social Skills: Intimidation 3, Persuasion 2, Socialize 2, Streetwise (Gangs) 3, Subterfuge 2

Merits: Allies (Snakes) 2, Potency 1, Contacts (Gangs) 2, Danger Sense, Fast Reflexes 2, Status (Snakes) 4

Max Willpower/per Turn: 10/1

Morality: 3

Virtue: Fortitude

Vice: Wrath

Initiative: 9

Defense: 3

Speed: 12

Health: 7

Dread Powers: Dread Attack (Claws) •••, Enhanced Senses •••, Unholy Grace

Weapons/Attacks:

Type	Damage	Range	Dice Pool	Special
Glock 9mm	2(L)	20/40/80	9	
Bite	3(L)	na	7	Target must be grappled
Claws	3(L)	na	9	

Requiem: Copperhead is likely of clan Gangrel.

Storytelling Hints: Genially belligerent. Copperhead is the type of guy that will punch you too hard in the shoulder, jokingly, and then roll his eyes if you complain. Though no coward, Copperhead will still beat feet if a fight looks like it's going against him. His tasking of messing with the Ashwood Abbey is self-appointed, but he has enough pull in the Snakes that no one but Carlee can tell him to stop (and so far, she hasn't). Copperhead hopes to eventually catch the Abbey with their pants down so he can launch a raid on the Art Museum and swipe the rumored horde of mystic artifacts they keep inside.

HEINRICH KOENIG
SERGEANT-AT-ARMS

Abilities:

Academics (dice pool 5) - The Special Collection is organized and filed in a way that only makes sense to Heinrich and it may even take him a short while to find a specific item.

Occult (dice pool 6) - Not every item brought to him is actually worth bothering with and he can usually discriminate between treasures and junk.

Firearms (dice pool 7) - He isn't called sergeant-at-arms for nothing.

Intimidation (dice pool 5) - Heinrich is generally unimpressed with threats or blustering intended to get past him and to the Special Collection.

Heinrich Koenig, Sergeant-At-Arms, Ashwood Abbey

Born to rich parents of pure German stock, the Heinrich quickly grew bored with the life of ease his parent's wealth and privilege allowed him. Falling in with other social delinquents near his own age, Heinrich was visiting an exclusive house of ill-repute when the expensive prostitute he had hired for the evening suddenly grew fangs, *in flagrante*, and attacked him. Keeping his wits about him, Heinrich seized his wallet from the bedside table and jammed it into the creature's mouth. While she was distracted, he tackled her to the floor and quickly restrained her using his belt and the electrical cord from a lamp. The kicker was, she seemed *into* it. Hissing, laughing, spitting. Happy to continue the game, Heinrich bound the whore to the bed and proceeded to get his money's worth. After he had finished, he quickly redressed and left an extra $100 tip on the dresser (he did not, however, *untie* the creature) and took his leave, feeling more alive than had since childhood.

Word of the incident spread to the Ashwood Abbey, who immediately invited Heinrich to join their numbers. Since his initiation, Heinrich has risen through the ranks of the Abbey to his current position of sergeant-at-arms,

keeper of the Special Collection at the Philadelphia Museum of Art. Slower now than he was when he first encountered a vampire and sporting several dashing scars on his body, Heinrich still goes hunting now and then, but most of his pleasure is found in denying access to the items contained in the Special Collection to the Aegis Kai Doru. Although the items of the Special Collection aren't generally loaned out, Heinrich has been known to look the other way when Abbey members of good standing (Status •• or more) come for a specific item. Especially if they bring him an amusing diversion in female (or even close to female) form.

REQUIEM

The vampire factions in the city are approximations of vampire covenants. The Serpents are roughly a Carthian analog, the Wyrms are mainly Ordo Dracul and the Blue Bloods are pretty much the Invictus. Other covenants have very little power in the city (or simply may not exist) and will ally themselves with one of the ruling factions from time to time. Usually, though, they just try to stay out of the way and mind their own business.

Wyrms

The Wyrms are the youngest faction in the city, only really rising to prominence in the late 1800s. The current moniker of Wyrms has evolved from the original name "Dragons," which was inspired by their hording of esoteric texts and mystic relics. Consisting mainly of vampires drawn from the intelligentsia of the numerous colleges and institutes found throughout the city, the Wyrms are the least expansionist faction overall. Mainly content to simply hold on to what they have, the Wyrms will sometimes enter the fracas as the aggressor to claim a building of historical significance or some random piece of the city that has no apparent value to anyone but them.

Of all the hunter groups in Philadelphia, the Wyrms seem to clash most frequently with the Aegis Kai Doru and the Loyalists of Thule over rare tomes or antiquities. On one memorable occasion, all three groups entered into a pitched three-way battle for possession of a statue thought to have been sculpted in the lost lands of Mu. The Wyrms control western and northwestern parts of the city and one of their primary repositories of knowledge is found among the tombs and buildings of the Laurel Hill Cemetary. Currently, the Wyrms aren't at war with either of the other two factions, though the Blue Bloods believe they have spotted Wyrm scouting parties near Independence Hall.

Antagonist: The Shadow Revenant

Name: Laurence Zbikowski

Quote: *(Whispered from the shadows)* *"Hungry."*

Background: People are vanishing from the streets of West Philadelphia. No outcry has appeared in the newspapers yet and the police have been slow to link the disappearances (plus, their busy with all those murders). All the same, businesses that thrive after dark have noticed a drop in sales as their customers have begun, subconsciously, to avoid the streets at night. No one can put a name to the dread they feel, but they *know* on some primal level that something haunts the night. The Wyrms know it too; the difference is they are pretty sure who it is.

A little over a month ago, the Wyrms sent a leech named Zbikowski to North Philly to spy on the activities of the Snakes. When Zbikowski never returned they assumed he had been discovered and killed by their rivals, even though the Serpents denied having killed any Wyrms lately. Then the killings be-

gan. Corpses were found near Wyrm nests, drained of blood, with a look of horror on their pallid faces. Each body bore the distinct marks of death at the hands of a frenzied vampire and, worse, none of the bite marks had been sealed shut with a lick. The Wyrms alerted their faction to the possibility that a mad vampire, a revenant, was loose in the area and as the days turned into weeks, were forced to alert the other factions as well. Soon a city-wide hunt was on for the revenant and after a month of fruitless searching the Wyrms began to suspect that Zbikowski might not be dead after all. Zbikowski was sent into enemy territory because of his mastery over shadows and his stealth. Knowing the identity of the revenant hasn't helped the Wyrms capture him, however, and it's only a matter of time until one of the bodies is found by a human (or worse, a hunter) and the real trouble begins.

Description: Zbikowski is a short, balding man with beady brown eyes and an unremarkable face. Even with such an apparently unoffensive demeanor, Zbikowski projects an aura of distaste that made people avoid him even before he went mad. Zbikowski is dressed in the tatters of what used to be a cheap suit, which is now splattered with mud and blood. Oddly for a revenant, Zbikowski rarely makes any noise at all, even when he kills.

Storytelling Hints: Zbikowski is the revenant. While spying for his faction on the northside he was unfortunate enough to encounter the Blood Boil (see p. 210) and went insane after slaughtering an entire family in their home during his frenzy. Not really rational, per se, Zbikowski possesses a feral cunning and remembers just enough of his old habits to drop the bodies of his victims off near Wyrm holdings for disposal.

THE BEAST TRIUMPHANT

Vampires who are reduced to Morality 0 become non-sentient beasts, following a mindless reptilian pattern of "Hunt, Feed, Kill, Sleep, Repeat." In this persistent state, they are as much a threat to vampires as to humans. Vampires refer to such creatures as revenants (though some call them *draugr*). The behavior of a revenant is very similar to undead bloodsuckers that have returned from the grave without knowing the embrace of a vampire, leading some scholars to believe that the very first vampire may have risen on its own.

THE SHADOW REVENANT

Mental Attributes: Intelligence 1, Wits 4, Resolve 4

Physical Attributes: Strength 3, Dexterity 4, Stamina 3

Social Attributes: Presence 1, Manipulation 1, Composure 2

Mental Skills: None. Because of his insanity, any Mental Skill roll is reduced to a chance die.

Physical Skills: Athletics 3, Brawl 4, Stealth (Stalking) 4, Survival (Urban) 4, Weaponry 2

Social Skills: Intimidation (Hollow Stare) 4, Streetwise 3

Merits: Potency •••, Danger Sense, Fleet of Foot •••

Willpower: 36

Morality: 0

Virtue: Fortitude

Vice: Gluttony

Initiative: 6

Defense: 4

Speed: 15

Health: 8

Dread Powers: Enhanced Senses •••, Lurker in Darkness •••, New Face ••••, Unholy Attribute (Dexterity) •••

Weapons/Attacks:

Type	Damage	Range	Dice Pool	Special
Bite	3(L)	7		Target must be grappled
Punch	3(B)	7		

Requiem: Zbikowski likely belongs to clan Nosferatu.

Location: Laurel Hill Cemetery

The Laurel Hill Cemetery was founded in 1836 on a plot of land well north of the city, overlooking the Schuylkill River. Designed to be an alternative to the squalid and overcrowded church cemeteries that were the usual places of rest for the dead, Laurel Hill also embraced the idea of religious tolerance prevalent in Philadelphia allowing anyone with the means to bury their loved ones in a place of serenity. The cemetery attracted the attention of the wealthy magnates of the day and great stone mausoleums were constructed to house their remains. The gothic splendor of the cemetery increased over the years with the addition of more and more elaborately-constructed mausoleums, statuary and tombstones. Philadelphia eventually expanded to absorb Laurel Hill, but it remains a place of calm beauty and was named a National Historic Landmark in 1998.

The Wyrms decided early on they would need a secure place to store their collections and settled on Laurel Hill for the security provided by its windowless tombs. Binding the caretakers to their wills, the Wyrms moved into the cemetery and constructed an elaborate series of underground passages that connected one mausoleum to another and to the chapel and superintendent's house. Choosing mainly to settle in the stone houses of dead family trees, the Wyrms moved their books, artifacts and other personal items into the warren they had created and continued with their esoteric pursuits. The warren has evolved and expanded over the years to connect nearly every mouldering tomb in the cemetery in a maze that serves as additional protection to the faction.

Story Seeds:

The Caretaker: The leader of the Wyrms is a mysterious vampire known only as the Curator. It is said that only the Curator knows the locations of every tome, artifact or curiosity piece that rests in the warren under Laurel Hill. The Curator is believed to be a lone vampire that has dwelled in the cemetery for over a century, though it is possible the title is one of rank that changes over time. In either case, both the Aegis Kai Doru and the Loyalists of Thule would dearly love to capture the Curator and use his knowledge to plunder the collections of the Wyrms. Recently, a rumor has spread to both hunter organizations that a caretaker of Laurel Hill and personal assistant to the Curator has managed to break the bonds of blood. If this rumor is true, the caretaker may be one of the most hunted men in the city with the agents of the Wyrms, the Aegis Kai Doru and the Loyalists of Thule all desperately searching for him.

The Traitor: Varina Navotny was well-respected by the hunters of Philly for her ability to seemingly pull information from thin air. Of indeterminate age (guesses ranged from 60 to 80), Varina visited the homes and headquarters of nearly every hunter cell in the city at one time or another to give advice or impart information. So when Varina walked alone into the Laurel Hill Cemetery one night and returned several months later a vampire, the shock was felt throughout the city. It was with heavy hearts that the hunters she had befriended surrounded her house intent on putting her to rest. To their surprise they found Varina sitting calmly in her rocking chair, awaiting their arrival. She quietly explained she had chosen the life of a vampire over the wasting illness of age and went on to reveal what she had learned from the Wyrms. Varina plays a dangerous game of double-agent now, spending her nights gathering information for her mortal friends in return for payments of blood.

THE CURATOR

The shadowy figure known only as the Curator not only leads the Wyrms in their struggles with the other factions he/she also oversees and dictates the direction of their research and experiments. For the last century the Curator has carefully guided the other vampires towards a single discovery that would, if successful, give the Wyrms power over every vampire in the city. The Curator believes that all vampires come from a single source and that the blood of all vampires bears the mystic signature of the ultimate source. If the Wyrms could learn to tap into the power of that source they could gain control over the properties of vampiric blood that form the foundation of vampire's supernatural powers and abilities.

Recently, the Wyrms have made what they believe could be a breakthrough on this front. The Curator and his most trusted lieutenants have begun work on a ritual that would empower the Wyrms with the ability to deny other vampires the use of their blood to heal wounds and fuel Dread Powers. If the ritual succeeds the other factions will be nearly helpless to resist a full-out Wyrm offensive. It is entirely possible that the Curator's ghoul assistant knows full details of this plan and this could be the reason the Wyrms are so desperate to capture him (see "The Caretaker," above).

No hunter has, as yet, managed to set eyes on the Curator as he rarely emerges from the warren underneath Laurel Hill Cemetery. If a hunter cell did take the fight to the Wyrms and managed to overcome the vampires that nest there, the blood slaves and the devious traps set to discourage visitors they might be able to corner the Curator. Storytellers with troupes that undertake this (likely suicidal) course of action should portray the Curator as an extraordinarily powerful vampire lord with Potency 5 and full command over *any and all* of the Dread Powers listed in this book or the **Hunter** corebook. A cell should not emerge victorious from a fight with the Curator without suffering losses, if they emerge at all.

Dr. Sanjog Buchar, Null Mysteriis

Operating from a renovated house on in West Philadelphia, Dr. Buchar and his Null Mysteriis assistants work to discover the causes (and possibly a cure) for the disease called vampirism. The son of Indian immigrants, Buchar graduated from medical school magna cum laude in the field of hematology and finished his internship in near record time. Returning to school after his internship for more training, Dr. Buchar was board-certified as a hematopathologist in 1995 and has been published in several well-respected medical journals. Shortly after the turn of the millennia, Dr. Buchar was running lab tests for a fraternity brother when he noticed some unusual qualities to the blood. The notes that came with the test claimed the sample came from a 19-year-old woman, but the blood show signs of age and decay he wouldn't have expected to see in so young a patient.

Intrigued, he delivered the results of his tests to his friend and asked to see the case files associated with the patient. His friend, Dr. John Lloyd, showed Buchar the files and asked if he would like to meet the patient. Lloyd explained that the nature of the patient required she be kept outside the hospital and gave Dr. Buchar an address to meet him at later that evening. Buchar was surprised when the address turned out to be an old stone house on the west side of the city, with bricked over windows and a steel security door. An intercom was set to one side of the

door and he noticed a small camera hidden in the shadows tracking his movements. He pressed the intercom, identified himself and after a short delay was buzzed into the building. There he saw his first vampire.

After joining the Null Mysteriis, Dr. Buchar worked with Lloyd and other scientists with little success at discovering the causes of the vampiric disease, but a recent breakthrough has given him new hope. Within the last year the Null Mysteriis has captured a number of vampires that seem to be in the early stages of the disease and he has succeeded in identifying a strange pathogen in the blood of his subjects. Dr. Buchar named the pathogen "Kali" in reference to the creator/destroyer goddess of his parent's homeland. Dr. Buchar hopes that a successful treatment for the disease will be found soon so he can announce his findings to the public and rid the world of the vampirism.

Kali

The Kali disease discovered by Dr. Buchar and his associates isn't really a root cause of vampirism. Instead, Kali is a new disease that is slowly spreading through Philadelphia that mimics many of the symptoms of the vampiric condition. The disease began when a Wyrm fed from a human infected with a rare blood disease and became a carrier. The disease mutated inside the body of the vampire and the next time he fed it was passed to his victim. Luckily, the vampire that began the plague was killed shortly thereafter by TFV agents, but not until he had spread the disease to several more of his victims.

Kali is spread by direct contact with blood or other bodily fluids and is particularly weak outside a host body, dying in under a minute. The disease isn't particularly contagious, meaning that most people with a healthy immune system fight it off with little difficulty. People that are already sick or have a weak immune system are more at risk. A character that comes in contact with the Kali disease must succeed at a Stamina + Resolve roll in order to avoid catching the disease. Symptoms of the disease include a heightened sensitivity to sunlight, akin to mild cases of Xeroderma Pigmentosum, which can lead to a greater chance of suffering from basaliomas and other skin malignancies; enhanced sense of sight and smell (the afflicted find strong organic scents, like garlic for example, repugnant); an increase in energy during night time hours only and an addict's craving for blood (both human and animal).

These are all classic symptoms of vampirism, and it isn't much of a surprise that many of those suffering from Kali disease have begun to claim and believe that they are vampires. This has already lead to a few tragic cases of mistaken identity when a hunter also believed the disease victim was a vampire and were horrified when the "sugger" they staked wept real tears and coughed up lungfuls of blood. Oddly, "patients" suffering from the disease (captured by Null Mysteriis) claim it is the act of drinking blood, the pleasure it gives them combined with the distress of their victims that forms the addiction.

Mechanically, humans afflicted with Kali disease suffer a -1 penalty to any actions taken during the day and a -2 penalty if they are exposed to direct sunlight. They gain a +2 bonus to any Perception-based rolls, a +1 bonus to any actions taken after sunset and a bonus dot of Stamina at night. Sufferers also acquire an addiction to drinking human blood, specifically from a living person, for the rush of pleasure and fear involved in the act. This addiction is identical to that of habitual cocaine use (**World of Darkness Rulebook**, p. 176) in intensity.

Although Kali dies quickly outside a body and isn't easily transmitted, the disease *is* supernatural in origin and doesn't respond to mundane methods of treatment. Only the blood of a real vampire, with its own unique qualities, and only in significant quantity (say, two liters worth), either ingested or injected directly into the body of the inflicted, will cure the disease.

Blue Bloods

The faction that eventually became known as the Blue Bloods was first formed by the wave of European vampire immigrants in the late 18th century. Many of the new vampires came from noble human stock and regarded themselves a step above the vampires already extant in Philadelphia. Individually the Europeans stood little chance at carving out domains in neighborhoods long held by the American vampires, so they bound together to form a new faction to wrest power for themselves. Over the centuries the backgrounds of the vampires that choose to align with the Blue Bloods has changed; instead of noble lineages they come from the nouveau riche, political dynasties and high society, but their attitude has not. The Blue Bloods believe they have a right, a mandate even, to rule Philadelphia by night.

Unlike the Snakes, the Blue Bloods prefer to work through subtlety and misdirection to make gains in the city, rather than brute force. They will fight only after exhausting every other possible avenue of approach and when they do fight they prefer to hire or "persuade" others to do their fighting for them. No other faction in the city has the ear of as many mortal politicians and high ranking officials as the Blue Bloods. Other than their low-grade fracas with the Snakes, the Blue Bloods are currently locked in battle with the Union over the fate of the Walnut Street Theatre. The vampires have decided the Theatre would make the perfect headquarters for their faction and are working behind the scenes

to make their idea a reality. The Blue Bloods control the southern and southeastern regions of Philadelphia.

Antagonist: Henry Ashton

Quote: "*It seems a citizen's action group is protesting our new development plans. Squash them like so many bugs if you please, Mr. Douglas.*"

Background: Originally from London, Henry Ashton was forced out of England when his plans to take control of the city were discovered prematurely. Fearing assassination, Ashton fled to the United States and took up residence in Philadelphia around the middle of the 19th century. Ashton hadn't dwelled in the city for more than a couple years before he joined his lot with that of the Blue Bloods, admiring the qualities that faction represented. With the aid of his faction, Ashton set about creating a financial empire for himself, investing heavily in the newly invented telephone, phonograph and incandescent lamp. When the profits from those enterprises finally began to bear fruit, Ashton turned to the tried and true business of land acquisition and speculation. Stepping over the corpses (sometimes literally) of other vampires and mortal alike, by the turn of the 21st century, Ashton had created a virtual kingdom for himself in and around Philadelphia. At a conservative estimate Ashton owns 10% of the land in the city, through dummy corporations and a variety of real estate conglomerates (and while 10% may not seem like a lot, consider that's roughly equivalent to ten to fifteen square miles of valuable real estate in the hands of a single monster).

Though neither the eldest or most powerful vampire in the Blue Bloods by anyone's estimations, Ashton's gains allowed him to take control of the faction. The power to grant or deny building permits (through his contacts in city hall); combined with his leverage over development plans and his outright ownership of several prominent politicians put him in a position of authority that the rest of the faction couldn't deny. The gains made under Ashton's leadership have mainly come in the areas of business and politics and he hopes to use these gains to redraw the map of Philadelphia in ways that favor the Blue Bloods. New zoning laws, migration of traditional neighborhood boundaries and the beefing up of security all over the city are all part of his plan to drive the other factions so deep into hiding they won't be able to resist being absorbed.

Description: Henry Ashton is a genteel figure that dresses in conservatively cut suits that are probably a decade or so behind current trends. Embraced in his late 50s, Ashton is bald as a cue ball, though lacking in the facial lines one would expect from a man his age. Ashton stares out at the world from behind pale blue eyes that seem to regard the activities of others with a detached amusement.

HENRY ASHTON

Mental Attributes: Intelligence 5, Wits 4, Composure 4

Physical Attributes: Strength 2, Dexterity 4, Stamina 2

Social Attributes: Presence 4, Manipulation 5, Composure 3

Mental Skills: Academics 3, Investigation 2, Occult 4, Politics (Philadelphia) 5

Physical Skills: Brawl 1, Firearms 2, Stealth 1, Weaponry (Rapier) 5

Social Skills: Empathy 3, Expression 2, Intimidate 1, Persuasion 5, Socialize 5, Subterfuge 5

Merits: Allies (City Hall) 5, Allies (Big Business) 4, Contacts (City Hall, Police, Fire Department, Big Business, Professional Hitmen) 5, Disarm, Fighting Finesse (Rapier), Potency 3, Resources 5, Retainers (Ghouls) 5

Max Willpower/per Turn: 15/2

Morality: 3

Virtue: Prudence

Vice: Greed

Initiative: 8

Speed: 11

Health: 7

Dread Powers: Alter Memory •••••, Confuse •••, Enhanced Senses ••, Hypnotism ••••, Impress •••, Sleep ••, Unholy Grace ••••

Weapons/Attacks

Type	Damage	Range	Dice Pool	Special
Bite	2(L)		3	Target must be grappled
Rapier	2(L)		10	

Requiem: Henry Ashton is likely clan Ventrue.

Storytelling Hints: Ashton never deigns to dirty his hand with the bloody side of leading a faction, relying instead on hired help and ghoul retainers. He deals with potential rivals to his leadership by interfering with their preferred method of hunting. A favored nightclub will suddenly shut down for "renovations," a previously darkened street corner will sprout a plethora of lights seemingly overnight or willing mortals prized by a rival will turn up dead or missing. The crown jewel of Ashton's rule was meant to be the Walnut Street Theatre and he is quickly becoming obsessed with gaining control of it at any cost.

Location: The Walnut Street Theatre

In continual operation since 1809, the Walnut Street Theatre is the oldest theater in America. Originally named The New Circus and the home of equestrian acts, the theater underwent renovations to include a main stage and orchestra pit and opened for its first production in 1812. The theater has undergone a number of expansions and renovations over its 200 year history, resulting in a maze of rooms, hallways and staircases that can easily befuddle the uninitiated. Named the Official State Theatre of Pennsylvania, Walnut Street Theatre can boast of past performances by an assortment of celebrities.

Two years ago, a consortium of Blue Bloods decided to buy the theater from the current non-profit owners to use as their fashionable seat of power in the city. Plans were made, the proper wheels were greased and everything seemed set in motion for the vampires to acquire the theater until the local chapter of the International Alliance of Theatrical Stage Employees (IATSE) threatened to boycott operations if the sale was finalized. The ringleader of the boycott was one Teddy Wordsworth, who just happened to belong to *the* Union. Through his contacts in the Union, Teddy learned the identities of his potential employers and immediately appealed to Joey Carcione, a local Union bigwig, for assistance. Together, Joey and Teddy put together the plan of a threatened boycott to play for time while the Union worked against the vampires. So far the plan has succeeded. The Union has managed to buy up 41% of the interests in the theater, helped in no small part by selling the bits and pieces (and occasionally still kicking) of Blue Blood vampires to the Cheiron Group.

For their own part, the Blue Bloods haven't sat around idly waiting for the Union to give up and have succeeded in procuring 48% of the theater. Both groups are in negotiations for the final 11% which is owned by an elderly patron of the arts named Thelma Eiche. Mrs. Eiche, a widow for 23 years, is thoroughly entertained by the attention she receives from both groups and has no intention of selling her interests before she dies. This deadlock has left the Union and the Blue Bloods in a perpetual state of war in which both sides are playing dirty.

The Blue Bloods arm their goon squads with firebombs and send them around to houses owned by Union members. The vampires attack and intimidate the Union's financial backers, which forces the Union to either hire or play bodyguard, neither of which they are in a good position to do. In return, the Union seeks out the mortal gophers of the Blue Bloods during the daylight hours and kneecaps them or "encourages" them to seek new employment. They have also started a city-wide petition that would force the sale of the Theatre to the Union rather than to the "Foreign Investment Group" the Union claims is after it. The struggle wears on and on with both sides seeking the final edge, either politically, financially or through attrition, that will place them in firm control of the theater.

Story Seeds:

The Will: Mrs. Eiche was recently observed by both Union and Blue Blood agents to have entered the offices of her lawyers. After a quick scramble to verify that her assets remained unchanged (requiring a few bribes paid to the lawyer's secretary), both sides have come to the conclusion that Mrs. Eiche has updated her will. The old woman's reticence to sell her interest in the theater is well known to everyone involved in the struggle and questions have been raised as to whether she has deeded the remaining 11% to one side or the other. After a botched Blue Blood kidnapping attempt on her lawyer resulted in his death, the only way to verify the contents of her will is perusal of the document itself. The problem is that no one is quite sure where the will is. Mrs. Eiche keeps safety deposit boxes at several banks and is known to have a personal safe in her manor. Both sides are desperate to see the will and plans are being hatched to find out what it contains.

Consultations: Even with time on their side, the Blue Bloods are eager to end their embarrassing standoff with the Union. The idea that any plan of theirs could be thwarted by mere humans, *blue collar* humans at that, drives the faction as a whole to distraction. Even without majority ownership of the theater, if the threat of boycott posed by the IATSE were ended, the vampires would effectively control the venue. To facilitate the end

CLIQUE

Ashton has gathered a small coterie of like-minded vampires to his side. He encourages them to speak their minds to him and values hearing opinions from people other than the usual blend of toadies and bootlickers that tend to congregate around authority figures. The clique includes (possible Requiem clans in parenthesis):

Devine (Daeva): An opera singer in life, Devine is very nearly Ashton's personal pet. Vampires outside the clique are frequently surprised by her intelligence on the rare occasions she decides to speak her mind.

Antonio (Mekhet): Serves as Ashton's head of intelligence. Antonio has assembled a formidable spy network in the city and can usually be found at Travesty.

Charles (Ventrue): Ashton's second-in-command and also his childe. Charles is completely devoted to Ashton, possibly as a result of a blood bond.

CHESTER HOLMES DOUGLAS III

Mental Attributes: Intelligence 3, Wits 3, Resolve 2

Physical Attributes: Strength 2, Dexterity 2, Stamina 2

Social Attributes: Presence 3, Manipulation 3, Composure 3

Mental Skills: Academics (Law) 4, Computer 2, Investigation 2, Occult 1, Politics 3

Physical Skills: Brawl 1, Drive 1, Weaponry 1

Social Skills: Empathy 2, Expression (Courtroom) 3, Intimidation 1, Persuasion 3, Socialize 3, Subterfuge (Doubletalk) 3

Merits: Allies (Blue Bloods) 2, Contacts (City Hall) 3, Eidetic Memory, Resources 4, Status (Law Firm) 4

Willpower: 5

Morality: 6

Virtue: Temperance

Vice: Gluttony

Initiative: 5

Defense: 2

Speed: 9

Health: 7

Dread Powers: Hypnotism ••, Unholy Attribute (Manipulation) •

Requiem: Chester could be portrayed as the ghoul of a Daeva.

of this threat, the Blue Bloods have hired a consultation firm named Oak, Winsthrop, Hayes and Jefferson to put an end to the stage hands union in Philadelphia.

The firm, specializing in union busting, sent in a senior consultant named Zachary Jordan to deal with, and hopefully break, the IATSE. It soon became apparent that Mr. Jordan was more than a simple union buster when Joey Carcione received a visit from ATF officers who busted "the Grocer" for unlicensed gun possession. A tip-off from a friendly contact at city hall revealed that the feds got their information from one Zachary Jordan. Mr. Jordan has figured in several other underhanded attacks on both Union and IATSE members, and, tempted as they are to simply kill him, the Union has yet to come up with a solution to this new dilemma.

Antagonist: Chester Holmes Douglas III

Quote: *"Yes sir. I understand sir. I'll take care of it."*

Background: Chester numbly followed the path planned out for him starting in high school, through law school and into the family law firm. Respectability, responsibility and dependability were Chester's watchwords; they dictated the girls he dated, the woman he eventually married and even the conception of his two children. No one ever told him what was expected of him; no one had to. The closest Chester ever came to excitement was the annual convention he attended with his father in Las Vegas, during which he usually hired a prostitute to do the things his wife never would. It was during his latest trip to Vegas that Chester met the Blue Blood vampire that had been sent out west specifically to seduce him. When he drank blood from the breast of his lover, Chester finally did something unexpected. Since that night he lives for the rush, the thrill of adrenaline that washes through him when he drinks vampiric blood. People might call him damned, but as far as Chester is concerned, he already lived in hell. He gleefully embraces his new addiction.

Description: Chester is the personification of your average WASP. Even when he isn't dressed in a business suit and tie, Chester presents himself in a solemn and reserved manner. His hair is always neat and trim, with a part that looks like it was done with a razor and he never allows even the hint of a five o'clock shadow to darken his jaw.

Storytelling Hints: Chester's law firm represents the major interests of the Blue Bloods in Philadelphia. He headed the team that engineered the Walnut Street Theatre buyout, manages political contacts and, by and large, makes unlife easier for the vampires that he serves. The only time his reserve slips is directly after he has fed from a vampire. While he's flush with blood he becomes downright chatty and has been known to let secrets slip.

Jamel Spurlock, South Side Slayers

Standing an easy 6'2", with light brown skin and a gentle smile, Jamel doesn't fit the profile most people would expect from a hunter. Jamel goes to work every day at his nine to five job, spends weekends grilling in his backyard (when the weather is good) and is well-liked by his neighbors and co-workers. A solid family man, Jamel has a

happy marriage and two beautiful children, James and Laticia. The qualities of character that make him such a success in both his professional and private life also catapulted him into leadership of a small hunter cell that calls itself the South Side Slayers. A string of missing children reports in his neighborhood led to the formation of a neighborhood watch, which Jamel was placed in charge of. Spurred by police failure to apprehend the kidnapper, the neighborhood watch took matters into their own hands. It was early evening when Jamel and his friends burst in to the abandoned home they had tracked to kidnapper back to. They surrounded the man armed with baseball bats, stun guns and a single pistol (just in case) intending to take the kidnapper alive. The man hissed at Jamel, baring fangs and attacked. After the fight was over, two of Jamel's friends were dead, victims of the slashing claws of the thing that had been eating their children. Just as Jamel was wondering what to do with the body, it turned to dust.

In the five years following that night, the South Side Slayers put down half a dozen other monsters, each one different and more terrifying than the last. Jamel resigned to himself to protecting the neighborhood from things the police couldn't or wouldn't believe existed. Then his baby girl got sick. Laticia had never been a very energetic child, always smaller and sicklier than other friends her age. With the onset of puberty she stopping growing taller, yet seemed to grow *older* somehow. At 15 she looked an underdeveloped 20 and a milky cataract formed over her left eye. The family physician ran a battery of tests then referred Jamel to a specialist. The specialist ran even more tests before finally telling him that Laticia suffered from Werner's Syndrome, an autosomal recessive disorder that was responsible for her rapid aging. His compassion obvious in his tone, the doctor explained there was no treatment for the disease and sufferers rarely lived past 50, sometimes dying as early as their mid-thirties.

Though devastated by the news, Jamel swore that Laticia would live as normal a life as possible. Unwilling to risk losing any time with his child, Jamel told the South Side Slayers he was retiring and dedicated himself to her care. The newspapers ran stories about Laticia and the family was inundated with cards and letters expressing their support for the family. Late one evening there was a knock on his door. Outside stood a well-dressed white man who shook Jamel's hand and offered him a business card. He told Jamel that there was a cure to be had for his daughter's malady, if Jamel was man enough to seek it. The card read Chester Holmes Douglass III, Attorney At Law.

The South Side Slayers were surprised, albeit pleased when Jamel returned to lead the cell. The other hunters attributed his return to the near-miraculous recovery of Laticia, who was growing again and seemed healthier

VAMPIRE BLOOD— THE MIRACLE CURE!?

Obviously not every ailment can be cured by a dose of vampire blood. In Laticia's case the rapid aging that comes from Werner's Syndrome is held in check by the side-effect of diminished aging that comes from habitually drinking vampiric blood. Of course, this choice of treatments comes with problems all its own in the form of addiction and the possibility of becoming bonded to a vampire.

Though, who says Cheiron isn't working on something that makes vampire's blood into a very genuine miracle cure? Sure, there'll be side effects (two pages worth in teensy-weensy font), but that's the nature of modern pharmaceuticals…

than ever, if a little manic. More active than ever before, the hunter cell has taken to killing vampires well outside their usual territory and Jamel always seems to know where to find them. If Jamel seems more somber these days, it's only to be expected given what he went through. For his part, Jamel knows he is being used by the vampires he now serves and through him the cell. He figures it's worth the price. As long as he continues to play ball, every month a different man shows up at his house carrying a vial filled with vampire blood and a cocktail of other ingredients he doesn't like to dwell on. He tries to think of it as medicine and Laticia never asks any questions.

The Independents

Not every vampire in the city is caught up in the struggle for supremacy evidenced by the major factions. Any number of vampires go about their nightly business with no thought to the future, no interest in expanding spheres of influence, pretty much just doing their own thing. Not that this makes them any less of a threat to humans in the city. Just because they aren't as organized doesn't mean they aren't dangerous.

Location: Travesty

Travesty is a night club/live performance venue that is popular with club goer and musicians on the bleeding edge of culture and music. Bathed in a perpetual gloom, the club is mainly lit by flashing lights, neon signs and dim rows of floor lights. Travesty

hires two or three bands each week to give live performances and, about once a month, hosts either a gothic burlesque or industrial/street wear type fashion show. The high level of security provided by the club is one of the reasons the place is so popular. Large, intimidating men guard the entrance and wander around the club watching for signs of trouble and guests must pass through a series of exceptionally sensitive metal detectors before they are allowed in. The metal detectors, in fact, are part of the show. Customers that set off the alarms on the way in are thoroughly searched, on the spot, and given the nature (and piercings) of the club's clientele, this can lead to an interesting spectacle. Anyone that objects to this treatment is turned away, accompanied by taunts and jeers from the watching crowd.

Travesty is unique in the city for reasons other than the nightly strip tease at the door. For starters, the club is owned by a vampire. That by itself isn't unusual; vampires own or have a share in any number of clubs in Philadelphia. The club also counts any number of vampires among its customers, but, again, that isn't unusual either. What is unusual is the lack of vampire-on-vampire violence that takes place in the club. See, Travesty is considered neutral ground (known as "Elysium" to older bloodsuckers) by the vampires of Philadelphia. It is the one place where Blue Blood, Snake and Wyrm alike can mingle, fairly secure in the knowledge no harm will come to them. The peace is backed partly by the blood-enhanced mortal security, partly by the vampire childer of the owner that keep an eye on the place, but mostly by the threat of violent retaliation from the vampires that frequent the club. Any vampire that gets too frisky in Travesty quickly finds he isn't welcome and woe to the leech that kills on neutral ground. The alley behind the bar is lightly dusted with the ashes of vampires that failed to practice self-control.

Travesty serves a vital role in the city, it's a place where immortal enemies can get together and discuss their differences over a drink. More information is traded or exchanged in one night at Travesty than could be obtained anywhere else in the city over the course of weeks.

And what of hunters? Hunters don't play by vampire rules… or, most don't. Certainly hunters that catch a whiff of the veritable nexus of vampire activity going on in Travesty will have little interest in pursuing the peace. Or will they? For one thing, messing with Travesty brings a whole world of pain down upon one's head. Another thing is that a few hunters have learned to play the game, and use Travesty in much the same way as the vampires: as a place to broker deals, gain information, and make poorly-veiled threats without immediately backing it up with a Molotov cocktail.

Story Seeds:

The Long Walk Home: The club itself is neutral ground, but anyone outside the club is fair game. Come closing time, security conducts a rigorous sweep of Travesty, ushers drunk or tardy individuals out and locks the doors. It is considered dishonorable in the extreme to attack someone exiting the club, it has, however, been known to happen. Smart vampires make sure they leave in groups and even elders gather their fellows to them before starting out. Hunters aren't bound by the same social rules of engagement as vampires and more than one cell has staked out the exits watching for their quarry to leave. This can lead to complications if the cell hasn't noticed the other undead in the crowd.

The Contact: The cell has received a message from an unknown informer to meet them at Travesty. The message, in the form of a handwritten note, was unsigned and contained hints of information about the target the cell is currently hunting. The author promises more information once they meet and instructs the cell to sit at a certain table at midnight. If the cell doesn't know about Travesty, they might believe the message is a trap. Cautious hunters that scope out the club before midnight can't help but notice a large number of vampires entering the place, which is unlikely to ameliorate their suspicions. The combination of hunter paranoia and ignorance of the strict ground rules of neutrality at Travesty could combine into a nasty surprise for cells that go into the club looking for trouble.

Antagonist: Darlington

The vampire owner of Travesty, known only by the name of Darlington, is something of a mystery in the city. As far as the other vampires of Philadelphia can tell, Darlington never leaves the club and hardly anyone even knows what he looks like. Considered the best source of information in the city on anything weird going on, Darlington receives a steady stream of visitors

THE UNSTATTED MR. NAYLOR

Unlike most of the antagonists in this book, Naylor/Darlington goes without a stat block for a good reason. If used properly, no one will ever even *see* Naylor. Even if a hunter cell managed to kill the fake Darlington (thus earning themselves some enemies, by the way), Naylor would just set up a new decoy and his apparent immortality would only add to his reputation.

Another possibility that some Storytellers might find appealing is that there isn't an Elias Naylor either. The Darlington vampire in the basement is still a fake, but he works for someone else. Maybe he gets his information from a hunter conspiracy that uses the club as a front to sow discord among the vampire factions. Maybe the info comes from a sorcerer that gets paid in vampire blood. The possibilities are many and varied.

during business hours (and *only* during business hours). Very few of these visitors ever get to see him directly, most are ushered into a room that contains a video camera, a microphone and a pair of speakers bolted to the wall. It's from this room that Darlington makes deals,

sells information and generally conducts his business in a dignified and professional manner with mortals (including the occasional hunter), vampires and other supernatural oddities alike. The select few that have met Darlington personally say he is distinguished in both appearance and demeanor. They describe his lair, in the cellar of the building, as posh, comfortable and modern without any trappings of the grotesque that many vampires can't seem to resist displaying.

None of these people have any idea what they are talking about. No one, including his supposed childer, has ever actually met him. The vampire that lives in the cellar and pretends to be Darlington is actually a vampire that made a deal to remain in the club as a kind of decoy, in return for protection from the vampire's enemies. The fake Darlington receives his information through a small earpiece through which the real Darlington whispers instructions or is comprehensively briefed on what to say before meeting with a client. The real Darlington never enters the club, instead speaking to his visitors via direct link from a building on the outskirts of town and Darlington isn't even his real name.

The *real* "Darlington" is a vampire named Elias Naylor who has been active and awake for nearly 200 years. Naylor initially settled far away from the lights of fledgling Philadelphia, ensconced in a manor with his retainers, mainly mortal descendants of his, from which he fed selectively. As the city grew and expanded, Naylor knew that, eventually, it would encompass his domain and so he began to set up a network of informants and spies to keep him apprised of the activities in the city to ensure he wasn't disturbed. Over the years his network grew and expanded, all behind a double blind of secrecy (most of his agents don't have any idea where their information goes) until Naylor could have become a power in the city, maybe even prince if he so chose.

Completely uninterested in the tedious business of rule that would come with such a burden, Naylor was far more entertained by simply gathering and doling out information, always from the shadows, to people or vampires in the city he found interesting. When the expansion of Philadelphia finally halted just shy of his home, Naylor gave a sigh of relief and began to ponder what he might do with the network he had created. In a flash of inspiration, the idea for the nightclub appeared in his head. Now, Naylor watches, with amusement, the antics of the souls that come to his club in search of his wisdom.

Antagonist: Max Barclay

Quote: *"The blood is the power."*

Background: Max was a witch before his embrace, a seeker of all things dark and mysterious. In the shadows of Philadelphia, Max found more than he had bargained for and would up a vampire in thrall to his sire. Not exactly pleased by this turn of events, Max returned to his study of magic in secret, puzzling out the ways in which he might regain some of his old power in his new form. Years of fruitless study left him nearly convinced that magic was forever beyond his reach until he found a tome hidden among his master's belongings that seemed the answer to his prayers. The tome, *Ritus Sanguis*, detailed mad blood rituals in erratic calligraphy. Max began to practice the rituals he found in the book and eventually managed to destroy his sire and escape from his slavery.

More recently, Max has heard stories about the objects of power and the books of shadow kept by the Aegis Kai Doru and has begun to plot ways of taking them for himself. In particular, his interest was piqued by mention of a tome kept by the hunters that sounds like a companion volume to *Ritus Sanguis*, which outlines more spells and rituals that might increase his power. Slowly and with great caution, Max has begun to dig up information about Aegis Kai Doru and its agents. He has set spies to watching known homes of Aegis Kai Doru member and even sent agents to Travesty to ask subtle questions (going in person would be foolish and might even alert his prey) about the pursuits and habits of the hunter group.

Description: Max is tall and skinny with a full head of black hair that might tactfully be described as disheveled. Although he no longer needs to wear glasses to improve his eyesight, Max still has the habit of pushing the phantom lenses back up his nose, especially when he's deep in thought or reading a book.

Storytelling Hints: Max is desperate to regain the power he held in life before he was made a vampire. It took him years of study to realize that the blood that now flows through his veins is the root of new magical powers that might actually be stronger than those he knew as a witch. So while most vampires only deal with one thirst, Max suffers from two connected thirsts. He thirsts for blood and for the power that comes from ritual use of that blood. This combination of hungers makes him seem a bit manic at times. Max has created a new cabal (some might call it a cult) that consists of mortal assistants to aid him in his work. None of his ghouls are true witches and Max keeps them in line not only through the blood bond but also with false promises of mystical power.

MAX BARCLAY

Mental Attributes: Intelligence 4, Wits 3, Resolve 3

Physical Attributes: Strength 2, Dexterity 3, Stamina 3

Social Attributes: Presence 3, Manipulation 3, Composure 3

Mental Skills: Academics 3, Computer 2, Crafts (Ritual Tools) 2, Investigation 3, Occult (Magic) 4, Science 2

Physical Skills: Brawl 2, Drive 1, Firearms (Pistol) 2, Larceny (Security Systems) 2, Stealth 4, Weaponry 1

Social Skills: Expression 3, Persuasion 3, Streetwise 2, Subterfuge 3

Merits: Contacts (Travesty) 2, Encyclopedic Knowledge, Potency 2, Resources 4, Retainer (Ghouls) 3

Max Willpower/per Turn: 13/1

Morality: 6

Virtue: Faith

Vice: Envy

Initiative: 6

Defense: 3

Speed: 10

Health: 8

Dread Powers: Agonize •••, Hypnotism ••, Shadow Harvest •, Tendrils •••, Unholy Attribute (Intelligence) •••

Requiem: Max could be portrayed as Mekhet.

The Cainites

The Cainites have been building up their numbers in the city. They think something big is coming (though some believe it's some*one*, not something, perhaps an elder vampire come to roost in the City of Brotherly Love). They've been recruiting, perhaps wantonly so; yes, their numbers are growing, but at what cost? If the young Cainites are reckless and without proper training, what good does that do anybody?

Location: St. Peter's Church of Philadelphia

Built on land donated by Thomas and Richard Penn, the construction of St. Peter's Church began in 1757. Largely unchanged since, the Episcopal Church is filled with light on bright Sunday mornings, courtesy of the large clear windows that surround the balcony and is modestly appointed. Large brass organ pipes are set directly over the altar and swell with music to celebrate the worship of God. All of the Christian hustle and bustle helps mask what lurks beneath the building.

The Cainite Heresy came to Philadelphia about a hundred years back—wild-eyed zealots with no mercy in reserve when it comes to the vampires or their kin. Once, the Cainites may have been religious (certainly the conspiracy still has the light trappings of that religion), but the religion hasn't truly been present in them for as long as any living member can remember. Their "religion" is the hunting of vampires, plain and simple—so, while St. Peter's Church held little interest to them from a spiritual point-of-view, it was interesting because first how defensible it was and second because there exists the theory that the creatures of the night cannot abide holy ground.

So, the Cainites dug a communal safehouse beneath the church. They put in a stockpile of weapons. They put in racks and closets of apotropaics (holy wafers, bulbs of garlic, loaves of bread baked with blood). And then they hunted.

From holy ground they moved through the darkened streets of Philadelphia leaving bloodless corpses or ashy outlines of bodies in their wake. The Cainite's activities remained largely unchanged for the next 50 years, when the heretics decided on a different course of action.

They'd heard tell of some truly ancient vampire—a deified figure some of the creatures worshipped. The figure was reportedly Longinus, the same figure who thrust the spear into Christ's side (and it was this act, some creatures of the night believe, that imbued the Roman with the cursed condition of eternal unlife). Some of the vampires claim that Longinus is truly their progenitor, the first of the damned race. Some of the monsters believe that this so-called "Dark Father" remains up and walking around.

It occurred to the Cainites that the best thing to do would be to destroy this mystical patron. If the old stories were true, destroying the progenitor of the fiends would eliminate *all* the fiends in one fell swoop—and, even if it wouldn't, it might throw all of their wretched society into disarray. At which point it would be easy to pick off the maddened, the melancholic.

Of course, finding Longinus was a pipe dream. No evidence was left of his passing. No sign of his coming or going. If they couldn't find him, then perhaps they could bring him to them? They'd witnessed the truth that particularly aged vampires (centuries dead) often chose to—or needed to—feed on their own kind (and what an ideal scenario that was, monsters eating monsters). Could he be summoned with a meal, the way a pie cooling on a windowsill might summon any number of fools with stomachs growling?

The Cainites instructed their members to capture, rather than kill, any elder vampire they uncovered. They then staked and buried the elder vampires in shallow graves ringing the church cemetery. The occasional moan of despair that emanates from the interred undead, combined with the presence of spirits drawn to the graveyard to feed on their mingled rage and pain has resulted in the cemetery at St. Peter's being declared one of the most haunted places in Philadelphia. (Far from being displeased by such attention, the heretics feel that rumors of hauntings bolster their scheme.) Essentially, the Cainites created a blood larder in Philadelphia meant to lure Longinus out of hiding.

Did it work? The Cainites waited for ten years to no avail. Then, one night? A few Cainites came back from a night's worth of hunting to find the shallow graves exhumed. All the elders were gone. And in the safehouse, the remaining Cainites were all dead—no signs of trauma or wounds, their bloodless bodies sitting or lying in normal positions (one was face down in a bowl of soup).

The Cainites today are just starting to get their numbers back up. They still hold the hidden safehouse beneath the church grounds, but it's growing more difficult to do so (and it doesn't help that it seems to stir the hunt-

ers of both the Long Night and the Malleus Maleficarum to fits that someone is basically squatting in a forbidden subbasement of holy ground). Most Cainites now linger off-site in various smaller caches and safehouses throughout the city. They are recruiting. Heavily.

Clint Thiessen, Cainites

Quote: *"You know the question. All there is, is the question."*

Background: Six years ago (it seems a lifetime to him), Clint's ex-wife, Christy, began to complain of nightmares and was diagnosed with anemia. The two had separated amiably a year earlier and still communicated with each other via email and greeting cards on the holidays. The affection Clint retained for her led him to knock on the door of her apartment, late one evening, to check on how she was doing. At his knock, the door swung open, apparently not having been latched or closed properly. Calling his ex-wife's name as he entered, Clint turned to hang his coat on a hook by the door when he was attacked from behind and beaten to unconsciousness. When he awoke, aching and bruised, he found himself lying in bed. Christy sat nearby on a chair, clasping her legs to her chest, watching him with her chin resting on her knees.

Her eyes almost seemed to glow in the dim light of the bedroom and he could see streaks of wetness running down her cheeks. In the flash of light provided by a passing car, Clint saw, revolted, that she wept tears of blood. He sat up, fighting off a sudden wave of dizziness and felt something warm and sticky on his neck. Touching his neck, Clint held his fingers up and saw they were coated with blood.

Christy lunged at him and Clint drew back instinctively, thinking she was about to attack him. Instead, she threw her arms around his neck and sobbed into his shirt. Christy reached behind him and, seemingly without effort, broke off a jagged section of the headboard and handed it to him. Clint numbly accepted the broken piece of furniture without really thinking about it. Christy guided his hand, and the make-shift stake, over her heart and smiled sadly at him, revealing long pointed canines that had not been present during their marriage. He drove the stake home and passed out. The next morning when he awoke, blinking in the bright sunlight that streamed in the room, he found the stake on the floor, covered in greasy ashes.

Clint reported Christy as missing the following week, just before he sold most of his possessions, his home and car, and moved into a small, Spartan apartment on the west side of town. It wasn't long after that the Cainites came looking for him. They asked him the question. His answer was to join them.

Description: Clint is a thin, hawkish man in his early thirties with a rapidly retreating hairline and the

CLINT THIESSEN

Mental Attributes: Intelligence 2, Wits 3, Resolve 4

Physical Attributes: Strength 2, Dexterity 3, Stamina 2

Social Attributes: Presence 2, Manipulation 2, Composure 4

Mental Skills: Academics 2, Computer 2, Investigation (Rumors) 3, Medicine (Anatomy) 2, Occult 3

Physical Skills: Athletics 2, Brawl 1, Drive 1, Stealth (Shadows) 3, Weaponry (Stake) 4

Social Skills: Persuasion 3, Streetwise 2, Subterfuge 3

Merits: Endowment (Denials) 3, Resources 2, Status (Cainites) 1, Unseen Sense (Vampires)

Willpower: 8

Morality: 6

Virtue: Justice

Vice: Wrath

Initiative: 7

Defense: 3

Speed: 10

Health: 7

burning eyes of a fanatic. He rarely seems to blink—his wide eyes are often staring holes through whomever or whatever he's looking at.

Storytelling Hints: Clint is intense. Unpleasantly so. He's really quite the zealot, and has little comfort level in the thought that others might not walk the same path.

OTHER CAINITES

Other Cainites—ones the characters might actually encounter—include:

Celia Carroll: Violent provocateur within the sect. Celia is a hardliner, and prefers to provoke her vampire enemies out into vulnerable places or positions. If she can work to force the creatures to destroy themselves, all the better. Celia isn't friendly. She's downright cold, actually. Still, she's not a monster. She's not James Argus (below): innocents do not deserve to be thrown into this timeless struggle.

Serge Wrightson: Smile and mumble, smile and mumble. Serge is just an old janitor, isn't he? Mopping the floors at 30th Street Station, he's not much to look at. Sometimes he whistles to himself. Other times, he ducks into the supply closets, removes a grate, crawls through it, and enters a long-forgotten (and crumbling) room where the local Cainites keep records and information held in fireproof lockboxes.

Elba Bloom: Elba is scared. Scared of her own people. Once, she maybe bought into the Cainite conspiracy. No longer. She's frightened by what she's seen, and what the others believe and do. She wants out, but has no idea how to make that happen. The question gives her no confidence. It only terrifies her.

James Argus: This is what James Argus often says: "No hope in small victories." To him, it's balls to the wall. Burn all the vampires or don't bother lighting the match. Except… well, that makes him pretty much a merciless, terroristic sociopath. He'll kill two innocents to get to one vampire without flinching. He believes the purpose of the Cainites is absolute and unyielding. That makes him a very dangerous man.

HUNTER: THE VIGIL
WITCH FINDERS
You can't trust magic.
You can't trust a witch.
Something has to be done.
Sin must be paid.
AVAILABLE NOW
978-158846-722-5
WW55554
$31.99 USD

HUNTER: THE VIGIL™
SPIRIT SLAYERS™

They shall have no rest,

these men that are wolves.

They shall eat ashes.

They shall be tormented

with fire and silver

in the presence of us.

God's holy angels.

For use with

HUNTER™
THE VIGIL

COMING JANUARY 2009

www.white-wolf.com
Suggested for mature readers

White Wolf
Publishing